Anatomy & Physiology
Plain and Simple

A Coloring Review Guide

Shelley H. Montgomery

and

Anne Catherine Mueller

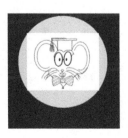

First paperback edition October 2019

Book cover design by Anne Catherine Mueller
Dr. L. Rat character by Shelley H. Montgomery

ISBN 978-1-7341671-0-8 (paperback)

www.biologysketchnotes.com
www.ateacherontheedge.wordpress.com

Lab Rat Press

DEDICATION

This book is dedicated to Nancy Hill, a wonderful Mom, Nana, and the BEST Anatomy and Physiology teacher. She inspired countless students, as well as her daughter and granddaughter, during her 43 year teaching career. Her influence continues to be felt throughout many areas of our small community in the students she encouraged to pursue careers in the medical field. She always encouraged me to write a book, so I hope this one will make her proud.

TABLE OF CONTENTS

List of Illustrations and Sketch Notes

ACKNOWLEDGMENTS

Writing a book is harder than we thought and more rewarding than we could have ever imagined. None of this would have been possible without the support and encouragement of our husbands, Jeff Montgomery and Nick Mueller. Thank you for always believing in us.

CHAPTER 1. INTRODUCTION TO ANATOMY & PHYSIOLOGY

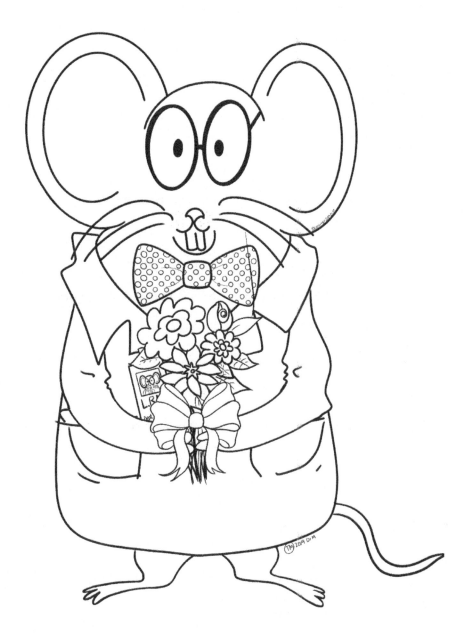

The Human Body: An Orientation

I. Overview of Anatomy and Physiology

    A. <u>Anatomy</u>-studies *structure*.

    B. <u>Physiology</u>-studies *function*.

    C. "Structure determines function" means that the *composition or shape of a structures* determines *the job* that it performs.

II. Levels of Structural Organization

    A. Chemical level

        1. <u>Atom</u>-smallest unit of a substance.

        2. <u>Molecule</u>-2 or more atoms bonded together.

        3. <u>Organelle</u>-"*little organ*"; basic unit of cells.

    B. Cellular level

        4. <u>Cell</u>-smallest unit of living things.

        5. <u>Tissue</u>-cells with common functions.

            Types:

                a. <u>Epithelial</u>-covers surfaces & lines cavities

                b. <u>Muscle</u>-movement

                c. <u>Connective</u>-supports and protects organs

                d. <u>Nervous</u>-communicates with electrical impulses

        6. <u>Organ</u>-made of at least 2 tissue types (usually 4).

        7. <u>Organ System</u>-organs that work together.

    C. Organismal level

        8. <u>Organism</u>-all levels working together to promote life.

III. Characteristics of Living Things

    A. Have these things in common:

- <u>Reactions</u>-occur in all living organisms
- <u>Responsiveness/irritability</u>-respond to outside conditions
- <u>Movement</u>-locomotion from within
- <u>Growth</u>-increase in size because new material is produced too fast
- <u>Differentiation</u>-development of cells into specialized state

- Reproduction-occurs at the cellular level (mitosis) or organismal level
- Digestion-food is physically and chemically changed into simple substances
- Excretion-removal of wastes

B. Depend upon physical and chemical changes that occur within body parts (called metabolism).

    1. Anabolism-builds new substances; uses energy.

    2. Catabolism-breaks substances down, generates energy.

C. Metabolism results in a patient's vital signs of temperature, breathing, blood pressure, and pulse. Death occurs when there are NO vital signs. In clinical death, there are no brain waves. In biological death, there is no pulse and no heartbeat.

IV. Survival Needs of Organisms-quantity and quality are both important. Organisms need these things to survive:

- Nutrients-chemical substances from food used for energy and cell building.
- Oxygen-chemical reactions to release energy from food require oxygen.
- Water-fluid base for reactions, accounts for 60-80% of body weight.
- Heat-too low, reactions will be slow; too high, proteins don't function, and death occurs.
- Pressure-force exerted on body's surface (by air); necessary for breathing and gas exchange.

V. Homeostasis *"steady state"*

A. Communication within the body is essential for homeostasis.

B. Accomplished chiefly by the Endocrine and Nervous Systems using *electrical signals* delivered by *nerves* or *blood-borne hormones* as information carriers.

C. The factor/event being regulated in the body is called the *variable*.

D. All homeostatic control mechanisms have at least 3 components:

    1. Control center-receives information, determines response; Example-brain, spinal cord

    2. Receptor (sensor/"receives")-area/structure that monitors conditions & sends information to the control center; Example-skin

    3. Effector ("effects")-produces a response or changes a condition; Example-muscle, gland

E. Pathways that information follows within this control mechanism:

    1. Afferent-information travels *from receptor* to control center.

    2. Efferent-information travels *from control center* to effector.

F. Results of the response "feed back" to increase or decrease the stimulus.

    1. Positive feedback-stimulus increases.

    2. Negative feedback-stimulus decreases.

VI. Feedback

    A. Positive Feedback "stimulatory" (see **Figure 1-1**)

        1. Always <u>increases</u> the original stimulus; called "cascade"

        2. Not used for moment-to-moment well-being.

        3. Produces unstable body conditions and can cause death.

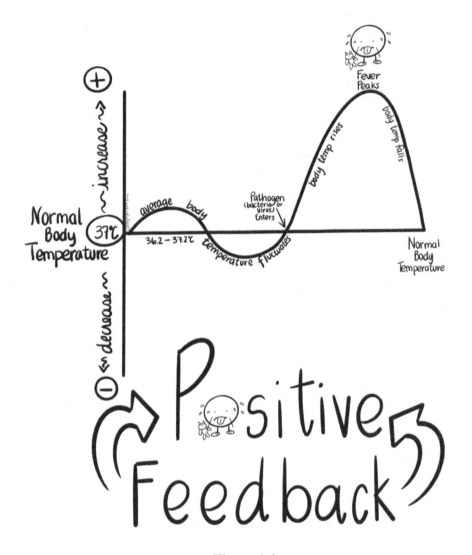

Figure 1-1

<u>Example</u>-Fever causes body temperature to increase when a pathogen is encountered. This continued increase in temperature produces less than optimal conditions for the survival of the pathogen (positive feedback). When numbers of pathogens decrease, the body's temperature gradually falls until it reaches a normal range.

B. Other examples of positive feedback include:

        1. <u>Good</u>-breastfeeding by infant, childbirth, blood clotting

        2. <u>Bad</u>-cancer

C. Negative Feedback "inhibitory"

    1. Responds by <u>decreasing</u> the original stimulus; used in making adjustments for moment-to-moment well-being of body.

    2. Returns body to normal state.

    3. Goal is to prevent sudden, severe changes in the body.

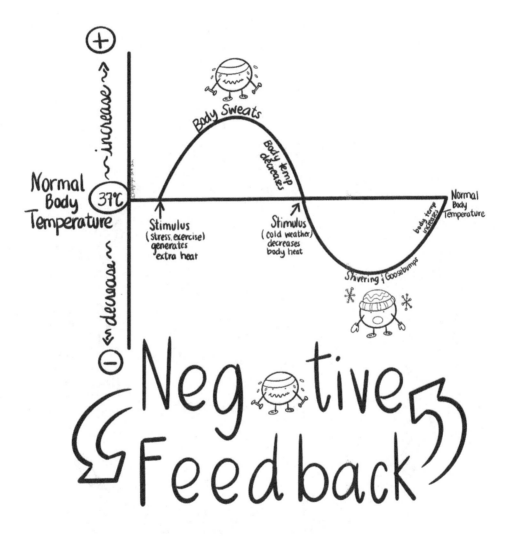

Figure 1-2

D. Examples of negative feedback

    1. Thermostat in hypothalamus (shown in **Figure 1-2**)

    2. Withdrawal reflex

    3. Insulin response/glycogen response

    4. Blood pressure/cardiac output

E. Steps of a specific negative feedback mechanism example (**Figure 1-3**)

    1. <u>Insulin response</u>-regulates *high* blood sugar
- Increase in blood sugar
- Pancreas secretes insulin
- Insulin causes increased uptake of glucose by cells
- Blood sugar returns to normal

    2. <u>Glycogen response</u>-regulates *low* blood sugar
- Decrease in blood sugar
- Glucagon secreted by pancreas
- Causes liver to secrete glucose into blood
- Blood sugar rises and returns to normal

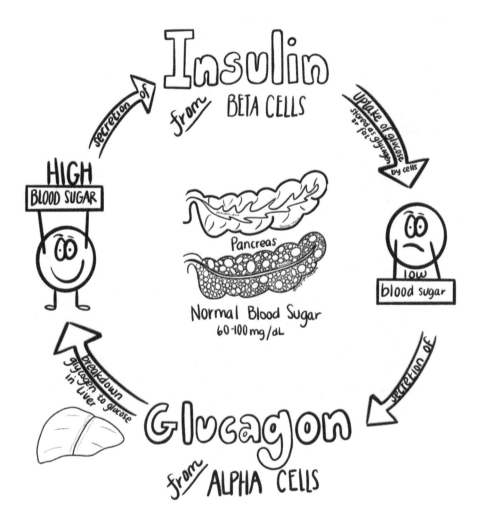

Figure 1-3

Cellular Communication

I. Cellular communication is essential to integrate and coordinate the systems of the body so they can participate in different functions. It is also a vital mechanism for maintaining homeostasis within the body. (see **Figure 1-4**)

    A. Different modes of cell communication differ in terms of distance and speed.

    B. Chemical signaling molecules (first messengers) provide the major means of intercellular communication; they include ions, gases, small peptides, protein hormones, metabolites, and steroids.

    C. Receptors are the receivers and transmitters of signaling molecules; they are located either on the plasma membrane or within the cell.

    D. Second messengers are important for amplification of the signal received by plasma membrane receptors.

II. Cell to Cell Communication

    A. Communication between cells occurs primarily through *chemical* means.

    B. It is absolutely necessary in order for multicellular organisms to survive and function.

III. Types of Signaling (Classified by Distance)

    A. <u>Direct</u> (autocrine or juxtacrine)-"cell to cell contact"/NO distance

        1. Involves <u>physical contact</u> between cells or organisms; like someone handing you a note meant just for your eyes; very specific.

        2. <u>Autocrine</u>-cell produces and secretes its own signaling molecules; important in cell development so cells have correct identification.

        3. <u>Juxtacrine</u>-passage between cells via gap junctions (as in adjacent cardiac muscle cells which allow action potential to continue through).

        4. Often involves <u>antigen-presenting cells</u> (APC) that serve as "hands" on surface of plasma membrane. These are specific receptors for *specific molecules* such as in a specific immune response.

    B. <u>Local</u> (paracrine)-"nearby"/Close distance

        1. Molecules released into a <u>localized area</u> and bind to receptors on *nearby* cells; like sending an email or text to someone who is not close enough for you to touch.

        2. Examples of local regulators include:

            a. Neurotransmitters released at synaptic cleft (gap) between neurons such as those responsible for pain relief (natural endorphins); some drugs produce a "high" by altering communication between neurons that are mediated by dopamine.

            b. Growth factors released for general growth and repair.

            c. Cells in nose respond to pollen attaching to antibodies attached to mast cells by producing histamine

C. <u>Long Distance</u> (endocrine)-"far apart"/Great distance

    1. Involves cells <u>far apart</u> or for <u>large audiences</u> of cells; like posting on social media so that anyone who is your "friend" can see it.

    2. Signal is sent to many cells, but few cells act.

    3. Examples include:

        a. <u>Hormones</u>-released from 1 part of body and travel to a different part of body; Ex. brain causing pituitary gland to release Human Growth Hormone (HGH) which travels through bloodstream to all types of cells but mainly bone cells and muscle cells react to it by growing.

        b. <u>Pheromones</u>-chemicals used to attract mates when released into the environment.

III. Ligand *"the signal molecule"*

A. Binds to the receptor protein (the "hands") on the cell membrane or inside the cell. There are specific "hands" for specific ligands and they must fit for activation. Different ligands can initiate different responses.

B. The attachment of the ligand to the receptor protein causes the receptor protein to change shape (called a <u>conformational shape change</u>). This activates a series of events known as the <u>signal transduction pathway</u>.

C. <u>Extracellular example</u> (on the cell membrane)-includes *protein ligands* such as growth hormone.

D. <u>Intracellular examples</u> (inside the cell)-include *steroid hormones* (including sex hormones, the most common type in the body) and nitrous oxide gas which relaxes muscles and dilates blood vessels (how nitroglycerin works to relax heart).

IV. Signal Transduction Pathway (STP)

A. BIG picture of the pathway:

    1. Typically converts an intercellular signal (between cells) into an intracellular signal (within a cell) that triggers a response.

    2. Can also be thought of as the triggering of a molecular event (or series of events) in order to produce an outcome.

B. Parts of the pathway:

    1. <u>Reception</u>-certain chemical/molecule binds to its corresponding membrane receptor protein. <u>Example</u>-If someone specifically dials your phone number and calls your phone, you hear the ring and know there's a call, but will not know what they want until you answer it and change the ringing into words you can understand.

    Receptors are of 2 types:

        a. <u>Surface</u>-on cell membrane.

        b. <u>Intracellular</u> (*"intra"*=within)-within/inside cell cytoplasm or nucleus.

    2. <u>Transduction</u>-*"to change or carry through"*

a. Series of actions to change the signal to something that the cell can understand.

b. Usually involves making something or turning on/off an enzymatic process as a response.

c. The "signal" is passed from one molecule to another using protein kinases (which *add* phosphorous molecule from ATP to protein to *turn it on*) and phosphorylation (in which protein phosphatase *removes* phosphorus molecule to *turn process off* and *stop* signal).

> 1). Signal is passed protein to protein, each *modifying* the next in some way, until it reaches the target molecule (which works to change the behavior of cells). Signals can be *amplified* to turn small signal into a large response, or *stop* the response entirely

> 2). Example-When you answer your phone, you must put your phone to your ear, say "hello", listen to the other person's words, answer them, and you can either continue the conversation *(amplify)* or hang up *(stop)*. All of these are a series of steps to transform the "ringing" of the phone into words you can understand.

3. Response-usually involves either changing the *activity of enzymes* already inside the cell or affecting transcription or translation (gene expression) at the DNA level inside the nucleus.

> a. Example-Once you have heard why the person was calling, you hang up the phone and do what they asked, or don't, thus completing the pathway with the action you performed as the response.

> b. Response can occur at a *molecular level* (such as an increase in transcription of certain genes or activation of particular enzymes) and at a *macroscopic level* (when there is a change in outward behavior or appearance of the cell as in cell growth or cell death).

> c. Response and Gene Expression

>> 1. Gene expression-when information from a gene is used by the cell to *produce a product* (usually a protein); the instructions of the cell are *"expressed"*.

>> 2. Production of the *product* is accomplished via 2 ways:

>>> a). Transcription-making mRNA, a disposable copy of DNA.

>>> b). Translation-reading DNA's instructions from mRNA and "translating" it into a protein/product.

>> 3. The response can alter either transcription, translation, or both to change the amount of product/protein produced by the cell.

>> 4. Example-Some responses cause cell migration, changes in cellular identity, and the start of apoptosis (programmed cell death).

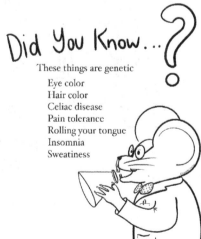

Did You Know...?

These things are genetic
Eye color
Hair color
Celiac disease
Pain tolerance
Rolling your tongue
Insomnia
Sweatiness

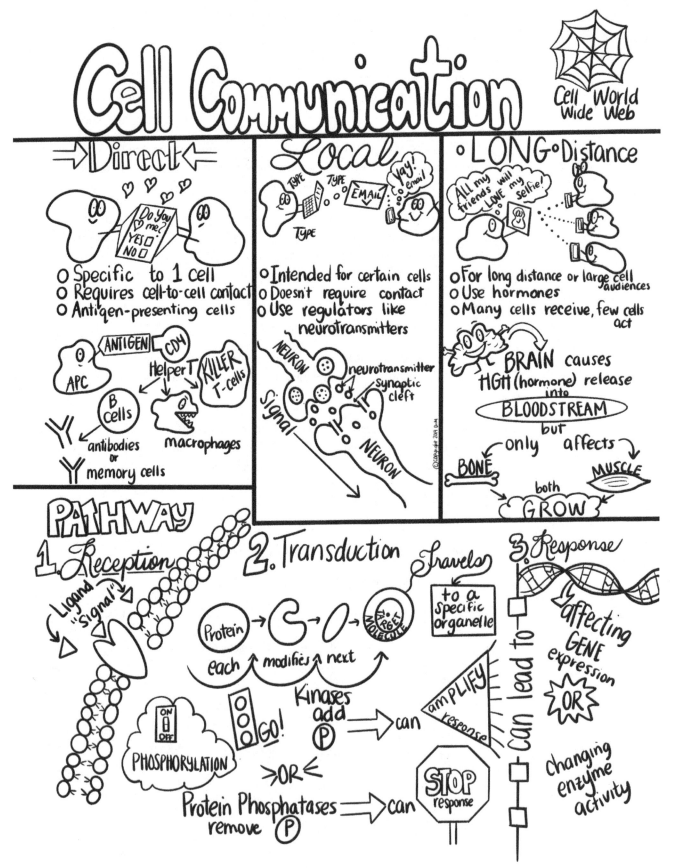

Figure 1-4

Body Cavities and Membranes

I. The human body can be divided into two main cavities, the <u>dorsal cavity</u> (back side) and the <u>ventral cavity</u> (belly side).

    A. <u>Dorsal body cavity</u>-protects organs of the nervous system and has two subdivisions:

        1. The <u>cranial cavity</u> is the area within the skull and contains the brain.

        2. The <u>spinal (vertebral) cavity</u> contains the vertebral column and spinal cord.

    B. <u>Ventral body cavity</u>-protects most of the organs in the body and consists of two major subdivisions, the thoracic and abdominopelvic cavities, and several minor body cavities including the <u>orbital</u> (contains the eyes), <u>nasal</u> (contains a respiratory and olfactory region), <u>oral</u> (contains tongue, teeth, and gums), and <u>otic</u> (middle ear bones). The 2 major subdivisions are: (see **Figure 1-5**)

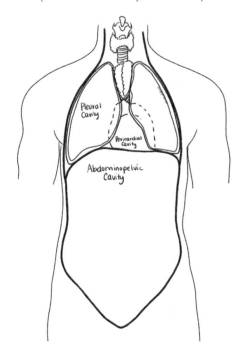

        1. The <u>thoracic cavity</u> is the superior division and is surrounded by the ribs and muscles in the chest. It is further subdivided into:

            a. Two lateral <u>pleural cavities</u> (each pleural cavity contains a lung) and the <u>mediastinum</u> (a wedge-shaped cavity located between the superior regions of the two thoracic cavities that contains the esophagus, thymus gland, and trachea).

            b. The <u>pericardial cavity</u> lies within the mediastinum in the center of the chest. It contains the heart.

        2. The <u>abdominopelvic cavity</u> is the inferior division and is separated from the thoracic cavity by the <u>diaphragm</u>. It has two major subdivisions:

            a. <u>Abdominal cavity</u>-contains the kidneys, ureters, stomach, spleen, liver, intestines, gallbladder, and pancreas.

            b. <u>Pelvic cavity</u>-contains the urinary bladder, rectum, anus, and reproductive organs.

Figure 1-5

II. The body cavities are lined with thin sheets of tissue called <u>membranes,</u> which cover a structure or line a cavity.

    The body's membranes are classified into 2 broad categories:

- <u>Epithelial membranes</u>-cutaneous (skin), mucous (mucosa), and serous (serosa); most are moist (except skin).
- <u>Synovial membranes</u>-lack epithelium; provide a smooth surface and cushioning through synovial fluid; found at joints.

    A. The <u>dorsal body cavity</u> is lined with three layers of protective membranes (the <u>dura mater</u>, <u>arachnoid</u>, and <u>pia mater</u>), which are called the <u>meninges</u>. They cover the brain and spinal cord.

B. The <u>ventral body cavity</u> contains cavities which are considered either <u>open</u> (to the air) or <u>closed</u> (not exposed to the air).

    1. <u>Open cavities</u>-lined with mucous membranes (mucosa); include the hollow organs of the respiratory, digestive, urinary, and reproductive tracts.

    2. <u>Closed cavities</u>-lined with double-layered serous membranes (serosa) separated by serous fluid, a watery substance that allows for lubrication and movement of organs. The inner membrane (<u>visceral</u>) clings to the organ and the outer membrane (<u>parietal</u>) lines the wall of the cavity. They are named according to their *location*:

        a. <u>Pleura</u>-membrane that lines the <u>pleural cavity</u>, which covers the *lungs* in the thoracic cavity.

        b. <u>Pericardium</u>-membrane that lines the <u>pericardial cavity</u>, which covers the *heart* in the mediastinum (middle part of the thoracic cavity).

        c. <u>Peritoneum</u>-membrane that lines the <u>abdominopelvic cavity</u> and many of the organs found within it.

C. Naming and Terminology

    1. The <u>visceral</u> layer of the membrane is the layer that <u>touches the organs</u>. Viscera means "organ".

    2. The <u>parietal</u> layer is the layer that forms the outer shell of the membrane and touches the surrounding structures, and <u>lines the wall of the cavity</u>. Parietal comes from a Latin word that means "*wall*".

    3. Typically, the serous membranes are named according to the *cavity and organ* with which they are associated. For example, the parietal pericardium lines the pericardial cavity and the visceral pericardium clings to the surface of the heart.

Body Cavities (Figure 1-6)

Cavity	Color
Cranial	
Spinal (Vertebral)	
Thoracic	
Abdominal	
Pelvic	

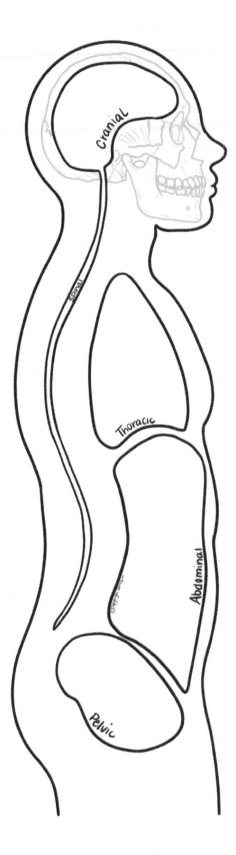

Figure 1-6

Body Cavities and Membranes (Figure 1-7)

Use **Figure 1-7** to help you visualize the arrangement of the body cavities. Color the body cavity, then outline the cavity with a contrasting color to represent the membrane that lines the cavity. Refer to pgs. 11-12 if you need additional assistance.

Cavity	Location (Dorsal or Ventral)	Membranes that Line this Cavity (Meninges, Serous, or Mucosa)	Organs/ Structures In this Cavity	Color
Cranial				
Spinal (Vertebral)				Not shown in Figure 1-7
Thoracic				
Oral				
Otic				
Nasal				
Orbital				
Cardiac (in Thoracic)				
Mediastinum (in Thoracic)				
Pleural (in Thoracic)				
Abdominal				
Pelvic				

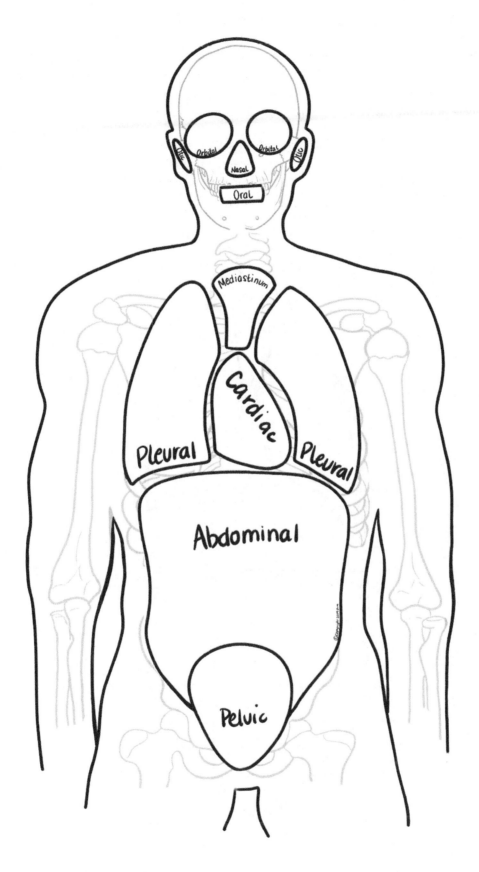

Figure 1-7

Abdominopelvic Regions

The regions of the abdomen are divisions used by physicians to help localize, identify and diagnose a patient's symptoms. There are two main forms of categorization: one that divides the abdomen into four quadrants and the second that divides it into nine regions. The method which divides the abdomen into 9 regions can further localize clinical symptoms to help physicians arrive at an accurate diagnosis more quickly.

The right and left hypochondriac regions are found superiorly on either side of the abdomen, while the epigastric region is located between them in a central, superior position. The right and left lumbar regions surround the central umbilical region that has the umbilicus (bellybutton or navel) as its center point. Finally, the right and left iliac regions are located inferiorly on either side of the hypogastric region, the most inferior of the central line of segments. (see **Figure 1-8**)

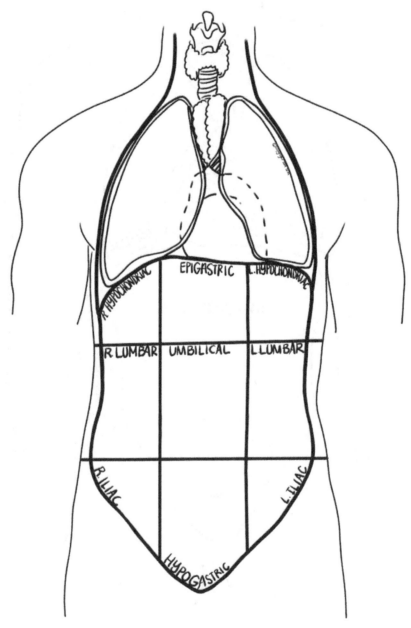

Figure 1-8

Most organs in the abdominopelvic cavity are part of multiple regions.

1. The <u>right hypochondriac region</u> contains parts of the liver, gallbladder, small intestine, and the right kidney, while the <u>left hypochondriac region</u> contains part of the spleen, colon (large intestine), pancreas, and the left kidney.

2. The <u>epigastric region</u>, located between the right and left hypochondriac regions, contains the majority of the stomach, as well as parts of the liver, pancreas, duodenum, spleen, and the adrenal glands.

3. The central <u>umbilical region</u>, located just inferior to the epigastric region, contains the umbilicus (navel), in addition to parts of the small intestine (duodenum, jejunum, and ileum).

4. It is flanked on either side by the <u>right lumbar region</u> containing the gallbladder, ascending colon, and the right kidney, and the <u>left lumbar region</u> which contains the descending colon, left kidney, and part of the spleen.

5. The lowest regions, the right and left iliac, are sometimes referred to as the *inguinal regions*. The <u>right iliac region</u> contains the appendix and cecum, while the <u>left iliac region</u> contains part of the descending colon and the sigmoid colon.

6. The central <u>hypogastric region</u> contains organs around the pubic bone including the urinary bladder, anus, and the reproductive organs.

Abdominopelvic Regions (Figures 1-8 and 1-9)

Color **Figure 1-8** on p. 16 and record your color choice in the chart below. Use the same colors to outline the corresponding region in **Figure 1-9**. Record the organs present in each abdominopelvic region using pgs. 16-17.

Region	Organs in this Region	Color
Right Hypochondriac		
Epigastric		
Left Hypochondriac		
Right Lumbar		
Umbilical		
Left Lumbar		
Right Iliac		
Hypogastric		
Left Iliac		

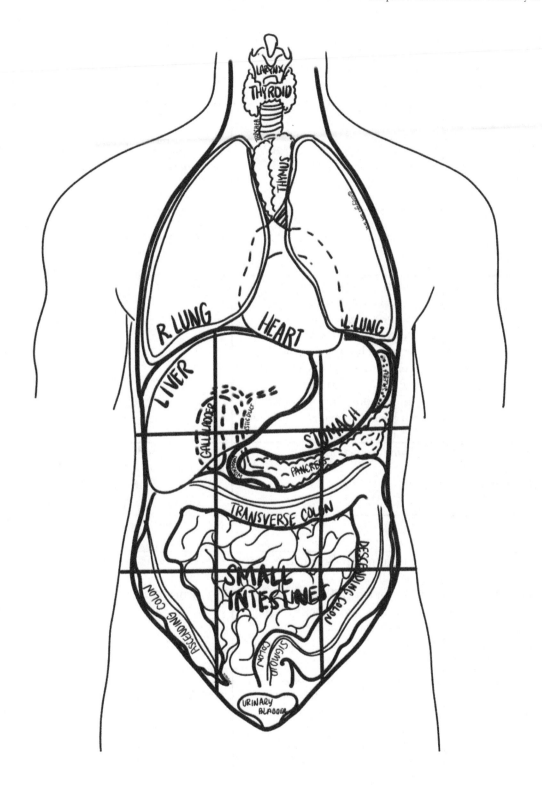

Figure 1-9

Organ System Overview

This chart provides the major functions and organs/structures for each body system. The function of the organ/structure is stated in parentheses after the name.

System	Organs	Functions
Skeletal	o Bones along with cartilage, ligaments, and joints (body support)	o Supports body o Site of skeletal muscle attachment o Stores minerals o Protects form blood cells
Muscular	o Muscles-smooth, cardiac, & skeletal (movement)	o Movement o Maintain posture o Produces heat
Nervous	o Brain (control of body) o Spinal cord (relay messages between body and brain) o Nerves (conduct impulses between body and brain) o Sensory receptors such as eye, ear, tongue (receive information from surroundings and generate nerve impulses to brain)	o Rapid response to stimuli
Integumentary	o Skin (protection)	o Covers body o Protection o Makes vitamin D o Contains receptors & glands
Endocrine	o Glands	o Secretes hormones that regulate processes
Cardiovascular	o Heart (pumps & circulates blood) o Red Blood Cells (carry O_2, nutrients, hormones to/from tissues for exchange) o White Blood Cells (protection and immunity)	o Transports nutrients, O_2, and hormones to cells o Removes metabolic wastes
Lymphatic	o Lymphatic vessels (tubes for fluid to return from blood) o Lymph nodes (cleanse blood, house immune cells) o Lymphoid organs including spleen (filters blood) and tonsils (gather and removes pathogens)	o Returns interstitial fluid leaked from blood to blood vessels o Transports WBC to and from lymph nodes into bones o Complements Cardiovascular system
Respiratory	o Nasal passages (inhale air) o Pharynx (throat, passageway for air) o Larynx (speech) o Trachea (passageway for air) o Bronchi (tubes leading to lungs for air passage)	o Supply O_2 o Remove CO_2

	o Lungs (O_2/CO_2 exchange) o Diaphragm (muscle that aids breathing)	
Digestive	o Mouth (take in food) o Esophagus (tube to stomach) o Stomach (chemical & physical digestion) o Small intestine (absorbs nutrients) o Large intestine/Colon (absorbs, transports waste, reclaims H_2O) o Rectum (waste storage before excretion) o Liver (detoxifies blood) o Cystic duct (tube bile travels through when secreted into duodenum) o Pancreas (produces insulin and other enzymes that break down food) o Gallbladder (stores bile) o Appendix (pouch of large intestine that contains lymphoid tissue) o Duodenum (1st part of small intestine and location where digestive enzymes & bile secreted)	o Break down food (mouth → small intestine) o Reclaim H_2O (large intestine)
Urinary	o Kidney (filters blood & removes toxins) o Ureter (tube from kidney to bladder) o Urethra (tube from bladder out of body) o Urinary Bladder (urine storage)	o Remove nitrogenous waste from blood o Salt/ electrolyte balance o Acid/base balance of blood
Reproductive	Male o Testes (produce sperm & testosterone) o Penis (delivers sperm to female) o Accessory glands (produce seminal fluid) o Duct System (transports sperm) Female o Ovary (produces eggs) o Fallopian Tubes (transport sperm towards egg) o Uterus (womb that holds fetus during pregnancy) o Vagina (canal that receives sperm)	o Produce offspring via sperm (male) and egg (female)

Major Organs and Functions (Figure 1-10)

Complete this chart by supplying the function of each organ as well as the body system to which it belongs. On **Figure 1-10**, color or outline each organ of the same system using the same color. Use the Organ System Overview chart on pgs. 20-21 for reference.

Organ/Structure	Function/ Description	Body System	Color
Larynx			
Trachea			
Lungs (R & L)			
Liver			
Gallbladder			
Cystic Duct			
Duodenum			
Large Intestine (Ascending, Transverse, Descending, and Sigmoid Colon)			
Appendix			
Heart			
Stomach			
Spleen			
Pancreas			
Small Intestine			
Urinary Bladder			

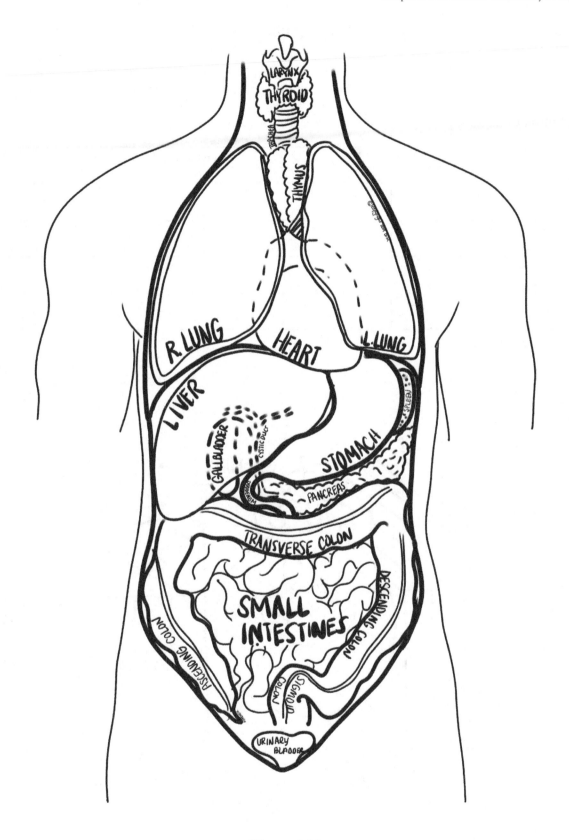

Figure 1-10

Body Planes & Directional Terms

<u>Anatomical position</u> is standing, with feet flat on the floor, and palms (anterior) surfaces facing forward. The body is always assumed to be in anatomical position when describing things in anatomical language.

I. Body Planes-The body can be divided into several planes/sections. (see **Figure 1-11**)

Plane	Divides Body Into:
1. Sagittal/ Mid-sagittal (median)	
2. Frontal (coronal)	
3. Transverse (cross-section)	
4. Oblique	

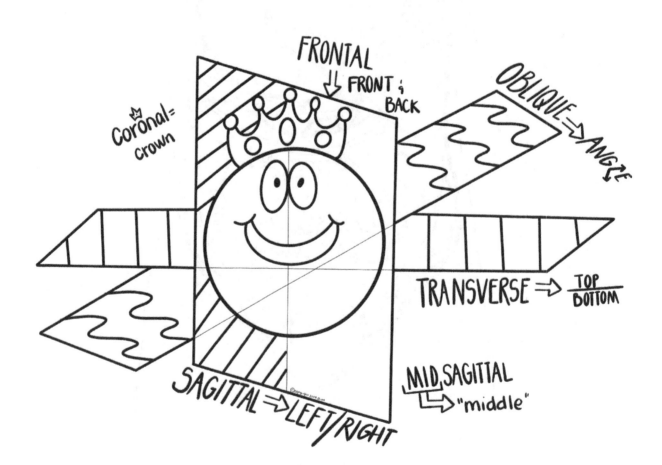

Figure 1-11

II. Directional Terms (use **Figure 1-12** p. 27 for reference)

<u>Helpful hint</u>: It is easier to remember the directional terms as opposites as they appear on this chart.

Directional Terms	
Term	**Definition**
Superior (Cranial)	
Inferior (Caudal)	
Anterior (Ventral)	
Posterior (Dorsal)	
Medial	
Lateral	
Intermediate	
Proximal	
Distal	
Supine	
Prone	
Superficial (External)	
Deep (Internal)	

III. Practice

Practice: Describe the anatomical relationship(s) that exist between each of the following parts. (There may be more than one answer for some of them). Always assume the body is in *anatomical position*. Answer should fit into the statement "The ____ is ____(anatomical term) to the ____" Refer to chart on p.25 as well as **Figure 1-12** for reference.

1. elbow and wrist-

2. nose and chin-

3. skin and kidneys-

4. lungs and heart-

5. toes to ankle-

6. scalp to skull-

7. diaphragm to lung-

8. heart to diaphragm-

9. head to neck-

10. esophagus to spine-

11. brain to spinal cord-

12. wrist to hand-

13. fingers to hand-

14. kneecap to knee joint-

15. eyes to nose-

16. ears to head-

17. thumb to hand-

18. little toe to big toe-

19. eyebrow to eye-

20. inside corner of eye to outside corner of eye-

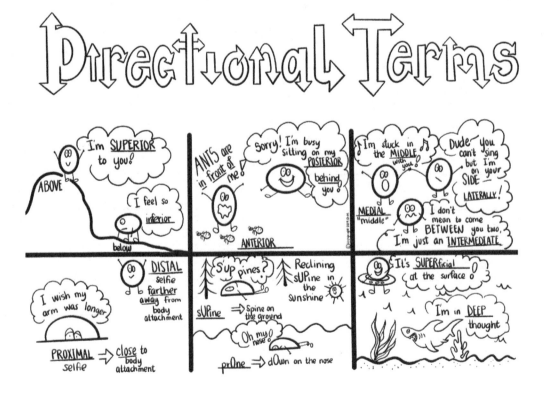

Figure 1-12

CHAPTER 2. INTEGUMENTARY SYSTEM

The Integumentary System

I. <u>Integumentary System</u>-largest organ in the body; includes the skin and its derivatives (hair, nails, and glands).

II. Functions

    A. Protection

        1. Provides a <u>physical barrier</u> to prevent bacterial and viral invasion of the body.

        2. Provides <u>chemical protection</u> by secreting *melanin* and *natural antibiotics* (defensin).

        3. Provides <u>biological protection</u> by producing cells (like Langerhans cells) that are involved in immune responses.

    B. Regulates Body Temperature

        1. Via *sweat production* when the body is too hot.

        2. In cold conditions, blood can be *pulled away* from the skin, thus reducing heat loss at the surface of the body.

    C. <u>Cutaneous Sensory Receptors</u>-located *throughout the skin*; function by detecting and responding to stimuli on the surface of the skin as well as stimuli external to the skin.

        a. <u>Meissner's Corpuscles</u>-detect touch (surface)

        b. <u>Pacinian Corpuscles</u>-detect pressure (deep)

        c. <u>Krause's End Bulbs</u>-detect low frequency and cold

        d. <u>Free Nerve Endings</u>-detect pain

    D. <u>Vitamin D Production</u>-begins when UV light hits special molecules in the skin. This molecule travels to the kidneys and liver where it is converted into <u>Calcitriol</u> (the active form of Vitamin D).

    E. <u>Blood Reservoir</u>-skin can store large supplies of blood.

    F. <u>Immunity</u>-produces cells that are involved in immune responses.

    G. <u>Excretion</u>-of waste materials via sweat production. Sweat is composed of salts, ammonia.

III. In 1 sq. inch of skin, you will find more than *1000 nerve endings,* yards of *capillaries*, 100 *sebaceous* (oil) *glands*, 150 *pressure sensors* (Pacinian= deep; Meissner's= surface), 75 *heat sensors*, 10 *cold sensors* (Krause's end bulbs), and millions of *cells*. The skin is the largest organ of the body (total area of about 20 square feet).

IV. Skin Structure

    A. Composed of two distinct layers: the <u>epidermis</u> (outer surface) and the <u>dermis</u>.

    B. The <u>hypodermis</u> (or superficial fascia) is not part of the skin but has some skin characteristics. It is made mostly of <u>adipose</u> tissue and anchors the skin to underlying structures.

Layers of the Skin

I. Epidermis (see **Figure 2-1**)

A. Most superficial layer of the skin.

B. Avascular (no blood supply) so is attached to the deeper dermis.

C. Contains accessory structures (hair, glands, and nails).

D. Skin's color is created by special cells located in the epidermis called melanocytes (produce the pigment melanin).

E. Also contains receptors called nociceptors (to detect pain), as well as tactile corpuscles (to detect light touch).

F. Composed of 4-5 layers of *keratinized, stratified squamous epithelium* depending on location.

1. Thin skin-has *four* layers of cells; these layers (from deep to superficial) are the stratum basale, stratum spinosum, stratum granulosum, and stratum corneum. *Most of the skin can be classified as thin skin.*

2. Thick skin-found only on the palms of the hands and the soles of the feet; has a fifth layer, called the stratum lucidum, located between the stratum corneum and the stratum granulosum.

G. Cells in all layers of the epidermis (*except the stratum basale*) are called keratinocytes. These cells make up approximately 95% of all epidermal cells. They also make and store the protein keratin.

H. Keratin-an intracellular fibrous protein that gives hair, nails, and skin their hardness, strength, and water-resistant properties.

II. Layers of the Epidermis (from superficial to deep)

A. Stratum Corneum (also known as horny layer)

1. *Most superficial layer* of the epidermis (layer exposed to the outside environment).

2. Named due to the increased keratinization (also called *cornification*) of the cells in this layer.

3. Made of 15 to 30 layers of cells.

4. Dry, dead layer that helps prevent the penetration of microbes and dehydration of underlying tissues.

5. Provides a mechanical protection against abrasion for the more delicate, underlying layers.

6. Cells in this layer are shed periodically and replaced by cells pushed up from the stratum granulosum. The entire layer is replaced during a period of about 4 weeks.

B. Stratum Lucidum (also known as clear layer)

1. Smooth, translucent layer of the epidermis located just above the stratum granulosum and below the stratum corneum.

2. Very thin layer of cells found only in the thick skin of the palms, soles, and digits.

3. Keratinocytes that compose the stratum lucidum are dead and flattened.

4. Cells are densely packed with a clear protein rich in lipids, which gives these cells their transparent (i.e. lucid) appearance and provides a barrier to water.

C. Stratum Granulosum (also known as <u>granular layer</u>)

    1. "Grainy" in appearance.

    2. Layer is three to five cell layers thick.

    3. Generate large amounts of the protein keratin.

    4. Contains lipids to create a water barrier.

D. Stratum Spinosum (also known as <u>prickly layer</u>)

    1. Composed of eight to 10 layers of tightly packed keratinocytes.

    2. Spiny cells have protruding processes and join together using structures called <u>desmosomes</u> which interlock and strengthen the bond formed between the cells.

E. Stratum Basale (also called the <u>stratum germinativum</u>)

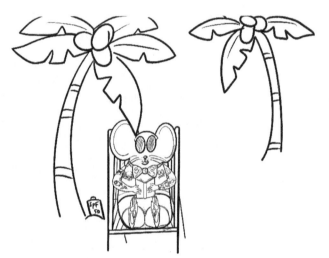

    1. Single layer of cells primarily made of <u>basal cells</u> (stem cells which are precursors of the <u>keratinocytes</u> of the epidermis).

    2. Deepest epidermal layer that attaches the epidermis to the <u>basal lamina</u>.

    3. Binds to the dermis via the <u>basement membrane</u>.

    4. Used to repair and produce new cells (or *germinate*).

<u>Mnemonic to remember layers of epidermis</u>- Come, **L**et's **G**et **S**un **B**urned

III. <u>Keratinization</u>-process in which cells develop in the stratum basale and *migrate upwards* over time; allows for the formation of new cells throughout the epidermis; typically, it takes *2-4 weeks* for new cells to reach the stratum corneum.

IV. Cell Types in the Epidermis

    A. <u>Keratinocytes</u>-produce keratin; sometimes called "prickle cells"

    B. <u>Melanocytes</u>-produce melanin; spider-shaped

    C. <u>Dendritic</u> (Langerhans) <u>Cells</u>-activate immune system; star-shaped macrophages

    D. <u>Tactile</u> (Merkel) <u>Cells</u>-sense touch

V. <u>Dermal-Epidermal Junction</u>-"glue" between stratum germinativum and dermis; location where blisters occur.

VI. Dermis

    A. Contains blood and lymph vessels, nerves, and other structures such as <u>sebaceous</u> (oil) <u>glands</u> (secrete sebum), and <u>sudoriferous</u> (sweat)<u> glands</u>, as well as sensors including <u>Ruffini Corpuscles</u> (to detect heat), <u>Krause's Corpuscles</u> (to detect cold), <u>Meissner's Corpuscles</u> (to detect touch), and <u>Pacinian Corpuscles</u> (to detect pressure).

    B. Also contains <u>hair follicles</u>, as well as the <u>arrector pili muscles</u> which raise hairs to cause "goosebumps".

C. <u>Avascular</u> so cells of this layer must get their oxygen and nutrients from capillaries in the dermis.

D. Made of <u>two layers of connective tissue</u> (Papillary and Reticular Layers) that form an interconnected mesh of elastin and collagenous fibers produced by fibroblasts.

    1. Papillary Layer

        a. More superficial layer that serves as an anchor point for the epidermis above and the deeper reticular layer.

        b. Has numerous <u>sensory</u>, <u>autonomic</u>, and <u>sympathetic nerve fibers</u> ensuring communication to and from the brain.

        c. Made of loose, areolar connective tissue.

        d. Projects into the stratum basale of the epidermis to form finger-like folds called <u>dermal papillae</u>.

            1). Within the papillary layer are <u>fibroblasts</u>, a small number of <u>adipocytes</u> (fat cells), and an abundance of small blood vessels.

            2). Also contains <u>phagocytes</u>, <u>defensive cells</u> (to fight infections), as well as lymphatic capillaries, nerve fibers, and <u>Meissner corpuscles</u> (touch receptors).

            3). Dermal papillae *increase the strength* of the connection between the epidermis and dermis.

            4). Also responsible for the fingerprints present on fingers and toes.

    2. Reticular Layer

        a. Much thicker layer composed of *dense irregular connective tissue* (resists forces in many directions allowing flexibility of the skin).

        b. Makes up around 80% of the dermis.

        c. Is well vascularized with arterioles and venules.

        d. Has a rich sensory and sympathetic nerve supply.

E. Sensors in Dermis

    1. <u>Meissner's Corpuscle</u>-detects light touch; found in dermal papillae.

    2. <u>Pacinian Corpuscle</u> (lamellar corpuscles)-detect pressure; found in dermis or hypodermis.

    3. <u>Krause's End Bulbs</u>-detect low frequency and cold; found in dermis.

VII. Hypodermis (called the <u>subcutaneous layer</u> or <u>superficial fascia</u>)

A. Layer directly below the dermis.

B. Serves to connect the skin to the underlying <u>fascia</u> (fibrous connective tissue wrapping that surrounds skeletal muscles anchoring them to surrounding tissues and groups of muscles).

C. Not strictly a part of the skin, although the border between the hypodermis and dermis can be difficult to distinguish.

D. Consists of well-vascularized, loose areolar connective tissue, and abundant adipose tissue (functions as a mode of fat storage and provides insulation and cushioning for the integument).

Layers of Skin (Figure 2-1)

Structure	Function/ Description	Color
Epidermis		
Stratum Corneum		
Stratum Lucidum		
Stratum Granulosum		
Stratum Spinosum		
Stratum Basale		
Basement Membrane		
Dermal Papillae		
Dermis		
Pacinian Corpuscle		
Hair Follicle		
Hair Root		
Hair Shaft		
Sebaceous (Oil) Gland		
Sebum		
Sudoriferous (Sweat) Gland		
Arteriole/Venule		
Hypodermis		
Adipose		

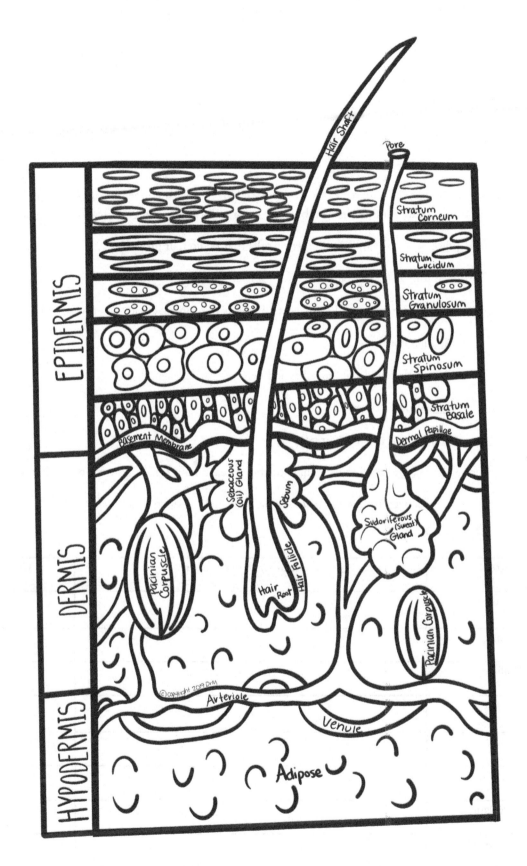

Figure 2-1

Appendages of Skin- Hair, Nails, and Glands

I. <u>Hair</u> (pili)-made of dead, keratinized cells; produced by hair follicles; contains hard <u>keratin</u>.

    A. Functions

        1. Warn of insects on skin.   3. Protects from heat loss.

        2. Guards against physical trauma.   4. Shields skin from sunlight.

    B. Hair Anatomy (**Figure 2-2**)

        1. <u>Hair follicle</u>-deep in skin; regulates hair growth; covered with <u>connective tissue sheath</u> (continuous with dermis). Location of the hair bulb where living cells divide and grow to build the <u>hair shaft</u>.

        2. <u>Hair papillae</u>-at base of follicle; cluster of cells that begin hair growth.

        3. <u>Hair root</u>-in follicle under skin.

        4. <u>Shaft</u>-visible strand; contains 3 parts that appear as concentric circles when viewed in cross section.

            a. <u>Medulla</u>-core

            b. <u>Cortex</u>-flattened cells around medulla

            c. <u>Cuticle</u>-outer layer

        5. <u>Dermal blood vessel</u>-around hair papillae

        6. <u>Arrector pili muscle</u>-small muscle that attaches to each hair; causes goosebumps when it contracts.

    C. <u>Hair growth</u>-most influenced by *nutrition and hormones* (especially testosterone)

Hair Anatomy (Figure 2-2)

Structure	Function/ Description	Color
Connective Tissue Sheath		
Hair Bulb		
Hair Follicle		
Hair Papilla		
Hair Root		
Hair Shaft		
Sebaceous Gland		
Arrector Pili Muscle		

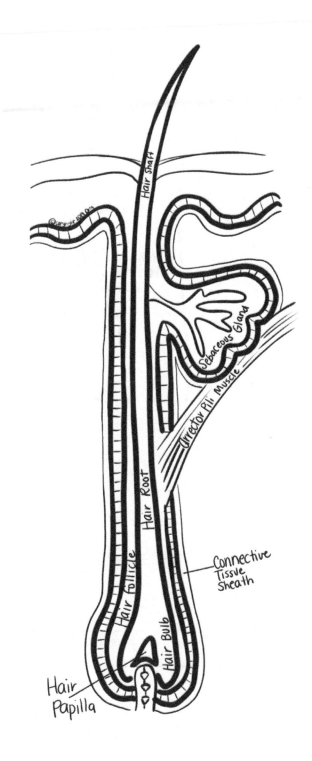

Figure 2-2

II. Nails-epidermal cells filled with keratin; function as a protective cover for distal, dorsal fingers and toes; contains 3 sections (free edge, nail plate, and root) (see **Figure 2-3**)

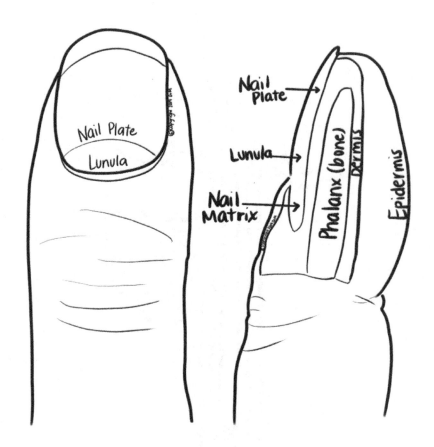

Figure 2-3

Nail Anatomy (Figure 2-3)

Structure	Function/ Description	Color
Lunula		
Nail Matrix		
Nail Plate		
Dermis		
Epidermis		

III. Glands (Associated with the Skin)

    A. <u>Sudoriferous</u> (Sweat) <u>Glands</u>-most numerous type; 2.5 million are distributed over the entire surface of the human body. There are 2 types:

        1. <u>Eccrine Sweat Glands</u>-merocrine; *most numerous type* of sweat gland. These are more common on the palms of the hands, soles of the feet, and the forehead for thermoregulation. Ducts are connected to pores where sweat is secreted.

        2. <u>Apocrine Sweat Glands</u>-located in the *axillary region* (underarm) and open directly into <u>hair follicles</u>. Secrete a milky, yellowish sweat when activated by nerves during pain and stress. The exact function of these glands is unclear. Modified apocrine glands include ceruminous glands that secrete ear wax and mammary glands that secrete milk.

    B. <u>Sebaceous</u> (Oil) <u>Glands</u>-located all over the body *except* the palms of the hands and soles of the feet. These glands open into <u>hair follicles</u>.

        1. <u>Sebum</u>-*oil* secreted by these glands. The functions of sebum include softening and lubricating the hair and skin, reducing water loss from the skin, and preventing bacterial growth on the surface of the skin.

        2. Secretion of sebum is *stimulated by hormones* (especially the sex hormones).

        3. <u>Acne</u>-inflammation of sebaceous glands that leads to the formation of pimples.

        4. <u>Blackheads</u>-occur when bacteria begin feeding on sebum.

IV. Skin Color

Skin has *3 pigments* that contribute to its color:

    A. <u>Melanin</u>-*brown or black* pigment; stored in <u>melanocytes</u>.

        1. All individuals have about the *same number* of melanocytes; differences in skin color patterns are caused by differences in the *amount of melanin* in the melanocytes.

        2. <u>Melanin</u>-*protects the skin* and the body from high levels of ultraviolet sunlight.

        3. <u>Freckles</u>-form when melanin accumulates in patches.

        4. <u>Albinism</u>-inherited *inability* of an individual to produce melanin.

        5. <u>Vitiligo</u>-partial loss of melanocytes from a small portion of the skin.

    B. <u>Carotene</u>-*yellow-orange* pigment; can be converted to vitamin A which aids in vision and proper skin growth and development; most obvious in palms and soles.

    C. <u>Hemoglobin</u>-*red* pigment in blood; color appears pinkish and can be seen in Caucasians due to lower levels of melanin.

    D. Humans have the same number of keratinocytes, so skin color differences are due to the *amount* and *form* of melanin a person possesses.

V. <u>Skin Cancer</u>-most are *noncancerous* (<u>benign</u>) and *don't spread* (<u>metastasize</u>). Risk factors include overexposure to UV radiation and frequent irritation of skin.

A. <u>Basal cell carcinoma</u>-least malignant and most common type of skin cancer. It is most common in areas exposed to direct sunlight and easily treated by surgical excision in 99% of cases.

B. <u>Squamous cell carcinoma</u>-2nd most common type; arises from keratinocytes in the stratum spinosum. It can grow and metastasize quickly and is usually seen as scaly, red papule on scalp, ears, lower lip, and hands. Early detection, surgical removal and radiation all are effective cures for this type.

C. <u>Melanoma</u>-cancer of melanocytes. Most dangerous type because it can metastasize but survival rates are good if detected early.

D. <u>ABCD Rule</u>-**A**symmetry, **B**order irregularity, **C**olor, **D**iameter; used to evaluate skin abnormalities for skin cancer risk.

Burns and Wound Healing

VI. Burns

A. Can be caused by heat, electricity, radiations, and chemicals.

B. Damaging effects of burns are caused by <u>denaturation of proteins</u> (destroys cells).

C. Threat to patient is dehydration and electrolyte imbalance because it can lead to renal shutdown and circulatory shock.

D. Evaluation of burns is done with the <u>Rule of Nines</u> (estimates volume of fluid loss) in which the body is broken down into 11 sections, each representing 9% of body surface (except genitals which account for 1%).

   1. Burns are classified by *severity*:

        a). <u>First degree burns</u>-epidermal damage only; Ex. sunburn

        b). <u>Second degree burns</u>-epidermal and upper dermal damage; blisters appear.

        c). <u>Third degree burns</u>-entire thickness of skin; skin will appear gray-white or blackened; skin grafts necessary.

   2. <u>Critical burns</u>-*more than 25% of body* covered with <u>2nd degree burns</u> or *more than 10% of body* covered with <u>3rd degree burns</u>.

   3. Common treatments of burns include debridement, antibiotics, temporary coverings, and skin grafts.

VII. Wound Healing

A. When tissue injury occurs, it stimulates the body's *inflammatory* and *immune* responses. Healing begins almost immediately.

   1. <u>Inflammation Response</u>-*generalized and non-specific* response to prevent further injury. (see **Figure 2-4**)

   2. <u>Immune Response</u>-*very specific* response against recognized bacteria, viruses, and toxins.

B. Tissue repair (wound healing) occurs in 2 major ways:

   1. <u>Regeneration</u>-replacement of damaged tissue by the *same kind* of cells.

   2. <u>Fibrosis</u>-replacement of damaged tissue by *dense fibroconnective tissue* (scar tissue).

C. Type of healing depends upon the *type of tissue* damaged and the *severity* of the injury.

D. Types of Wound Healing:

    1. <u>Epidermal wound healing</u>-involves *abrasion* of the epidermis. In this process, cells in the lower epidermis enlarge and migrate across the wound; thus, covering the site of injury.

    2. <u>Deep wound healing</u>-involves *damage* to the dermis.

Phases in this type of healing include:

    a. <u>Inflammatory Phase</u>-inflammation occurs to kill microbes, blood clots can also form here as well. (see **Figure 2-4**)

        1). <u>Platelets</u>-release *clotting proteins*.

        2). <u>Macrophages</u>-release *chemokines* to increase the immune response.

        3). <u>Mast cells</u>-release *histamine* to dilate blood vessels & make them more permeable.

        4). <u>Neutrophils</u>-remove pathogens by *phagocytosis*.

        5). <u>Macrophages</u>-release *cytokines* to start tissue repair.

    b. <u>Migratory Phase</u>-scab forms and cells begin to fill in under the scab.

    c. <u>Proliferative Phase</u>-epithelial cells grow under the scab.

    d. <u>Maturation Phase</u>-scab falls off.

Figure 2-4

Skin (Figure 2-5)

Structure	Function/ Description	Color
Epidermis		
Arrector pili muscle		
Artery		
Dermal Papillae		
Hair Follicle		
Krause's Corpuscle		
Meissner's Corpuscle		
Melanin		
Nociceptors (Free Nerve Endings)		
Pacinian Corpuscle		
Ruffini Corpuscle		
Sebaceous (Oil) Gland		
Sebum		
Sudoriferous (Sweat) Gland		
Tactile Corpuscle		
Vein		
Dermis		
Hypodermis		
Fat (Adipose)		

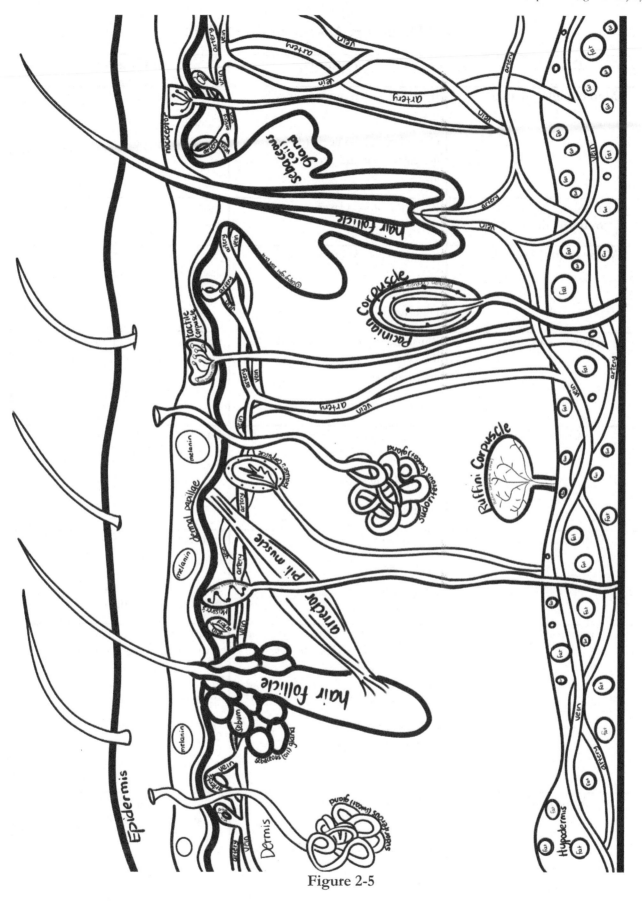

Figure 2-5

Unusual Disorders Associated with Skin

Disorder	Symptoms	Cause(s)
Methemoglobinemia	Blue skin (could result from hypoxia) Chocolate brown urine (due to increased iron and decreased oxygen levels)	Some medications Genetic (recessive)
Epidermolysis bullosa (EB) "butterfly disease"	Blistering of skin layers	Genetic (affects genes that make collagen in skin)
Malar (butterfly) rash	Butterfly-shaped rash on face Hair loss High fever	Autoimmune (most commonly associated with Lupus)
Kaposi's sarcoma	Bluish-purple lesions (spots) on legs, feet, face, genital area, mouth, or lymph nodes Decrease in immune system	Cancer in lining of blood and lymph vessels (associated with AIDS)
Cellulitis	Pain, tenderness, redness, and inflammation of skin Tight, glossy swollen skin Warmth in affected area	Bacterial infection (commonly due to Staph or Strep)
Urticaria (Hives)	Rash of round, red welts Intense itching Swelling	Chronic-linked to problems with immune system Acute-linked to allergy (like a medication, pollen, etc)
Dermatomyositis	Violet-colored or dusty-red rash on face, eyelids, knuckles, elbows, knees, and back Itchy and painful Can cause heart muscle inflammation (myocarditis) Muscle weakness	Unknown but may be associated with autoimmune disorders
Dermopathy	Red, swollen skin usually on shins and tops of feet Skin has an "orange peel" texture	Linked with hyperthyroidism (especially Graves Disease) or diabetes

CHAPTER 3. SKELETAL SYSTEM

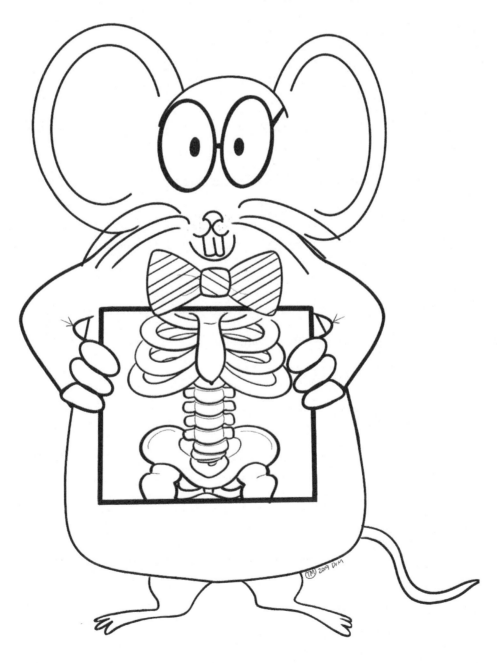

The Skeletal System

I. Skeletal System

    A. Gives the body shape and form.

    B. Helps to both protect and support the entire organism.

    C. Composed of fibrous and mineralized connective tissues that give it firmness and flexibility.

    D. Consists of bone, cartilage, tendons, joints, and ligaments.

II. Bones (see **Figure 3-1**)

    A. Adult human body consists of 206 bones; smallest bones are in the ear, largest bone is the femur.

    B. Bone-type of mineralized connective tissue containing *collagen* and *calcium phosphate* (a mineral crystal).

    C. Calcium phosphate-gives bone its firmness.

    D. Types include compact and spongy bone.

    E. Provides support and protection for organs.

    F. Work in partnership with skeletal muscle and other skeletal system components to enable body movement.

    G. Red bone marrow-produces blood cells (hematopoiesis).

    H. Yellow bone marrow-stores fat.

    I. Store important minerals and mineral salts (including calcium, phosphorus, and calcium phosphate).

    J. Composed of several layers:

        1. Periosteum (outside membrane)-covers the entire bone.

        2. Endosteum (inside membrane)-lines the medullary cavity.

    K. Primary types of bone tissue:

        1. Compact bone-dense, hard outer layer of bone that contains osteons (Haversian systems) tightly packed together.

            a. Osteon-cylindrical structure consisting of a central canal (Haversian canal) surrounded by concentric rings (lamellae) of compact bone.

            b. Haversian canal-provides a passageway for blood vessels and nerves.

        2. Cancellous (spongy) bone-located within compact bone. It is spongy, more flexible, and less dense than compact bone and typically contains red bone marrow (site of blood cell production).

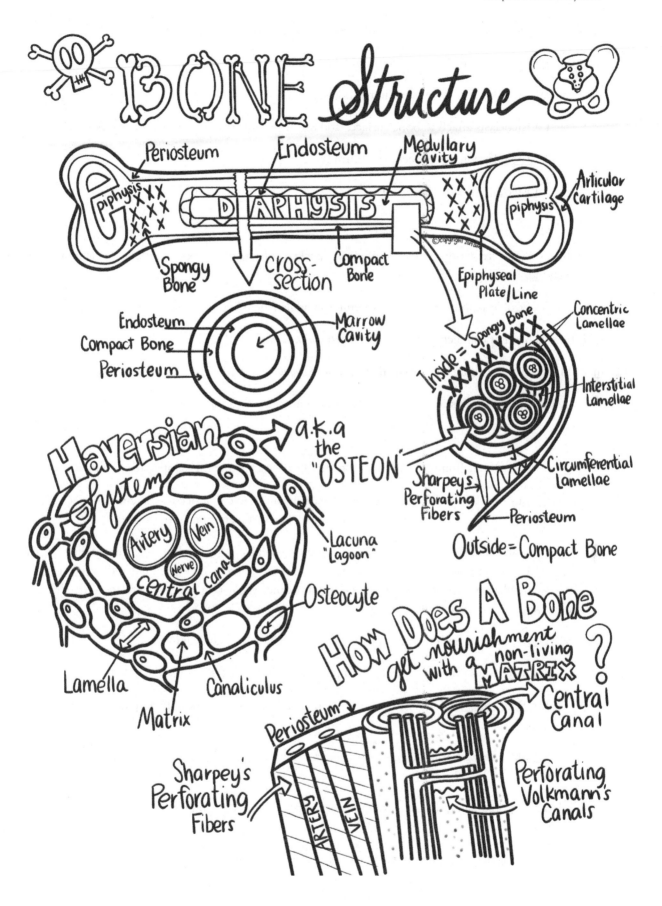

Figure 3-1

L. Consists primarily of <u>matrix</u> made up of collagen and calcium phosphate minerals.

M. <u>Remodeling</u>-constantly breaking down and rebuilding to replace old tissue with new tissue.

N. Major types of bone cells involved in remodeling:

    1. <u>Osteoclasts</u>-attach to bone surfaces and use acids and enzymes to break down bone.

    2. <u>Osteoblasts</u>-immature cells that form bone.

    3. <u>Osteocytes</u>-mature bone cells.

III. Cartilage

A. Fibrous connective tissue composed of closely packed collagenous fibers in a rubbery gelatinous substance called <u>chondrin</u>.

B. Provides flexible support for certain structures in adults, including the nose, trachea, and ears.

IV. <u>Tendon</u>-fibrous band of connective tissue that *connects muscle to bone*.

V. <u>Ligament</u>-fibrous band of connective tissue that *joins bones and other connective tissues* together at <u>joints</u>.

VI. <u>Joint</u>-where two or more bones or other skeletal components are joined together.

Types include:

A. <u>Fibrous</u> (synarthrodial)-immovable, held together by only a ligament. Example: teeth in their sockets.

B. <u>Cartilaginous</u> (synchondroses and symphyses)-partially moveable that occur where the connection between the articulating bones is made up of cartilage. Example: between vertebrae in the spine.

C. <u>Synovial</u> (diarthrosis)-freely moveable, most common type; has a <u>synovial capsule</u> surrounding the entire joint, a <u>synovial membrane</u> (the inner layer of the capsule) that secretes synovial fluid and <u>hyaline cartilage</u> (known as articular cartilage) which cushions the ends of the articulating bones. There are 6 types classified by shape of joint and movement allowed:

    1. <u>Hinge</u>-allows flexion and extension. Example: elbow or knee joint.

    2. <u>Pivot</u>-allows rotation of neck. Example: top of the spine (atlas and axis).

    3. <u>Ball and Socket</u>-allows flexion, extension, abduction, and rotation. Examples: shoulder and hip joint.

    4. <u>Saddle</u>-allows flexion, extension, adduction, abduction, and circumduction. Example: thumb joint.

    5. <u>Condyloid</u>-allows flexion, extension, adduction, abduction, and circumduction. Example: wrist joint.

    6. <u>Gliding</u>-allows gliding movements. Example: intercarpal joints.

Microscopic Anatomy of Bone (Haversian System/Osteon)

VII. Microscopic Anatomy of Bone (see **Figure 3-2**)

    A. <u>Haversian System</u> (Osteon)-the fundamental circular unit of compact bone; made of concentric rings of lamella surrounding a central canal.

    B. <u>Central</u> (Haversian) <u>Canal</u>-opening in the middle of an osteon; contains an <u>artery</u> (for oxygenated blood), <u>vein</u> (for deoxygenated blood), and <u>nerve</u> (for electrical impulses); run longitudinally along the long axis of the bone parallel to the bone's surface.

    C. <u>Perforating</u> (Volkmann's) <u>Canal</u>-canal the carries blood vessels and nerves; runs perpendicular to the Central Canal.

    D. <u>Canaliculi</u>-"*tiny canals*" that join Central Canal and lacunae to form a transport system.

    E. <u>Lacuna</u>-"*the lagoon*"; a cavity that contains a bone cell (osteocytes); arranged in concentric rings.

    F. <u>Lamellae</u>-rings of compact bone around the Central Canal; where lacunae are found. (see **Figure 3-3**)

        a. <u>Concentric Lamellae</u>-lamellae around the *outside of each osteon* (Haversian System).

        b. <u>Circumferential Lamellae</u>-lamellae around the *outside circumference* of the bone.

        c. <u>Interstitial Lamellae</u>-irregular wedges of lamellar bone *between osteons*.

    G. <u>Matrix</u>-intercellular substance found between cells made of collagenous fibers, ground substance (the organic part), as well as inorganic salts (hydroxyapatite); part of the bone tissue that forms most of the mass of the bone.

    H. <u>Osteocyte</u>-mature bone cell; resides within the lacuna and forms networks via canaliculi.

The Haversian System/Osteon (Figure 3-2)

Structure	Description or Function	Color
Central Canal		
Lacuna		
Osteocyte		
Matrix		
Artery		
Vein		
Nerve		

Did You Know... Layers of lamella around an osteon look like tree rings

Osteon layers

Figure 3-2

Figure 3-3

Cross-Section of a Long Bone (Lamellar Arrangement)

<u>Helpful hint</u>: Use pg. 47 for reference if you need assistance with this diagram.

Structure	Description	Color
Concentric Lamellae		
Interstitial Lamellae		
Circumferential Lamellae		

Match the following:

A. Central (Haversian) Canal   B. Concentric Lamellae C. Lacunae   D. Canaliculi   E. Bone Matrix

_____1. Tiny canals that connect lacunae

_____2. Nonliving, structural part of bone

_____3. Longitudinal canal that carries blood vessels and nerves

_____4. Where osteocytes reside

_____5. Layers of calcified matrix

Term Group	Which Term Doesn't Belong?	Why Do You Think It Doesn't Belong?
Epiphysis surface, Articular cartilage, Periosteum, Hyaline cartilage		
Hematopoiesis, Red marrow, Yellow marrow, Spongy bone		
Lamellae, Canaliculi, Circulation, Osteoblasts		
Osteon, Canaliculi, Central canal, Marrow cavity		

Ossification

VIII. Ossification

 A. Endochondral Ossification-forms most long bones in the body when cartilage is replaced with bone.

 1. Steps:

 a. Bone Collar Formation-primary ossification center develops in the center of the bone and osteoblasts secrete osteoid against the walls of the diaphysis, encasing it in compact bone. This bone collar gives the developing bone structural support to begin the hardening process.

 b. Cavitation-chondrocytes (cartilage cells) enlarge and signal hyaline cartilage to harden into bone in a process called *calcification*. Chondrocytes cannot receive nutrients so they die and leave small cavities creating room in the hardened bone for blood vessels to penetrate.

 c. Periosteal Bud Invasion-introduction of a nutrient source to the bone by a bud containing blood vessels and nerves. This allows nutrients, osteoblasts, and osteoclasts to enter the cavities left by the death of the chondrocytes. Osteoblasts secrete osteoid and give rise to spongy bone.

d. <u>Diaphysis Elongation</u>-diaphysis region (shaft of bone) begins to elongate in the medullary cavity as cells begin dividing in the primary center of ossification.

e. <u>Epiphyseal Ossification</u>-epiphyses (ends of the bone) develop their own secondary centers of ossification.

2. Can be remembered using this mnemonic "*Bones Can Prove Difficult Exams*".

- **Bones**=Bone Collar Formation
- **Can**=Cavitation
- **Prove**=Periosteal Bud Invasion
- **Difficult**=Diaphysis Elongation
- **Exams**=Epiphyseal Ossification

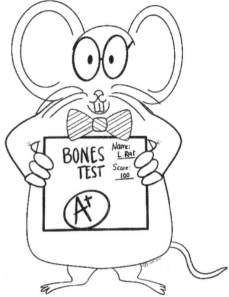

B. <u>Intramembranous Ossification</u>-develops directly from sheets of embryonic, mesenchymal (undifferentiated) connective tissue; forms the flat bones of the face, most of the cranial bones, and the clavicles (collarbones).

1. Steps:

a. <u>Ossification Centers</u>-connective tissue mesenchyme cells (embryonic cells) differentiate into <u>osteoblasts</u> and form clusters called <u>ossification centers</u>.

b. <u>Secrete Osteoid</u>-clusters of osteoblasts secrete osteoid which hardens. Trapped osteoblasts become <u>osteocytes</u>.

c. <u>Periosteum Forms</u>-small spikes of bone (<u>trabeculae</u>) radiate from the ossification centers and join neighboring bone trabeculae. <u>Periosteum</u> (outer covering of bone) forms.

d. <u>Compact Bone Forms</u>-compact bone develops above the trabecular bone and blood vessels condense into red marrow.

2. Can be remembered using this mnemonic "*Odd Students Play Cards*".

- **Odd**=Ossification Centers
- **Students**=Secrete Osteoid
- **Play**=Periosteum Forms
- **Cards**=Compact Bone Forms

IX. Bone Classification

Bones of the skeletal system can be classified into four (or sometimes five) major types, categorized by *shape* and *size*. The main bone classifications are:

1. <u>Long bones</u>-longer than they are wide; have a shaft (<u>diaphysis</u>) with heads at both ends (<u>epiphysis</u>); made of mostly compact bone. Example: femur

2. <u>Short bones</u>-usually cube shaped; made of mostly spongy bone. Example: carpals

3. <u>Flat bones</u>-thin & flattened; usually curved; made of thin layers of compact bone covering a layer of spongy bone. Examples: skull, ribs

4. <u>Irregular bones</u>-irregular shape; do not fit into the other categories. Examples: vertebrae, hip

5. <u>Sesamoid bones</u>-shaped like a sesame seed, form within tendons. Example: patella

Anatomy of a Long Bone

X. Anatomy of a Long Bone (see **Figure 3-4**)

A. <u>Diaphysis</u>-shaft of bone; made of compact bone.

B. <u>Epiphysis</u>-ends of bone; made of spongy bone.

C. <u>Periosteum</u>-outside covering of bone; made of fibrous connective tissue.

D. <u>Endosteum</u>-thin vascular membrane of connective tissue; lines the inner surface that forms the medullary cavity of long bones.

E. <u>Sharpey's Perforating Fibers</u>-secure periosteum to bone.

F. <u>Articular Cartilage</u>-covers external end (<u>epiphysis</u>) of bone; used to decrease friction at joints; made of hyaline cartilage.

G. <u>Medullary Cavity</u>-cavity of the bone shaft (<u>diaphysis</u>); contains yellow marrow (mostly fat) in adults; contains red marrow (for RBC production) in infants.

H. <u>Spongy Bone</u> (also known as <u>cancellous bone</u> or <u>trabecular bone</u>)-very porous; highly vascularized and contains red bone marrow that is used in <u>erythropoiesis</u> (RBC production). It is usually located at the ends of the long bones (the epiphyses), with the harder compact bone surrounding it; also found inside the vertebrae, in the ribs, in the skull and in the bones of the joints.

I. <u>Compact Bone</u> (also known as <u>cortical bone</u>)-dense material that is used to create much of the hard structure of the skeleton; formed from osteons.

J. <u>Epiphyseal Line/ Plate</u> (also known as the <u>growth plate</u> in kids)-hyaline cartilage plate near the epiphysis in the long bone; where new bone growth in length takes place; plate replaced by the <u>epiphyseal line</u> in adults.

Did You Know...?
If a growth plate fracture is not treated properly, the limb with the fracture could heal shorter or crooked compared to other limbs.

Anatomy of the Long Bone (Figure 3-4)

Structure	Description or Function	Color
Epiphysis		
Diaphysis		
Periosteum		
Endosteum		
Articular Cartilage		
Epiphyseal Line/ Plate		
Medullary Cavity		
Spongy Bone		
Compact Bone		

Match the following (can be used more than once):

A. Diaphysis   B. Epiphyseal Plate   C. Epiphysis   D. Red Marrow   E. Yellow Marrow Cavity

_____1. Site of longitudinal growth in a child

_____2. Site of fat storage in adults

_____3. Scientific name for the shaft of the bone

_____4. Site of erythropoiesis (RBC production) in adults

_____5. Site of compact bone in an adult

_____6. Site of spongy bone in an adult

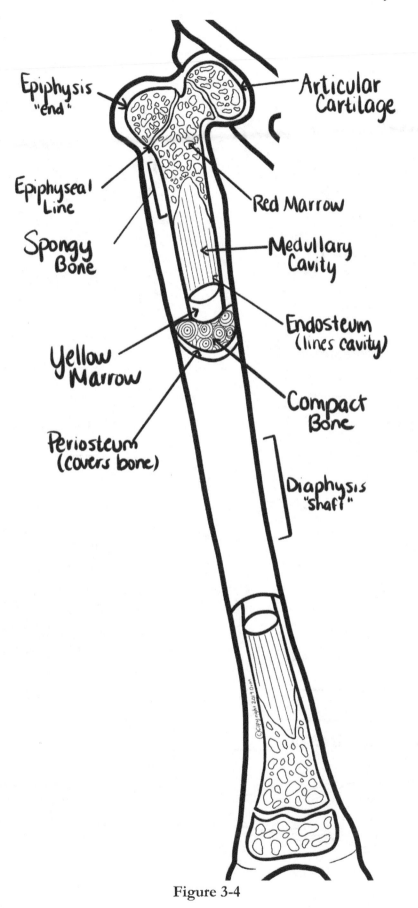

Epiphysis "end"

Articular Cartilage

Epiphyseal Line

Red Marrow

Spongy Bone

Medullary Cavity

Endosteum (lines cavity)

Yellow Marrow

Compact Bone

Periosteum (covers bone)

Diaphysis "shaft"

Figure 3-4

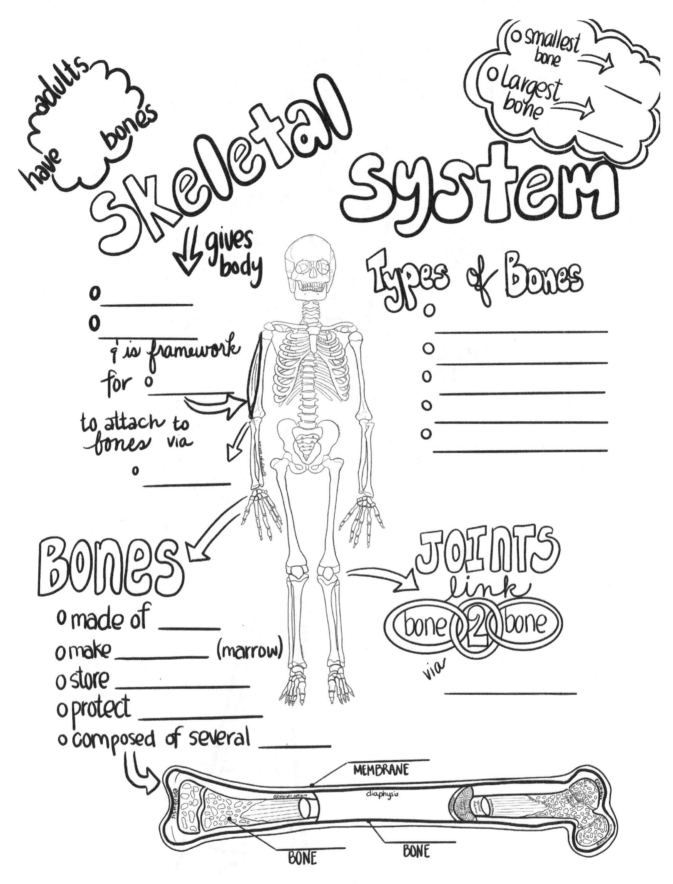

adults have _____ bones

Skeletal System

○ smallest bone →
○ largest bone →

gives body
○ _____
○ _____
& is framework for ○ _____
to attach to bones via
○ _____

Types of Bones
○
○ _____
○ _____
○ _____
○ _____

Bones
○ made of _____
○ make _____ (marrow)
○ store _____
○ protect _____
○ composed of several _____

JOINTS
link bone 2 bone
via _____

MEMBRANE
diaphysis
BONE   BONE

Figure 3-5

Fractures and Bone Healing

XI. Fractures

    A. Most commonly occur in the diaphysis of long bones.

    B. Most people will suffer at least 2 fractures over their lifetime.

        1. Under 75, the most common type is a wrist fracture.

        2. Over 75, the most common type is a hip fracture.

    C. Caused when the force applied to a bone is greater that it can handle.

    D. Most common forces that result in fractures are stretching, compression, and twisting (torsion).

    E. Can be classified as either <u>simple</u> (doesn't break skin) or <u>compound</u> (breaks through the skin).

    F. Low bone density can also contribute to fractures.

    G. Treatment of fractures includes immediate immobilization and splinting.

    H. Sometimes surgery to hold a bone in place with pins, plates, or screws is necessary if the fracture is compound, the bone has been shattered, or the fracture is displaced.

XII. Types of Fractures

Type and severity of a fracture is dependent upon the *strength* and *direction* of forces that cause a bone to break. There are 8 common types of fractures:

Type of Fracture	Characteristic of Fracture	Caused by
Transverse	Fracture occurs at an exact 90° horizontal angle	A bending force that causes the bone to snap in half
Oblique	Fracture occurs at an upward slant or angle	Trapping of 2 bones while the other twists over it (ex. Foot caught in a hole & leg twists)
Spiral	Fracture swirls around the bone	A twisting force
Greenstick	Incomplete fracture where bone bends rather than breaks	Bones being not completely ossified in children
Comminuted	Breaks in multiple pieces	Crushing injury
Avulsion	Ligament or tendon pulls away from attachment on bone & bone fragment breaks off with it	Muscle contraction that is stronger than the force that holds tendon or ligament to bone
Impacted	Fracture that occurs in center of bone where bone buckles into itself	Compression of bone from end to end
Fissure (or hairline)	Incomplete bone fracture where small lines are visible but do not pass through entire bone	Force that is not great enough to completely break the bone

XIII. Bone Repair and Healing (**Figure 3-6**)

    A. Bones are capable of repairing and remodeling themselves.

    B. The *length of time* a fracture takes to heal depends upon the *location* and *extent* of the fracture. It might take a few weeks to a few months.

    C. The healing process is initiated by cells in the <u>periosteum</u> (outer membrane surrounding bone) that respond to the stress of a fracture by triggering the <u>inflammation response</u>.

    D. Then, the periosteum produces cells which will develop into <u>chondroblasts</u> and <u>osteoblasts</u> that will fill the site of the fracture with cartilage, and later with bone.

    E. Steps in bone healing:

Step 1	Inflammation
White blood cells move to site of fracture in order to remove debris. This forms a hematoma that causes swelling, inflammation, and pain which will trigger the growth of new blood cells.	

Step 2	Soft Callus Formation
New blood vessels develop and grow into the hematoma in order to fuel the repair process as blood cells divide and multiply near the fracture. This happens over a 3-4 week period. A fibrocartilaginous callus made of collagen is formed to bridge the gap in the fracture.	

Step 3	Hard Bony Callus Formation
Approximately 2-3 months following the fracture, osteoblasts and osteocytes fill in the fibrocartilaginous callus with bone.	

Step 4	Remodeling
Any excess bone created during the formation of the bony callus (Step 3) is removed and bone is reconstructed. This remodeling improves blood circulation in the bone as well as making the bone stronger and more compact.	

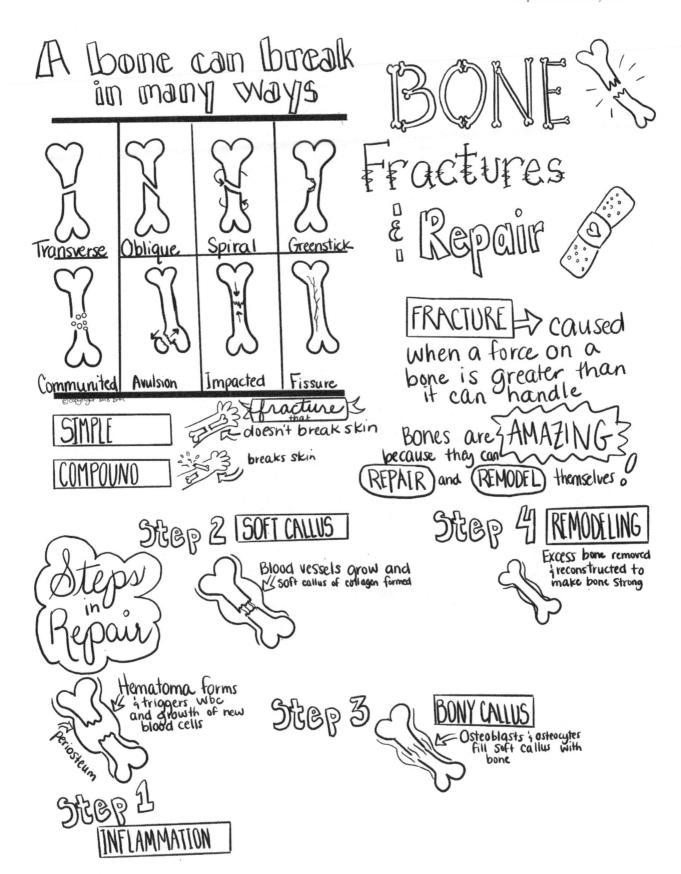

Figure 3-6

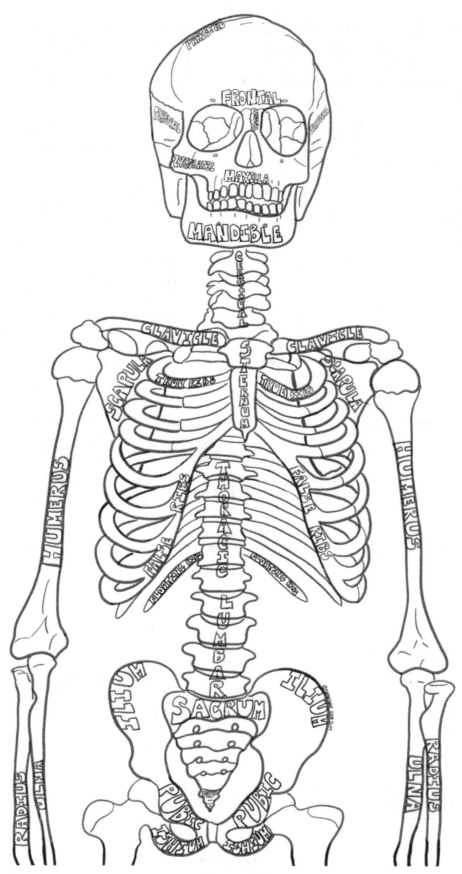

Figure 3-7

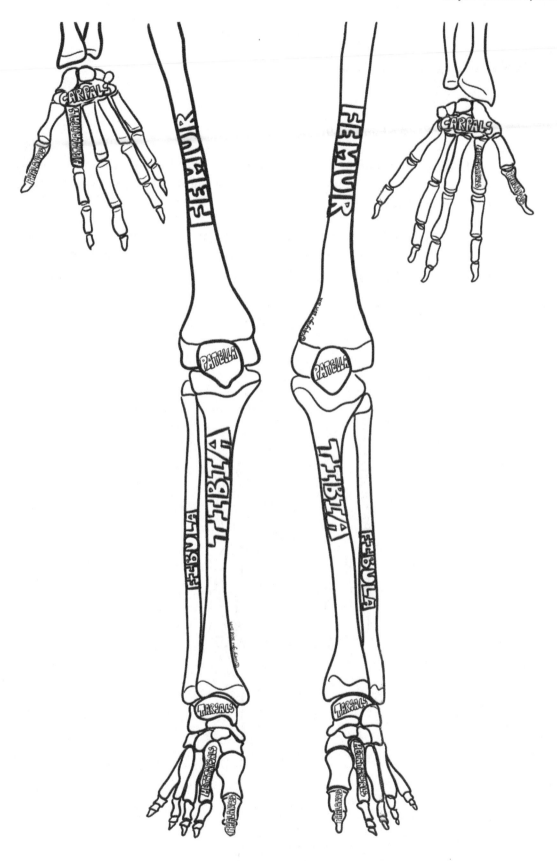

Figure 3-8

The Skeleton

I. The Human Skeleton (**Figures 3-7 and 3-8**)

    A.   Composed of 206 bones.

    B.   Two major divisions: (see **Figure 3-9**)

        1. <u>Axial Skeleton</u> (bones of the central axis of the body)-includes 80 bones that run along the midsagittal plane of the body; forms a central axis that includes bones of the skull, hyoid, vertebral column, and thoracic cage.

        2. <u>Appendicular Skeleton</u> (bones of the arms and legs)-includes 126 bones from the body limbs and structures that attach limbs to the axial skeleton; includes bones of the upper and lower limbs (arms and legs), pectoral girdles, and the pelvic girdle.

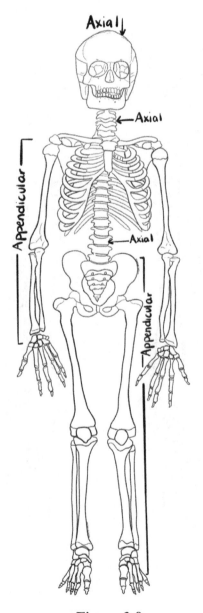

Figure 3-9

II. Skull (**Figures 3-10, 3-11,** and **3-12**)

    A. Composed of 2 major regions: the <u>cranium</u> and the <u>facial region</u>.

    B. Bones of the Cranium:

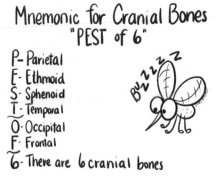

Mnemonic for Cranial Bones
"PEST of 6"
P- Parietal
E- Ethmoid
S- Sphenoid
T- Temporal
O- Occipital
F- Frontal
6- There are 6 cranial bones

        1. <u>Frontal bone</u>-thick plate that forms the forehead.

            a. <u>Supraorbital margin</u>-thickening over the eye.

            b. <u>Frontal sinuses</u>-cavities in frontal bone.

        2. <u>Parietal bones</u>-form most of the sides of the skull.

        3. <u>Temporal bones</u>-form the temple.

            a. <u>Zygomatic arch</u> (cheekbone)-formed where the <u>zygomatic process of the temporal bone</u> and the <u>temporal process of the zygomatic bone</u> meet.

            b. <u>Carotid canal</u>-space where carotid artery passes. (Since this artery is close to the ear, you can often hear your heartbeat and you may feel a pounding sensation in this area during heavy activity.)

            c. <u>Jugular foramen</u>-hole where jugular vein and 3 cranial nerves pass.

            d. <u>External acoustic meatus</u>-hole that leads to the auditory canal where ossicles (malleus, incus, stapes) are located.

            e. <u>Temporomandibular joint</u>-between temporal bone and mandible. <u>Mandibular fossa</u>-depression that articulates with the mandible to form this joint.

            f. <u>Mastoid process</u>-bump behind the ear where neck muscles attach.

            g. <u>Styloid process</u>-slender spike of bone behind the ear that is the anchor point for neck, tongue muscles, and ligaments that hold the hyoid bone in place.

        4. <u>Occipital bone</u>-back of skull.

            a. <u>Foramen magnum</u>-large hole where spinal cord passes through to attach to the brain.

            b. <u>Occipital condyles</u>-rounded knobs that articulate with vertebrae and allow for head nodding.

        5. <u>Sphenoid bone</u>-bat-shaped bone in the middle of the skull that articulates with all cranial bones.

            a. <u>Sella turcica</u> ("*Turk's saddle*")-surrounds and holds the Pituitary Gland in place.

            b. <u>Foramen ovale</u>-hole that forms a passageway for several cranial nerves.

        6. <u>Ethmoid bone</u>-upper portion of nasal cavity, forms part of the eye orbits at front of skull. The ethmoid connects to all the bones of the skull and face and essentially holds all of the bones in place.

            a. <u>Cribriform plate</u>-forms the roof of the nasal cavity and contains numerous small holes (olfactory foramina) through which olfactory nerves pass.

b. <u>Crista galli</u> ("*rooster's comb*")-ridge that serves as a site of attachment for the meninges.

c. <u>Perpendicular plate</u>-forms part of the nasal septum.

7. Major sutures of the skull:

a. <u>Coronal suture</u>-divides the frontal and parietal bones.

b. <u>Lambdoid suture</u>-divides the parietal and occipital bones.

c. <u>Squamous suture</u>-divides the parietal and temporal bones.

d. <u>Sagittal suture</u>-divides the 2 parietal bones.

8. Skull Development

a. The bones of the skull develop via <u>intramembranous ossification.</u>

b. Because of this, the skull bones are *not fully ossified* at birth. Instead, the bones are composed of <u>fontanelles</u> (soft spots) which allow the infant's head to be compressed during birth in addition to accommodating brain growth.

Anatomy of the Skull (Inferior View)-Figure 3-10

Structure	Description or Function	Color
Maxilla		
Zygomatic Bone		
Temporal Bone		
Palatine Bone (facial bone)		
Vomer (facial bone)		
Parietal Bone		
Styloid Process		
Jugular Foramen		
Carotid Canal		
Occipital Condyle		
Foramen Magnum		
Occipital Bone		

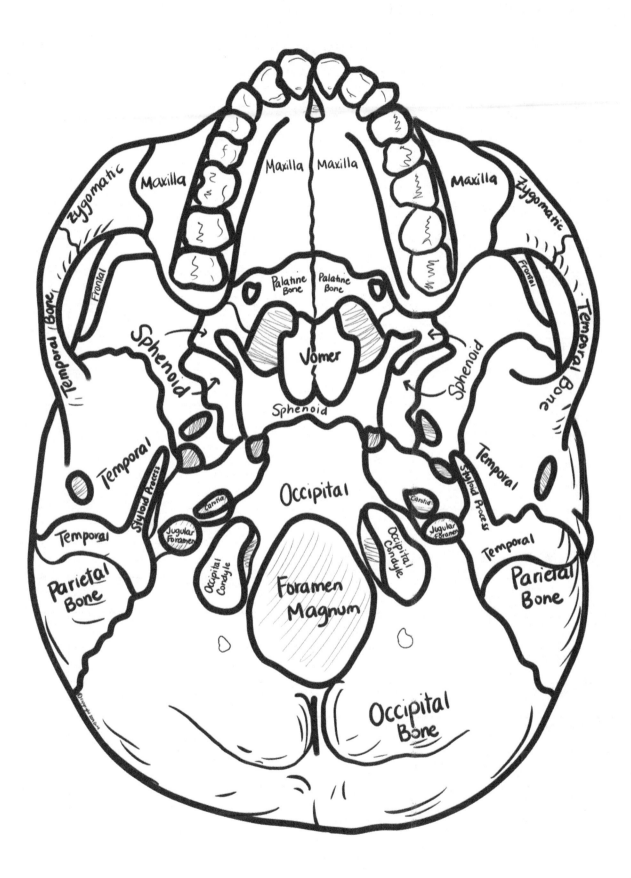

Figure 3-10

Anatomy of the Skull (Lateral View)-Figure 3-11

Structure	Description or Function	Color
Frontal bone		
Infraorbital Foramen		
Nasal Bone		
Sphenoid Bone		
Lacrimal Bone		
Ethmoid Bone		
Maxilla		
Zygomatic Bone		
Mental Foramen		
Mandible		
Zygomatic Process of Temporal Bone		
External Auditory Meatus		
Mastoid Process		
Styloid Process		
Temporal Bone		
Parietal Bone		
Occipital Bone		
Squamosal Suture		
Coronal Suture		
Lambdoid Suture		
Sagittal Suture		

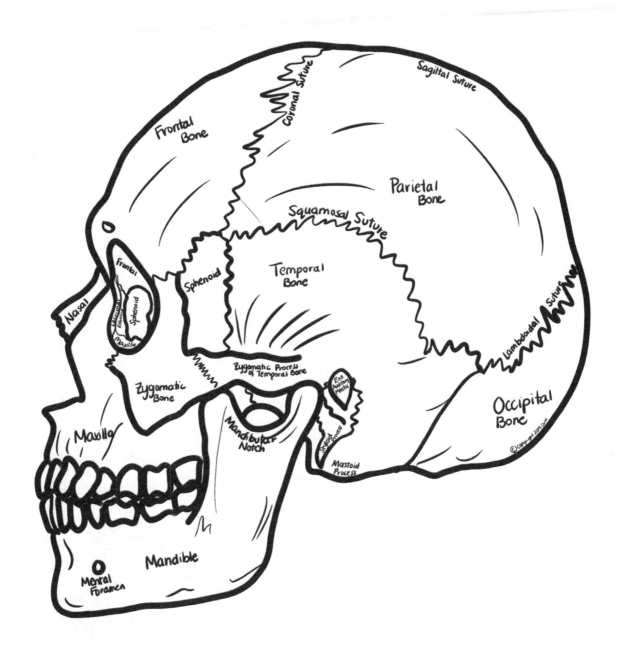

Figure 3-11

C. Facial Bones

    1. <u>Nasal bones</u>-form the bridge of the nose.

    2. <u>Nasal septum</u>-separates the right and left spaces in the nose. It is composed of the ethmoid bone, vomer bone and cartilage. Three bony processes in the nasal cavity known as <u>concha</u> (Middle, Inferior, Superior) form the walls of the nasal cavity.

    3. <u>Maxillae</u>-form the upper jaw (maxilla is singular). These paired bones hold the upper teeth in place and form the boundaries of three cavities: the roof of the mouth, the floor of the nose, and the floor of the orbits.

        a. Teeth are held in the <u>alveolar margins</u> of the maxillae.

        b. <u>Maxillary sinuses</u>-largest of the paranasal sinuses.

        c. <u>Cleft palate</u>-condition in which the maxillary bones are not completely joined; often leads to a cleft lip; can be repaired via surgery.

    4. <u>Zygomatic bones</u>-cheek bones that articulate with the maxilla, temporal bones, and sphenoid bone.

    5. <u>Mandible</u>-largest and strongest bone of the face that forms the lower jaw bone; holds the lower teeth in place.

        a. <u>Mental foramen</u>-passageway for nerves to the chin.

    6. <u>Vomer</u>-unpaired facial bone that forms part of the nasal septum.

        a. <u>Deviated nasal septum</u>-disorder in which the vomer is pushed to one side; often caused by trauma to the face.

    7. <u>Palatine bones</u>-paired L-shaped bones that form part of the hard palate (roof of the mouth) and the nasal cavity.

    8. <u>Lacrimal bones</u>-smallest and most fragile bones of the face; located at inner corner of eye under tear ducts.

    9. <u>Eye orbit</u>-cavity or socket that holds the eye. Blood vessels and nerves enter this area through the <u>Infraorbital Foramen</u> (below eye) and the <u>Supraorbital Foramen</u> (above eye).

    10. <u>Hyoid bone</u>-horseshoe shaped bone located in neck; location where tongue attaches.

<u>Mnemonic for Facial Bones</u>- "Virgil Can Not Make My Pet Zebra Laugh!" (**V**omer, **C**onchae (inferior), **N**asal bone, **M**axilla, **M**andible, **P**alatine bone, **Z**ygomatic bone, **L**acrimal bones)

Bone Markings

Marking	Description	Example
Articulations	Where two bones meet	Knee joint
Head	Prominent rounded surface	Head of femur
Facet	Flat surface	Vertebrae
Condyle	Rounded surface	Occipital condyles
Projections	Raised markings	Spinous process of the vertebrae
Protuberance	Protruding	Chin
Process	Prominence feature	Transverse process of vertebra
Spine	Sharp process	Ischial spine
Tubercle	Small, rounded process	Tubercle of humerus
Tuberosity	Rough surface	Deltoid tuberosity
Line	Slight, elongated ridge	Temporal lines of the parietal bones
Crest	Ridge	Iliac crest
Holes	Holes and depressions	Foramen (holes through which blood vessels can pass through)
Fossa	Elongated depression	Mandibular fossa
Fovea	Small pit	Fovea capitis on the head of the femur
Sulcus	Groove	Sigmoid sulcus of the temporal bones
Canal	Passage in bone	Auditory canal
Fissure	Slit through bone	Auricular fissure
Foramen	Hole through bone	Foramen magnum in the occipital bone
Foramina	Small hole in bone	Olfactory foramina of cribriform plate
Meatus	Opening into canal	External auditory meatus
Sinus	Air-filled space in bone	Nasal sinus

Anatomy of the Skull (Frontal View)- Figure 3-12

Structure	Description or Function	Color
Frontal Bone		
Parietal Bone		
Nasal Bone		
Sphenoid Bone		
Temporal Bone		
Ethmoid Bone		
Zygomatic Bone		
Lacrimal Bone		
Maxilla		
Perpendicular Plate		
Nasal Conchae		
Supraorbital Foramen		
Mental Foramen		

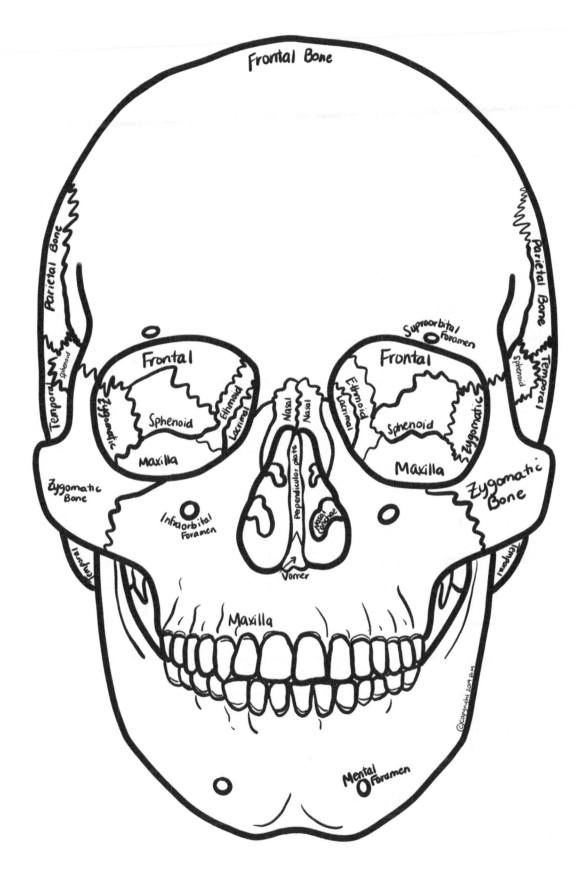

Figure 3-12

IV. Vertebral Column

    A. Regions of the vertebral column (33 individual bones)

        1. Cervical region-in neck; 7 vertebrae.

        2. Thoracic region-in chest; 12 vertebrae.

        3. Lumbar region-in lower back; 5 vertebrae.

        4. Sacral region-in hips; 5 vertebrae (fused).

        5. Coccygeal region-tailbone; 4 vertebrae (fused).

    B. Normal Curves of the Vertebral Column

        1. Cervical curve and Lumbar curve-concave.

        2. Thoracic curve and Sacral curve-convex.

Memory trick for vertebral column-The number of bones in each region can be remembered as the same times one would eat meals (breakfast, lunch, and dinner). Breakfast, 7am and the cervical has 7 bones; Lunch, 12pm and the thoracic has 12 bones; Dinner, 5 pm and the lumbar has 5 bones.

Vertebral Column (Figure 3-13)

Structure	Description /Location	Number	Concave/Convex	Color
Atlas				
Axis				
Cervical				
Thoracic				
Lumbar				
Sacral				
Coccyx				

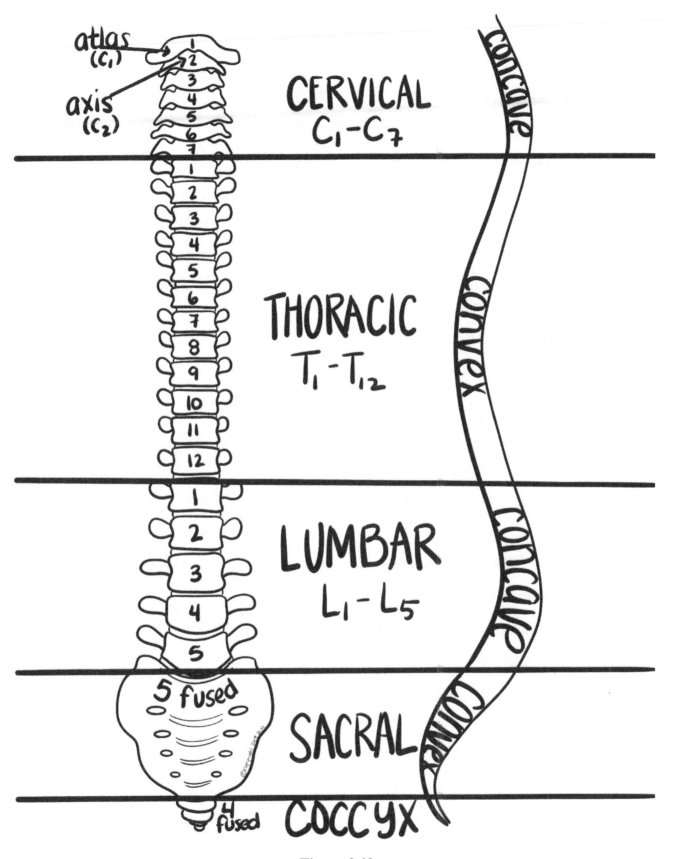

Figure 3-13

C. <u>Vertebrae</u>-bones that make up the spinal column; become larger as you move down the spinal column. (see **Figure 3-14**)

The major parts of a vertebra include:

1. <u>Intervertebral disc</u>-cartilage pad between the vertebrae.

2. <u>Body</u> (centrum)-major weight-bearing structure.

3. <u>Vertebral arch</u>-also bears weight.

 Composed of:

 a. <u>Pedicle</u>-forms the arches.

 b. <u>Lamina</u>-roof of the spinal canal that provides support and protection for the backside of the spinal cord.

4. <u>Vertebral foramen</u>-hole where spinal cord passes.

5. <u>Intervertebral foramen/foramina</u>-small holes where nerves pass.

6. <u>Processes</u>-project outward from vertebrae for muscle attachment.

 a. <u>Spinous process</u>-projects up from center.

 b. <u>Transverse processes</u> (2)-project outward to sides.

 c. <u>Articular processes</u>-fit with adjacent vertebrae.

7. <u>Atlas</u>-C1 vertebra; has no body. Supports head and allows you to nod *"yes"* .

8. <u>Axis</u>-C2 vertebra; has the <u>dens</u> process. Allows you to shake your head *"no"*.

 a. <u>Dens</u> (Odontoid Process)-pivot point on the axis for skull rotation.

D. <u>Sacrum</u>-triangular bone, composed of 5 fused vertebrae.

1. <u>Sacral foramina</u>-holes through which nerves and blood vessels pass.

2. <u>Sacral canal</u>-extension of the vertebral foramen on the sacrum.

E. <u>Coccyx</u>-tailbone, composed of 4 fused vertebrae.

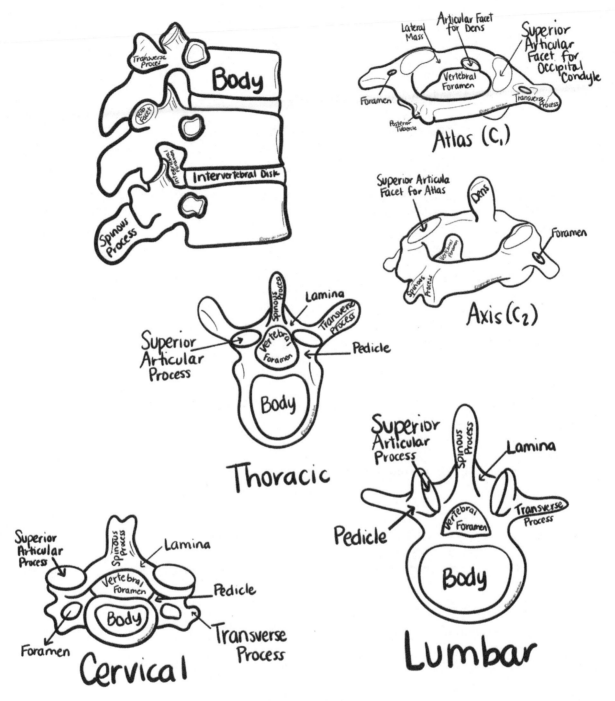

Figure 3-14

Vertebrae

Structure	Description or Function	Color
Body of Vertebra		
Transverse Process		
Spinous Process		

V. Sternum

 Major Regions

  1. <u>Manubrium</u>-superior portion.

   a. <u>Clavicular notch</u>-where clavicle attaches.

   b. <u>Jugular notch</u>-superior portion of the manubrium.

  2. <u>Body</u>-attaches to cartilages from ribs 2-7.

  3. <u>Xiphoid process</u>-primarily cartilage, becomes hardened (ossified) as we age; where abdominal muscles attach; used as a landmark for CPR.

VI. Ribs (12 pairs)

 A. <u>True ribs</u>-their cartilage attaches *directly* to the sternum.

 B. <u>False ribs</u>-their cartilage *does not attach directly* to the sternum.

 C. <u>Floating ribs</u>-do not attach to the sternum at all.

 D. Parts of a rib

  1. <u>Head</u>-attaches to the vertebrae, the <u>neck</u> is near the head of a rib.

  2. <u>Shaft</u>-forms the length of a rib.

  3. <u>Tubercle</u>-attaches to the thoracic vertebrae.

VII. Clavicle

 A. <u>Sternal extremity</u>-site where the clavicle articulates with the sternum.

 B. <u>Acromial extremity</u>-site where the clavicle articulates with the acromion.

VIII. Scapula

 A. <u>Acromion</u>-upper portion of scapula, forms the <u>acromioclavicular joint</u>.

 B. <u>Glenoid cavity</u>-depression (fossa) where the humerus attaches to form the shoulder joint.

 C. <u>Suprascapular notch</u>-notch through which major nerves pass.

 D. <u>Coracoid process</u>-posterior structure, site of muscle attachment.

 E. <u>Supraspinous fossa</u>-depression where the supraspinatus muscle resides.

 F. <u>Infraspinous fossa</u>-depression where the infraspinatus muscle resides.

 G. <u>Subscapular fossa</u>-depression where the subscapularis muscle resides.

IX. Humerus

   A. <u>Head</u>-articulates with the glenoid cavity to form the shoulder joint.

   B. <u>Anatomical neck</u>-site of the epiphyseal plate.

   C. <u>Greater tubercle</u>-knob, where major muscles attach.

   D. <u>Lesser tubercle</u>-smaller knob, also a site for major muscle attachment.

   E. <u>Deltoid tuberosity</u>-site where the deltoid muscle attaches.

   F. <u>Capitulum</u>-allows the humerus to articulate with the ulna.

   G. <u>Trochlea</u>-allows for articulation of the humerus at the elbow joint.

   H. <u>Coronoid fossa</u>-forms part of the elbow joint.

   I. <u>Olecranon fossa</u>-forms part of the elbow joint.

   J. <u>Medial and lateral epicondyles</u>-bumps that serve as sites for muscle attachment.

X. Ulna

   A. <u>Olecranon process</u>-prominence of the elbow.

   B. <u>Coronoid Process</u>-projection from the front of the ulna that forms part of the articulation of the elbow.

   C. <u>Radial Notch</u>-site of radial articulation with the ulna.

XI. Radius

   A. <u>Head</u>-nail-shaped structure that articulates with the ulna.

   B. <u>Radial tuberosity</u>-site for muscle attachment.

   C. <u>Ulnar notch</u>-low on the radius, articulates with the ulna.

<u>Mnemonic for elbow joint</u>-Which part of the humerus articulates with the radius vs. ulna?

CRAzy **TUL**ips

Capitulum (on humerus) = **RA**dius

Trochlear (on humerus) = **U**lnar

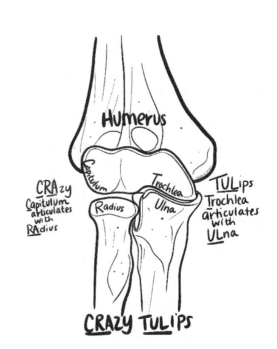

XII. Hand (**Figures 3-15 and 3-16**)

    A. <u>Carpals</u>-8 bones that form the wrist.

    B. <u>Metacarpals</u>-5 bones that form the palm of the hand.

    C. <u>Phalanges</u>-14 in each hand that form the fingers.

    D. <u>Disorders of the Forearm/Hand</u>:

        1. <u>Carpal Tunnel Syndrome</u>-causes pain, numbness, and tingling in the hand and arm; occurs when one of the major nerves to the hand (median nerve) is compressed.

        2. <u>Osteoarthritis</u>-degeneration of articular cartilage; very common in the hand and wrist; occurs as individuals age.

<u>**Mnemonic for Carpal Bones**</u>**- (Distal to Proximal, Palmar Aspect)"These Things Can Happen. Sensible Lovers Take Precautions"** (**T**rapezium, **T**rapezoid, **C**apitate, **H**amate, **S**caphoid, **L**unate, **T**riquetrum, **P**isiform)
**Note: The pisiform bone is <u>only</u> visible in the palmar aspect. It is not visible in the dorsal view of the hand.

Anatomy of the Left Hand (Palmar and Dorsal Aspects)-Figures 3-15 and 3-16

Structure	Description	Color
Distal phalanges		
Intermediate phalanges		
Proximal phalanges		
Metacarpals		
Trapezium		
Trapezoid		
Scaphoid		
Capitate		
Lunate		
Hamate		
Triquetrum		
Pisiform (*only seen in Palmar View) Figure 3-15		
Ulna		
Radius		

Palmar Aspect of Left Hand (Palm of Hand, Pisiform Bone Visible)

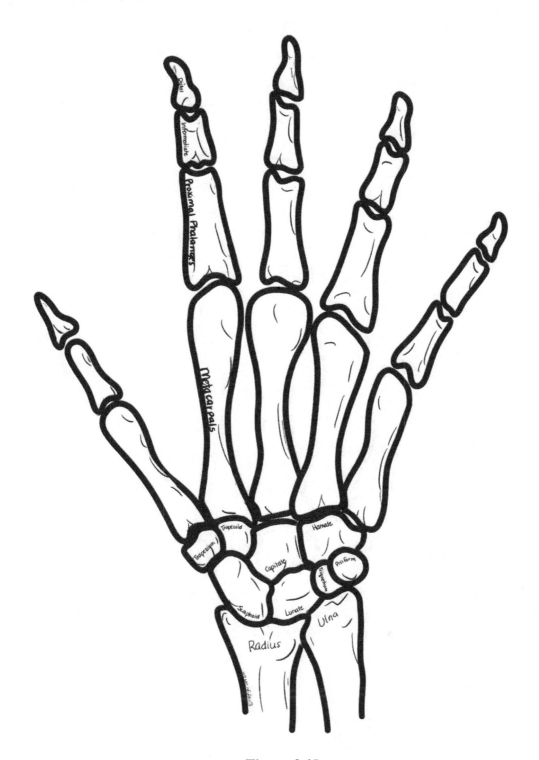

Figure 3-15

Dorsal Aspect of Left Hand (Top of Hand)

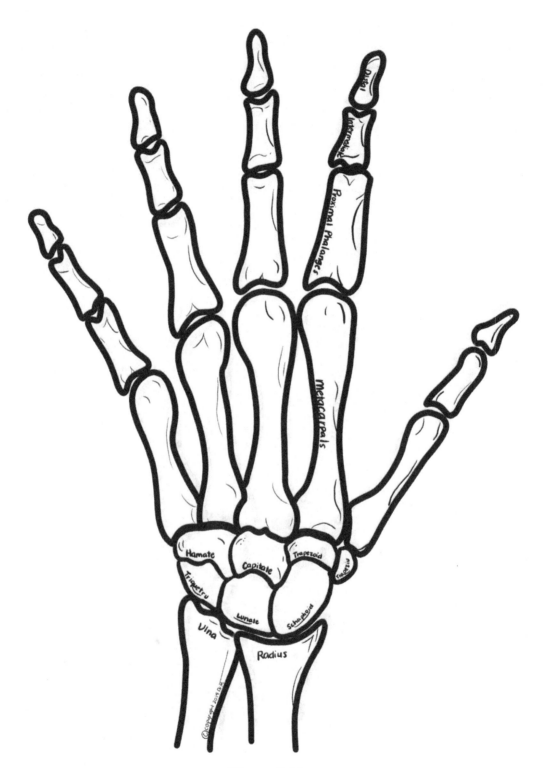

Figure 3-16

XIII. Pelvic Girdle

    A. Ilium

        1. <u>Sacroiliac joint</u>-site where the sacrum and ilium attach.

        2. <u>Greater sciatic notch</u>-allows passage of sciatic nerve to leg.

    B. Ischium

        1. <u>Obturator foramen</u>-large hole in pelvis where blood vessels and nerves pass.

        2. <u>Ischial tuberosity</u>-inferior surface of the ischial body, is rough and thickened but is strongest part of the hip bone supports our weight when we sit.

        3. <u>Acetabulum</u>-deep socket that receives the head of the femur or thigh bone.

    C. Pubis

        1. <u>Pubic symphysis</u>-formed by the rami of the pubic bones; held together by fibrocartilage and forms the pubic arch.

        2. Pubis is wider in females to allow for childbirth.

XIV. Femur

    A. <u>Head of femur</u>-forms the pelvic girdle.

    B. <u>Greater and lesser trochanters</u>-knobs for major muscle attachment, including the gluteal muscles.

    C. <u>Medial and lateral condyles</u>-articulate with the medial and lateral condyles of tibia forming knee joint.

 XV. <u>Patella</u> (kneecap)-increases leverage of the leg; held in place by the patellar ligament.

XVI. <u>Tibia</u>-second largest bone of the body.

    A. <u>Medial and lateral condyles</u>-articulate with medial and lateral condyles of the femur to form knee joint.

    B. <u>Medial malleolus</u>-forms the medial side (inner) of the ankle.

    C. <u>Tibial tuberosity</u>-site for patellar ligament attachment.

    D. <u>Fibular notch</u>-site where the fibula attaches to the tibia.

XVII. <u>Fibula</u>-smaller of the 2 bones in lower leg

    A. <u>Lateral malleolus</u>-forms the lateral side (outside) of the ankle.

<u>Mnemonic for bones of lower leg</u>-Which is lateral, tibia or fibula?

FibuLA is LAteral

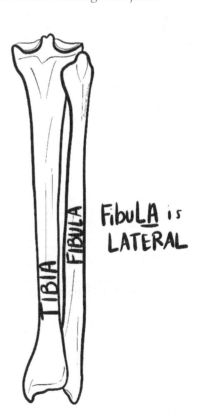

FibuLA is LATERAL

XVIII. Foot (see **Figures 3-17 and 3-18**)

A. <u>Tarsals</u>-7 bones that form the ankle.

B. <u>Metatarsals</u>-5 bones that form the arch of the foot.

C. <u>Phalanges</u>-14 in each foot that form the toes.

<u>Mnemonic for Tarsal Bones</u>- (right foot, superior to inferior, medial to lateral)- "Tiger Cubs Need MILC" (**T**alus, **C**alcaneus, **N**avicular, **M**edial Cuneiform, **I**ntermediate Cuneiform, **L**ateral Cuneiform, **C**uboid)

Anatomy of the Right Foot (Dorsal and Plantar Aspects)-Figures 3-17 and 3-18

Structure	Description	Color
Distal phalanges		
Intermediate phalanges		
Proximal phalanges		
Metatarsals		
Talus		
Calcaneus		
Navicular		
Medial Cuneiform		
Intermediate Cuneiform		
Lateral Cuneiform		
Cuboid		

Dorsal Aspect of Right Foot (Top of Foot)

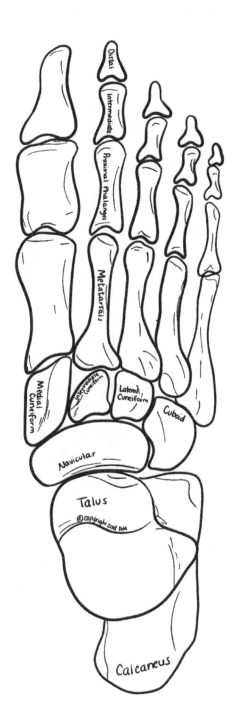

Figure 3-17

Plantar Aspect of Right Foot (Bottom of Foot)

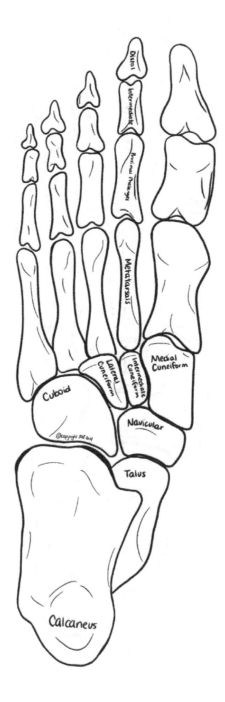

Figure 3-18

Bones

Bone	Description of Bone	Number Found in Body
I. Axial Skeleton— Skull & Face		
Cranium (8)		
Parietal		
Ethmoid		
Sphenoid		
Temporal		
Occipital		
Frontal		
Face (14)		
Vomer		
Nasal Conchae		
Nasal		
Maxilla		
Mandible		
Palatine		
Zygomatic		
Lacrimal		
Ear (6)		
Ossicles (Malleus, Incus, Stapes)		
Neck (1)		
Hyoid		
II. Axial Skeleton— Vertebral Column		
Backbone (26)		
Cervical Vertebrae		
Thoracic Vertebrae		
Lumbar Vertebrae		

Sacrum		
Coccyx		

III. Axial Skeleton— Thoracic Cage

Thoracic Cage (25)		
Ribs • True • False		
Sternum		

IV. Appendicular Skeleton—Pectoral and Pelvic Girdles

Pectoral Girdle/Upper Limbs (64)		
Scapula		
Clavicle		
Humerus		
Ulna		
Radius		
Carpals		
Metacarpals		
Phalanges		
Pelvic Girdle/Lower Limbs (62)		
Os Coxa (ilium, ischium, pelvic)		
Femur		
Tibia		
Fibula		
Patella		
Tarsals		
Metatarsals		
Phalanges		
	Total Bones	**206**

What We Learn from Bones

I. What Bones Can Tell Us

    A. Bones contain a record of the physical life. In fact, the term <u>osteobiography</u> literally translates as the "*story of a life told by the bones*";

    B. How to Distinguish Male from Female (see **Figure 3-19**)

        1. Overall appearance of the female's skeleton tends to be much smaller, smoother, and less knobby than a male's skeleton.

        2. <u>Skull</u>-male skull is larger and has more prominent features than the female skull.

Male	Female
Heavy and rugged	More delicate
Eye orbits are square	Eye orbits are rounded
Supraorbital ridge (brow) is sloping, heavy, and pronounced	Brow is more vertical, smooth, and flat
Cheekbones heavy & more laterally arched	Cheekbones lighter, more compressed, and lack lateral arching.
Occipital protuberance (bump at base of skull) very pronounced	Occipital protuberance almost absent
Chin square shaped	Chin rounded
Angle of jaw line is more angular (obtuse angle)	Angle of jaw line is more curved (acute angle)
Mastoid process (bump behind ear) large and prominent	Mastoid process (bump behind ear) small

        3. <u>Pelvis</u>-because of the anatomical differences needed for childbearing, this region of the body exhibits many differences.

Male	Female
Narrow	Wide
Pelvic opening is more constricted	Pelvic opening is rounder and larger (to accommodate childbirth)
Pubic arch angle is narrow and less than 90°	Pubic arch angle is broad and greater than 90°
Sacrum is small, narrow, and curved	Sacrum is broad, wider, and straighter
Obturator foramen appears rounded	Obturator foramen appears oval shaped

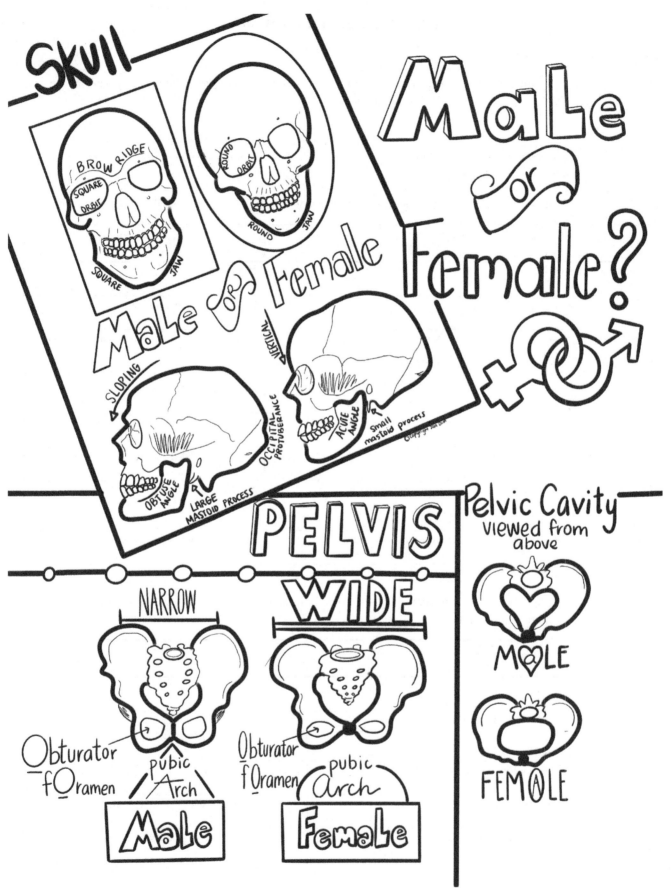

Figure 3-19

II. <u>How to Distinguish Age</u>-determined by examining features of certain bones (such as skull and long bones) and by looking for the presence or absence of cartilage.

    A. <u>Suture Marks</u>-zigzag appearance are found on the skull where bones meet and ossify; three main areas where skull bones meet and grow together can be identified: the lambdoidal, sagittal, and coronal.

    B. <u>Cartilaginous Lines</u> (epiphyseal)-appear as cartilage is slowly replaced with hard, compact bone. As bones complete ossification, this epiphyseal line mostly disappears.

III. How to Distinguish Height

    A. Measuring bones like the humerus or femur can help determine the approximate height of an individual.

    B. The mathematical formula derived from skeletal analysis between bone length and estimated height varies depending on the race and the bone examined. However, general formulas can be used:

      1. To calculate the estimated height based on the person's <u>femur</u>, first measure the femur in centimeters.

        a. If the subject is female, multiply the length by 2.47 and add 54.1 to arrive at the approximate height.

        b. If the subject is male, multiply by 2.32 and add 65.53. These calculations are accurate to within five centimeters.

      2. To calculate the estimated height based on the person's <u>humerus</u>, measure the humerus in centimeters.

        a. For a female subject, multiply the length in centimeters by 3.08 and add 64.67.

        b. For a male subject, multiply the length by 2.89 and add 78.1. Again, these calculations are accurate to within five centimeters of the subject's height.

CHAPTER 4. MUSCULAR SYSTEM

Microscopic Muscle Anatomy

I. <u>Myology</u>-the study of muscle tissue. Muscles account for nearly 50% of total body weight.

    A. Muscles are capable of transforming <u>chemical energy</u> (ATP) into <u>mechanical energy</u>. This mechanical energy is used to *generate force* and to produce muscle *movements*.

    B. Muscle is from the Latin *mus* which means "*little mouse*".

    C. Common prefixes for muscle include: <u>myo</u>-, <u>mys</u>-, and <u>sarco</u>-

II. Types of Muscle Tissue

    A. Skeletal (Key words: *skeletal, striated, voluntary*)

        1. Elongated cells; also called <u>muscle fibers</u>.

        2. Packaged into <u>skeletal muscles</u> (organs attached to bone and skin).

        3. Skeletal muscle fibers are the longest of all muscle and have <u>striations</u> (stripes) running through them.

        4. Also called <u>voluntary muscle</u> because it is under conscious control.

        5. Contracts rapidly, tires easily, and is very powerful.

    B. Cardiac (Key words: *cardiac, striated, involuntary*)

        1. Found only in the <u>heart</u>.

        2. Striated and is <u>involuntary</u> (not consciously controlled).

    C. Smooth (Key words: *smooth, non-striated, involuntary*)

        1. Found in walls of hollow organs.

        2. Not striated and is involuntary.

        3. Elongated cells.

III. Characteristics Shared by All Muscles

    A. <u>Excitability</u>-ability to respond to a stimulus by producing electrical signals (impulses) within the body; also a major property of nerve tissue; triggered and regulated by neurotransmitters and hormones.

    B. <u>Contractility</u>-ability to shorten and thicken (contract), therefore, generating force to do work; a characteristic is unique to muscle tissue.

    C. <u>Extensibility</u>-ability to stretch without damage to the tissue.

    D. <u>Elasticity</u>-the ability to return to its original shape after stretching or contracting.

IV. Functions

    A. <u>Movement</u>-skeletal muscles contract (shorten) to pull on bones producing movement; also move and position the eyeball, and create facial expressions.

    B. <u>Maintaining posture</u>-skeletal muscles help us sit upright and stand.

    C. <u>Stabilizing joints</u>-provide strength and support to joints.

D. <u>Produce heat</u> (thermogenesis)-can generate as much as 85% of our body heat; <u>Shivering</u>-involuntary contractions of skeletal muscles that greatly increases body temperature when the body is cold.

E. <u>Additional functions</u>-protect organs, form valves in the body, control pupil size; cause "goosebumps" to generate heat when cold.

V. Skeletal Muscle Anatomy

A. Each skeletal muscle is composed of numerous <u>myofibers</u> (*"muscle fibers"* or muscle cells), nerves, blood vessels, and connective tissues.

1. Myofibers run parallel to each other.

2. Parts of a Skeletal Muscle Fiber:

a. <u>Sarcolemma</u>-plasma membrane of muscle cell.

b. <u>Sarcoplasm</u>-cytoplasm of muscle cell.

c. <u>Myofibrils</u>-small thread-like structures in the sarcoplasm of muscle fibers. *These are the contractile elements of the muscle fiber.* They make up approximately 80% of muscle cell volume and run parallel to the length of the entire muscle fiber.

d. Numerous <u>mitochondria</u> that are involved in aerobic cellular respiration.

B. <u>Skeletal muscle</u>-an organ made of different tissues, as well as nerve and blood supply, connective tissue sheaths, and attachments.

C. Nerve and blood supply

1. Each muscle receives a <u>nerve</u>, an <u>artery</u>, and <u>veins</u>.

2. Skeletal muscle has nerves supplying every fiber.

3. Contracting fibers also require huge amounts of oxygen and nutrients, as well as waste product removal.

Skeletal Muscle Cross-Section

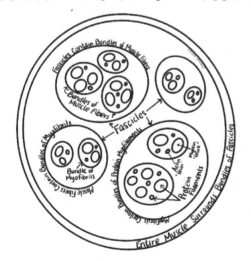

D. Skeletal muscle is packaged as a *series of tubes within other tubes.* It is easy to see this in **Figure 4-1**. The subdivisions include:

1. <u>Entire muscle</u>-made of bundles of long tubes called <u>fascicles</u> (*fasciculus*= singular form).

2. <u>Each fascicle</u>-composed of a bundle of <u>skeletal muscle fibers</u> (these are *skeletal muscle cells*).

3. <u>Each skeletal muscle fiber</u>-made of a bundle of <u>myofibrils</u>.

4. <u>Each myofibril</u>-made of two different <u>protein filaments</u> called <u>actin</u> (*thin* filament) and <u>myosin</u> (*thick* filament). Myosin contains small protruding heads which bind to regions of the thin filament actin.

Figure 4-1

E. Connective Tissue Sheaths (of skeletal muscle tissue)-the different bundles of tube-like structures that make up skeletal muscle are held together by *wrappings (sheaths) of connective tissue*. As shown in **Figure 4-2**, these wrap individual muscle fibers in order to support each cell, as well as reinforce and hold together the muscle and prevent the bulging muscles from bursting during strong contractions. These wrappings are (from exterior to interior):

Figure 4-2

1. Fascia-sheet of fibrous connective tissue deep to the skin that covers muscles.

2. Layers of Connective Tissue Sheaths Beneath the Deep Fascia (external to internal) (see **Figure 4-3**)

a. Epimysium-outer layer, nearest to the deep fascia; tough, fibrous connective tissue that completely *surrounds the outside* of an entire skeletal muscle.

b. Perimysium-*surrounds bundles of muscle fibers*; (called fascicles); made of fibrous connective tissue from portions of the epimysium that project inward and divide the muscle into compartments. Each compartment contains a bundle of myofibers (muscle fibers).

c. Endomysium-inner layer, surrounds and separates *each individual muscle cell* (called a myofiber or muscle fiber) within the fascicles; made of fine areolar connective tissue.

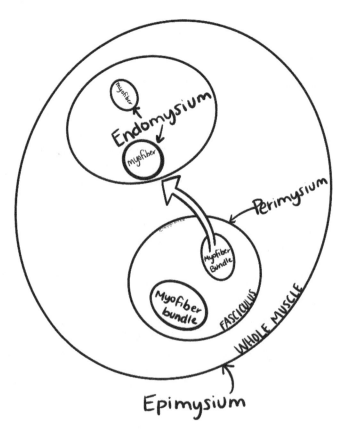

Figure 4-3

3. <u>Tendons</u>-connective tissue cords that attach *muscle to bone* (specifically to the periosteum of bone).

    a. <u>Tendon sheaths</u>-cover and protect some tendons in the human body.

    b. <u>Aponeurosis</u>-tendon that appears as a broad, flat layer over a muscle; also attach muscles to bone.

F. Sarcomere (the structural and functional unit for muscle contraction)

1. Arranged in a stacked pattern throughout striated muscle tissue. Segments are aligned end to end along a myofibril like boxcars. Each individual sarcomere is flanked by discs of protein called <u>Z lines</u>, which hold the myofilaments in place. The actin filaments radiate out from the Z discs to help to anchor the central myosin filaments in place. A sarcomere spans the area between the Z discs and contains an <u>A band</u> with half an <u>I band</u> at each end.

2. The overlap of the thick myosin filaments and thin actin filaments is responsible for producing the <u>striations</u> (stripes) visible in skeletal and cardiac muscle.

3. An individual sarcomere contains many parallel actin and myosin filaments. Movement of these two filaments relative to one another causes the lengthening and shortening of the sarcomere, thus producing <u>muscle contraction</u>.

G. Attachments

1. Skeletal muscles *attach to one bone* and *extend across a joint* to attach to another bone. When the muscle contracts, one of the structures usually remains stationary while the other moves. Skeletal muscle attaches to bones in at least 2 places:

    a. <u>Insertion</u>-attach to *movable* bone, usually distal to the body.

    b. <u>Origin</u>-attach to *immovable* or *less movable* bone, usually proximal to the body.

    c. <u>Belly</u>-part of the muscle between the origin and insertion.

2. Example-the *triceps brachii* muscle has four points of attachment:

- One insertion on the ulna
- Three origins (2 on the humerus and 1 on the scapula)

3. Attachments can be:

    a. <u>Direct</u> (fleshy)-epimysium fused to <u>periosteum</u> (outer membrane) of bone or <u>perichondrium</u> of cartilage.

    b. <u>Indirect</u>-connective tissue extends beyond muscle as ropelike <u>tendon</u> or sheet-like <u>aponeurosis.</u>

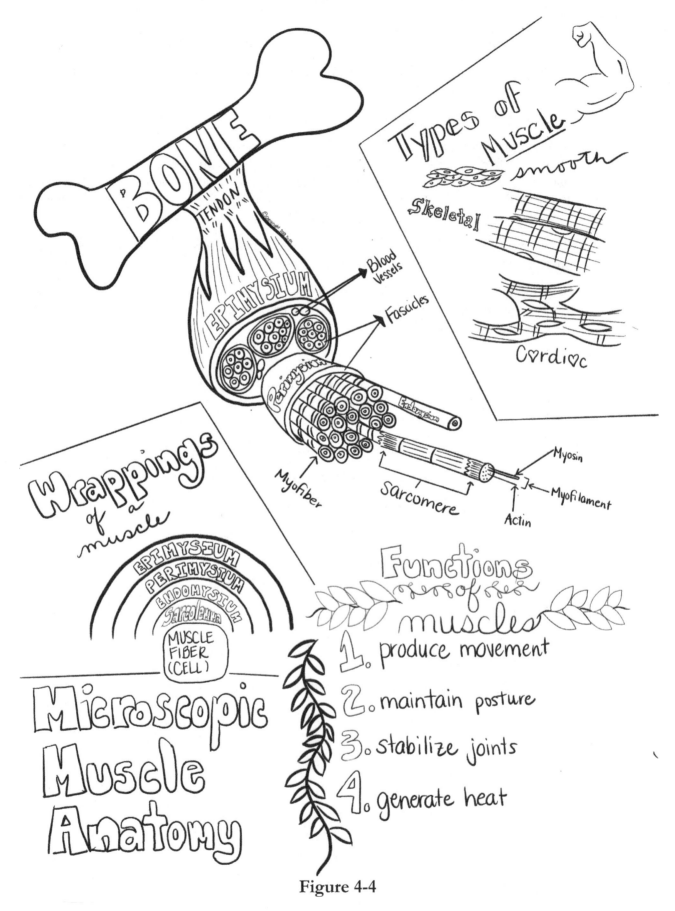

Figure 4-4

Muscle Contraction and the Sliding Filament Theory

I. Muscle Action

A. Muscular contraction produces an *action* or a movement of the appendage.

B. Muscle contraction tends to result in *different types* of movement. The movement performed is a *direct result* of the muscle attachment. A good example of this in action is the type of movements that occur when picking up a book. Each of these actions can be described in one of two ways:

1. The first way describes action in terms of the <u>bone</u> to which the muscle is attached or the <u>appendage</u> that is moved. For example, the *biceps brachii* performs *flexion* of the forearm as the forearm is moved.

2. The second way to describe a muscle's action is based on the <u>joint</u> (or *articulation*). For example, that same muscle, the *biceps brachii*, performs *flexion at the elbow*, in which the elbow is the joint.

II. Functional Roles of Muscles

A. The human body has *over 500* muscles responsible for all types of movement. Each of these muscles has a name.

B. There are seven ways to name a muscle:

- <u>Location on Body or Nearby Bone</u>-Example: *Rectus abdominis* is a flat muscle that covers the abdomen.

- <u>Action</u>-indicates the kind of movement that is generated by the muscle. The most common are: flexor (bends), extensor (straightens or extends), abductor (moves laterally away from the body), and adductor (returns back towards the body). Example: *Extensor digitorum longus* straightens the toes.

- <u>Direction of Fibers</u>-in relation to the midline of the body. The most common are: rectus (parallel), transverse (perpendicular), and oblique (diagonal). Example: *External oblique* covers the sides of the abdomen at a diagonal angle.

- <u>Shape</u>-Examples: *Deltoid* is shaped like a triangle; *Trapezius* is shaped like a trapezoid; *Serratus anterior* is serrated like a saw blade.

- <u>Number of Origins</u>-two (Example: *biceps*), three (Example: *triceps*), or four (Example: *quadriceps*)

- <u>Origin/Insertion Location</u>-Example: *Sternocleidomastoid* has the sternum ("*sterno*") and clavicle ("*cleido*") as its origins and the mastoid process ("*mastoid*") as its insertion.

- <u>Relative Size</u>-the most common are maximus (largest), minimus (smallest), longus (longest), and brevis (shortest). Example: *Gluteus maximus* is the largest muscle of the posterior hip, *gluteus minimus* is the smaller of the posterior hip muscles.

Mnemonic for Naming Muscles-LADS Only Love Sports
(<u>L</u>ocation, <u>A</u>ction, <u>D</u>irection of fibers, <u>S</u>hape, <u>O</u>rigin (number), <u>L</u>ocation of origin/insertion, <u>S</u>ize)

III. Steps to Muscle Contraction (see **Figure 4-5**)

1. A nerve impulse travels to the <u>neuromuscular junction</u> in a muscle cell. The <u>neuromuscular junction</u> is the point where the axons of the nerve meet with the muscle cell.

2. <u>Acetylcholine</u> (Ach) is released from the axon to receptors located on the sarcolemma.

3. The binding Ach causes <u>depolarization</u> of the sarcolemma by opening ion channels and allowing Na+ ions into the muscle cell.

4. Na+ ions diffuse into the muscle fiber and depolarization occurs.

5. Depolarization creates a wave of <u>action potential</u> (electrical current) across the sarcolemma.

6. Action potential travels across the sarcolemma and down the <u>T-tubules</u> which triggers the <u>sarcoplasmic reticulum</u> (SR) to release Ca^{+2}.

7. As Ca^{+2} levels rise, Ca^{+2} ions bind with <u>Troponin</u> which removes the blocking action of <u>Tropomyosin</u> from the <u>actin binding sites</u>.

8. <u>Myosin</u> is now ready to bind with the actin and form <u>cross-bridges</u> which begins the contraction process.

9. In order to contract, <u>ATP binds to the myosin</u>.

10. ATP is then <u>hydrolyzed</u> (broken down) to ADP and P, which gives the myosin the energy to "cock" its head to the high-energy position.

11. <u>Actin</u> and <u>myosin</u> bind together to form a cross bridge.

12. The myosin heads then pull the actin filaments inward ("*sliding filaments*") and release the ADP and P and return to a low energy position. The myosin is now ready for more ATP to bind and repeat the cycle. <u>This process will continue for as long as there are Ca^{+2} ions and ATP available.</u>

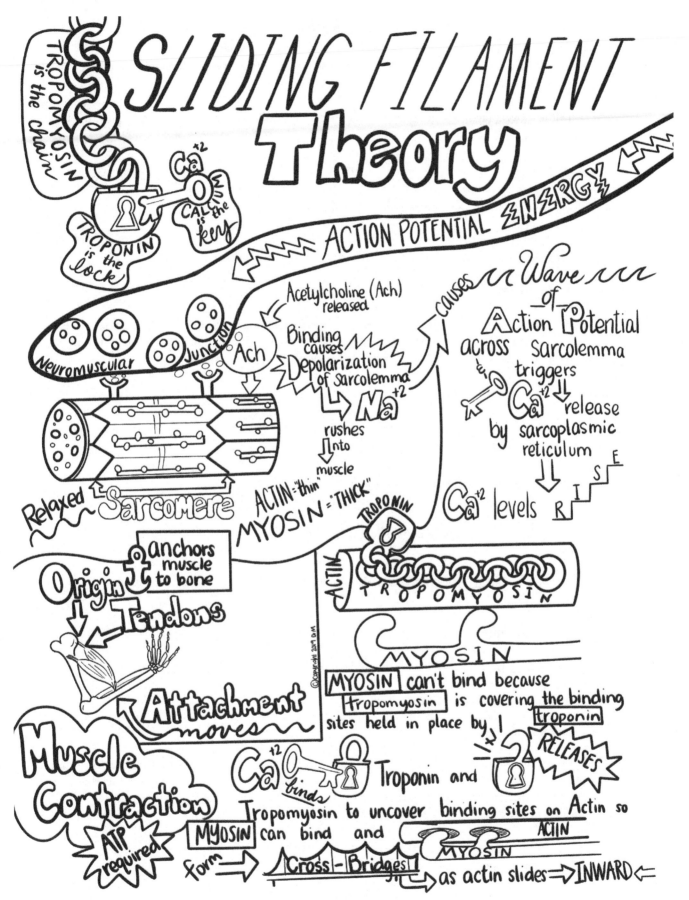

SLIDING FILAMENT Theory

TROPOMYOSIN is the chain

Ca^{+2} CA is the key

TROPONIN is the lock

ACTION POTENTIAL ENERGY

Acetylcholine (Ach) released

Ach

Binding causes Depolarization of Sarcolemma

Neuromuscular Junction

Na^{+2} rushes Into muscle

ACTIN = "thin" MYOSIN = "THICK"

causes Wave of Action Potential across Sarcolemma & triggers Ca^{+2} release by sarcoplasmic reticulum

Ca^{+2} levels RISE

Relaxed Sarcomere

anchors muscle to bone

Origin Tendons

Attachment moves

TROPONIN

ACTIN

TROPOMYOSIN

MYOSIN

MYOSIN can't bind because tropomyosin is covering the binding sites held in place by troponin

RELEASES

Muscle Contraction

ATP required

Ca^{+2} binds Troponin and Tropomyosin to uncover binding sites on Actin so MYOSIN can bind and form Cross-Bridges

ACTIN MYOSIN as actin slides INWARD

Figure 4-5

Muscle Actions

I. Muscles work in *groups*, rather than individually, to cause the movement of a body part. This cooperation between various muscles enhances movement, yet requires individual muscles play different roles depending upon their origin and insertion. These roles can be described as:

1. Prime movers (agonists)-muscles that are most responsible for the movement; provide the major force during contraction.

2. Antagonists ("*opposite*")-muscles that cause a movement *opposite* that of the prime mover; generally *attached to the opposite side of the joint* to which the prime mover is attached. For example, if the prime mover raises an arm, its antagonist pulls the arm down.

3. Synergists ("*work together*")-muscles that *assist* the prime mover; may stabilize a joint around which movement is occurring or refine the movement of the prime mover.

II. Muscle Actions (**Figure 4-13**)

A. The muscles surrounding synovial joints are responsible for moving the body. The orientation, placement, and coordination of these muscles allow the human body to produce a wide range of voluntary movements. These muscle actions are often paired (like *flexion* and *extension* or *abduction* and *adduction*).

B. Most common body movements:

1. Flexion and extension-movements *forward* and *backward* from the body, such as nodding the head yes or picking up an object.

- Flexion-*decreasing* the angle between two bones (bending).
- Extension-*increasing* the angle between two bones (straightening a bend).

Example-The *extensor carpi* extends (straightens) the fingers while the *flexor carpi* flexes (bends) the fingers.

2. Abduction and adduction-*side-to-side* movements, such as moving the arm laterally when doing jumping jacks.

- Abduction-moving *away* from the midline of the body. (Hint: *if you are abducted, someone takes you "away"*)
- Adduction-moving *towards* the midline of the body. (Hint: *"adds" to the body*)

Example-The *gluteus medius*, *gluteus minimus*, and *sartorius* are muscles that abduct the hip and move it away from the body. The *pectineus*, *adductor longus*, *adductor magnus*, and *gracilis* adduct the hip and bring it back towards the body.

3. Pronation and supination-commonly used to describe the unique *rotation* of the forearm so that the palm of the hand (anterior body surface) is either *facing up* or *facing down*. (Hint: remember that similar terms can also be used to describe the position of the body when it is lying face (anterior surface) up ("*supine*") or face down ("*prone*").

- Pronation-rotating forearm so *the palm is facing backward or down*.
- Supination-rotating forearm so *the palm is facing forward or up*.

Example-The *pronator teres* and *pronator quadratus* (muscles in the forearm) work together to achieve pronation by pulling on the radius bone of the forearm. The *supinator muscle of the forearm* and the *biceps brachii* of the upper arm supinate the forearm by pulling on the radius.

D. Elevation and depression-*up-and-down movements*, such as chewing or shrugging your shoulders.

- Elevation-moving a body part *up*.
- Depression-moving a body part *down*.

Example-Three muscles (*masseter*, *temporalis*, and *medial pterygoid*) are powerful closers ("*elevators*") of the mandible. However, unlike the other three muscles of mastication, the *lateral pterygoid* is the only muscle that helps in depressing the mandible (opening the jaw).

Common Muscles (Anterior)

Head & Neck
Frontalis
Orbicularis oculi
Temporalis
Orbicularis oris
Buccinator
Masseter
Zygomatic
Sternocleidomastoid
Trapezius
Platysma

Trunk
Pectoralis major
Rectus abdominis
External oblique
Internal oblique
Transverse abdominis

Arm/Forearm
Deltoid
Triceps brachii
Biceps brachii
Brachioradialis
Extensor carpi radialis longus
Extensor digitorum
Extensor carpi ulnaris
Flexor carpi ulnaris

Hip, Thigh, & Lower Leg
Sartorius
Rectus femoris (Quadriceps)
Vastus lateralis (Quadriceps)
Vastus medialis (Quadriceps)
Adductor longus (Adductor)
Iliopsoas (Adductor)
Pectineus (Adductor)
Gracilis (Adductor)
Gastrocnemius
Soleus
Tibialis anterior
Fibularis

Common Muscles (Posterior)

Trunk
Trapezius
Latissimus dorsi

Arm
Deltoid
Triceps brachii

Hips, Thigh, & Lower Leg
Gluteus maximus
Gluteus medius
Semimembranosus (Hamstrings)
Biceps femoris (Hamstrings)
Semitendinosus (Hamstrings)
Gastrocnemius

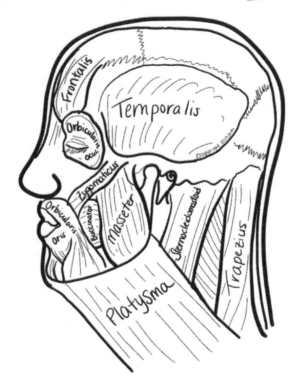

Figure 4-6

Muscle	Action	Color
Frontalis	Raises eyebrows	
Orbicularis oculi	Closes eyes	
Temporalis	Moves ears slightly	
Orbicularis oris	Puckers lips	
Buccinator	Holds food between teeth when chewing	
Masseter	Clenches teeth tightly	
Zygomatic	Raises corner of mouth as in smiling	
Sternocleidomastoid	Pulls head to 1 side, flexes neck or elevates sternum	
Trapezius	Shrugs shoulders; rotates & moves scapula	
Platysma	Draws angle of mouth downward when head leaned back	

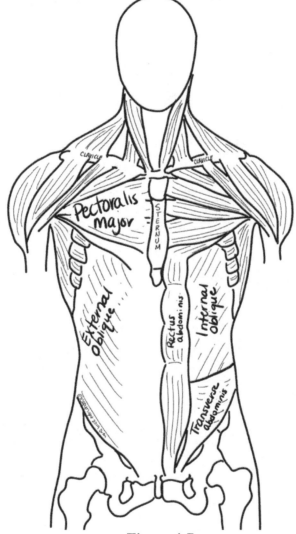

Figure 4-7

Muscle	Action	Color
Pectoralis major	Raises upper arm & pulls it across chest	
Rectus abdominis	Pulls ribs & pelvis in; curves back as in doing crunches	
External oblique	Tenses abdominal wall & compresses abdominal contents	
Internal oblique	Tenses abdominal wall & compresses abdominal contents	
Transverse abdominis	Compresses abdomen	

Muscles of the Hip, Thigh, and Lower Leg (Anterior)-Figure 4-8

Muscle	Action	Color
Sartorius	Longest muscle; flexes knee & hip, abducts & rotates thigh laterally (as in sitting cross-legged); draws 1 leg over the other, "tailor's muscle";	
Rectus femoris (Quadriceps)	Extends knee	
Vastus lateralis (Quadriceps)	Extends knee	
Vastus medialis (Quadriceps)	Extends knee	
Adductor longus (Adductors)	Adducts & flexes thigh	
Iliopsoas (Adductors)	Flexes hip at thigh	
Pectineus (Adductors)	Adducts, flexes, & medially rotates thigh; primary function is hip flexion	
Gracilis (Adductors)	Adducts (extends) thigh, flexes & medially rotates leg; highest muscle inside thigh	
Gastrocnemius	Points toes down; flexes (bends) knee; large calf muscle	
Soleus	Points toes down; small muscle that works with gastrocnemius	
Tibialis anterior	Flexes foot & raises toes	
Fibularis	Plantar flexes & everts foot; helps keep foot flat on ground	

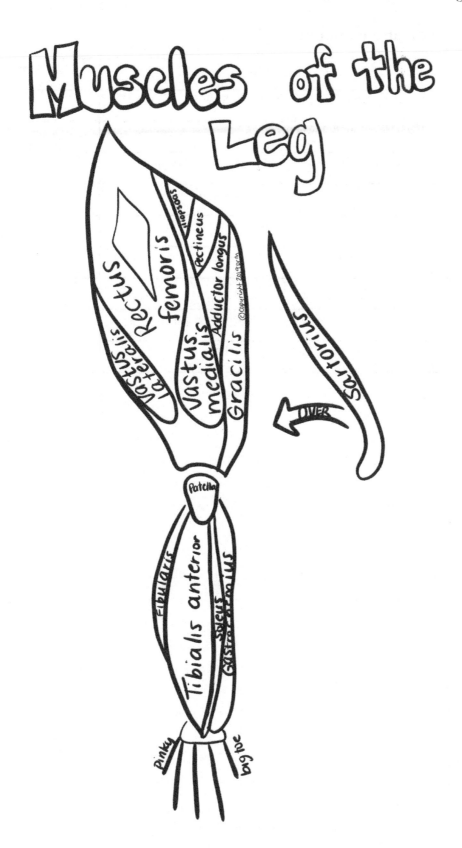

Figure 4-8

Muscles of the Arm and Forearm (Anterior)-Figure 4-9

Muscle	Action	Color
Deltoid	Raises upper arm & pulls it slightly forward	
Triceps brachii	Extends elbow & lower arm	
Biceps brachii	Flexes elbow & lower arm and rotates hand palm up	
Brachioradialis	Flexes lower arm (forearm) when palm is down	
Extensor carpi radialis longus	Extends wrist & abducts hand	
Extensor digitorum	Extends fingers	
Extensor carpi ulnaris	Extends wrist & adducts hand	
Flexor carpi ulnaris	Flexes wrist & adducts hand laterally (towards ulna)	
Pectoralis major	Raises upper arm & pulls it across chest.	

Muscles of the Arm

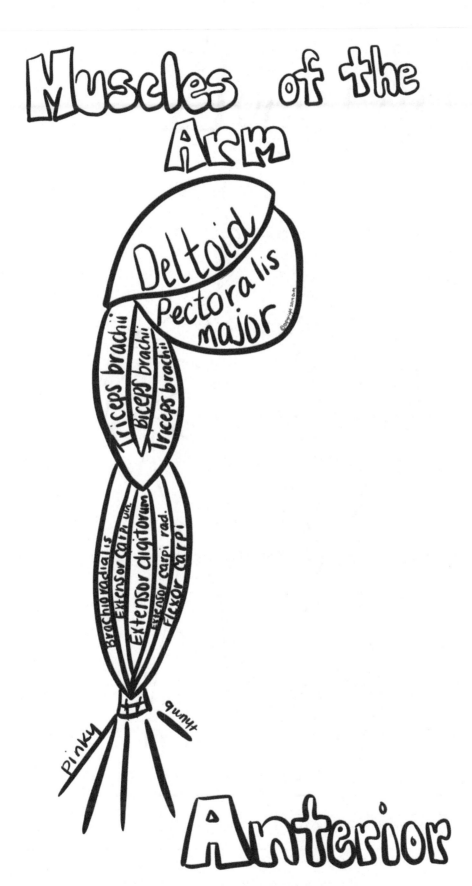

Anterior

Figure 4-9

Trunk

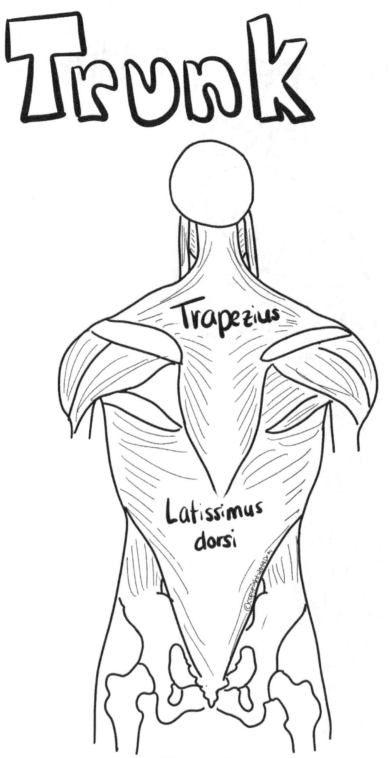

Figure 4-10

Muscle	Action	Color
Trapezius	Shrugs shoulders; rotates & moves scapula	
Latissimus dorsi	Lowers upper arm & pulls it back	

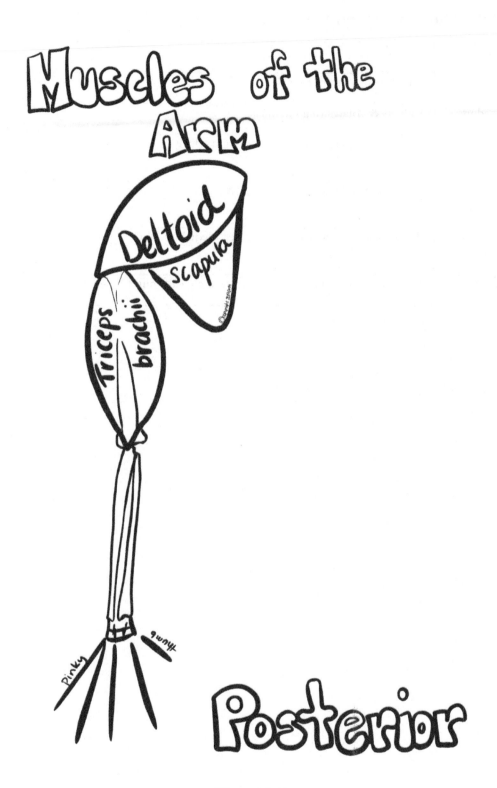

Figure 4-11

Muscle	Action	Color
Deltoid	Raises upper arm & pulls it slightly forward	
Triceps brachii	Extends elbow & lower arm	

Muscles of the Hip, Thigh, and Lower Leg (Posterior)-Figure 4-12

Muscle	Action	Color
Gluteus maximus	Extends thigh away from body at hip	
Gluteus medius	Abducts & rotates thigh medially	
Semimembranosus (Hamstrings)	Flexes (bends) knee, rotates lower leg medially & extends thigh	
Biceps femoris (Hamstrings)	Flexes (bends) knee, rotates lower leg medially & extends thigh	
Semitendinosus (Hamstrings)	Flexes (bends) knee, rotates lower leg medially & extends thigh	
Gastrocnemius	Points toes down; flexes (bends) knee; large calf muscle	

Muscles of the Leg

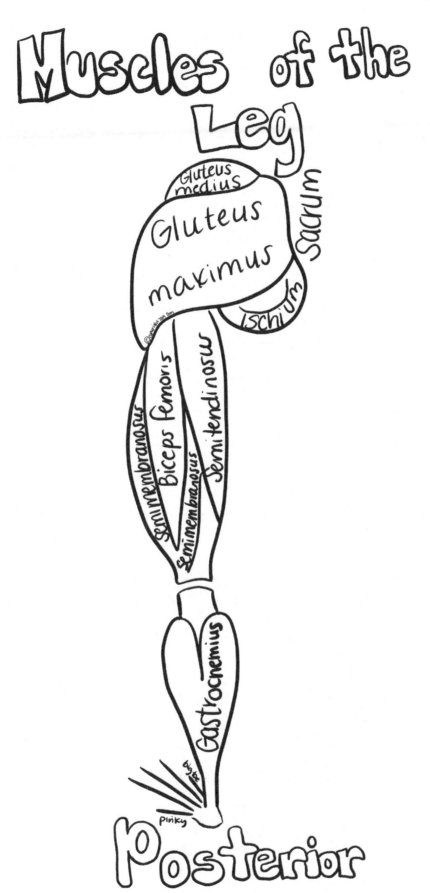

Posterior

Figure 4-12

Muscle Actions

Use the following pages to test yourself on the actions and locations of the most common muscles. Use pgs. 102-111 if you need additional assistance.

Head & Neck

Muscle	Action	Number	Color
Frontalis			
Orbicularis oculi			
Temporalis			
Orbicularis oris			
Buccinator			
Masseter			
Zygomaticus			
Sternocleidomastoid			
Trapezius			
Platysma			

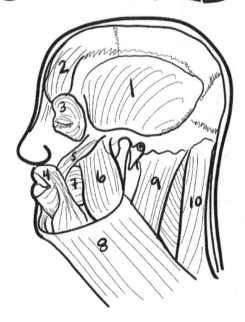

Trunk (Anterior)

Muscle	Action	Number	Color
Pectoralis major			
Rectus abdominis			
External oblique			
Internal oblique			
Transverse abdominis			

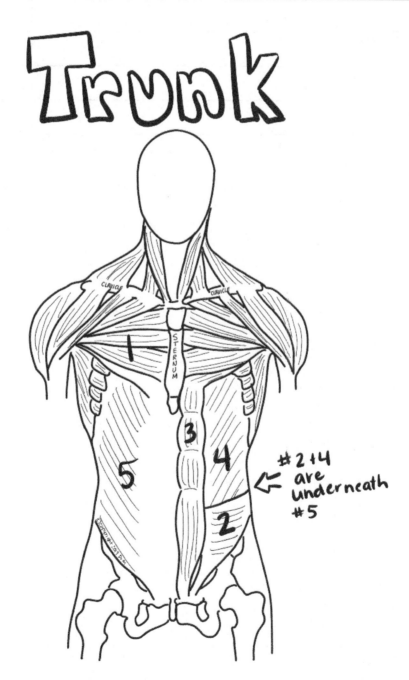

Arm & Forearm (Anterior)

Muscle	Action	Number	Color
Deltoid			
Triceps brachii			
Biceps brachii			
Brachioradialis			
Extensor carpi radialis longus			
Extensor digitorum			
Extensor carpi ulnaris			
Flexor carpi ulnaris			
Pectoralis major			

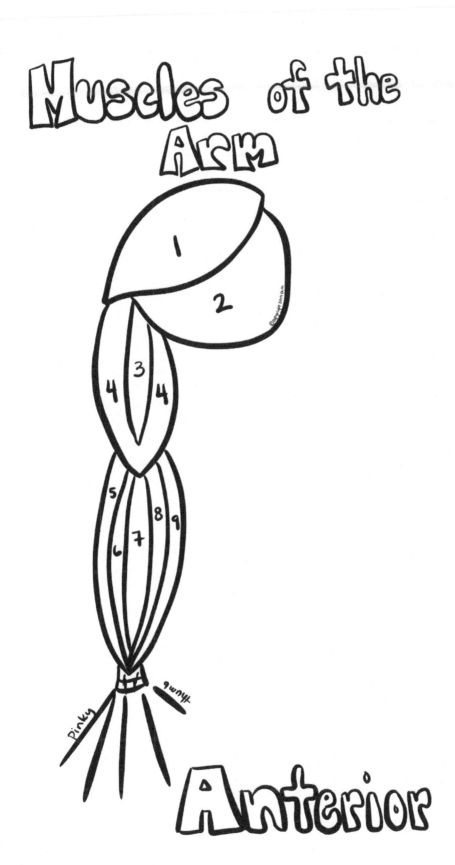

Hip, Thigh, & Lower Leg (Anterior)

Muscle	Action	Number	Color
Sartorius			
Rectus femoris (Quadriceps)			
Vastus lateralis (Quadriceps)			
Vastus medialis (Quadriceps)			
Adductor longus (Adductors)			
Iliopsoas (Adductors)			
Pectineus (Adductors)			
Gracilis (Adductors)			
Gastrocnemius			
Soleus			
Tibialis anterior			
Fibularis			

Muscles of the Leg

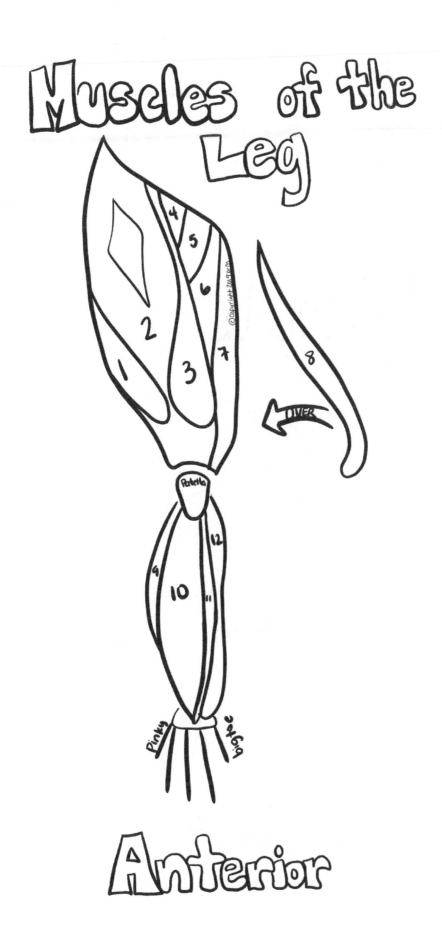

Anterior

Trunk (Posterior)

Muscle	*Action*	*Number*	*Color*
Trapezius			
Latissimus dorsi			

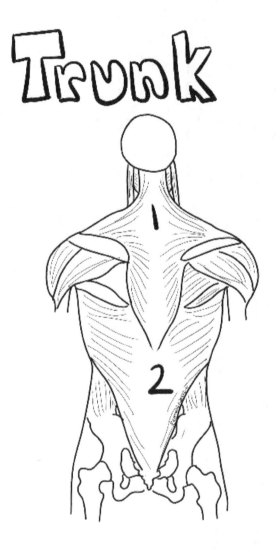

Arm (Posterior)

Muscle	Action	Number	Color
Deltoid			
Triceps brachii			

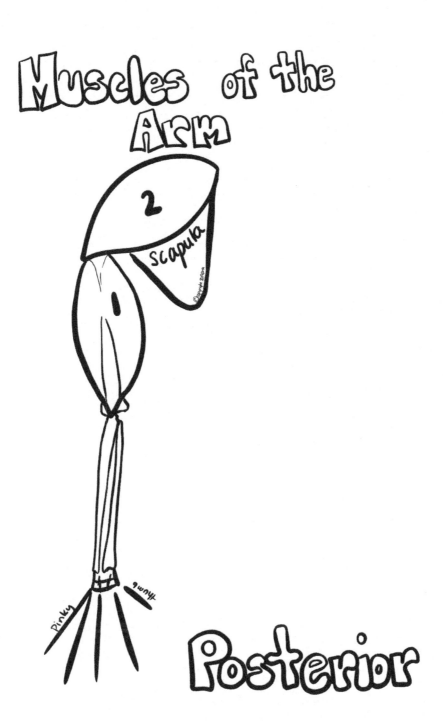

Hips, Thigh, & Lower Leg (Posterior)

Muscle	Action	Number	Color
Gluteus maximus			
Gluteus medius			
Semimembranosus (Hamstrings)			
Biceps femoris (Hamstrings)			
Semitendinosus (Hamstrings)			
Gastrocnemius			

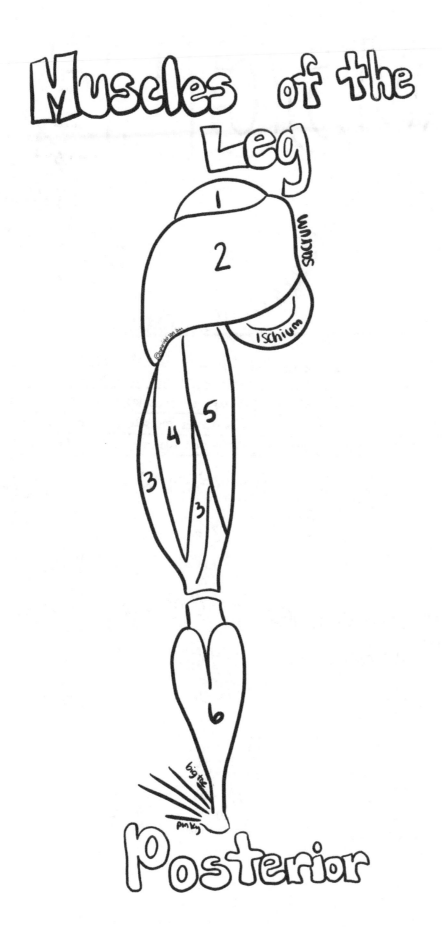

Muscles of the Leg

1

2

sacrum

ischium

5

4

3

3

6

big toe

pinky

Posterior

MUSCLE

ACTIONS

"all or none response"

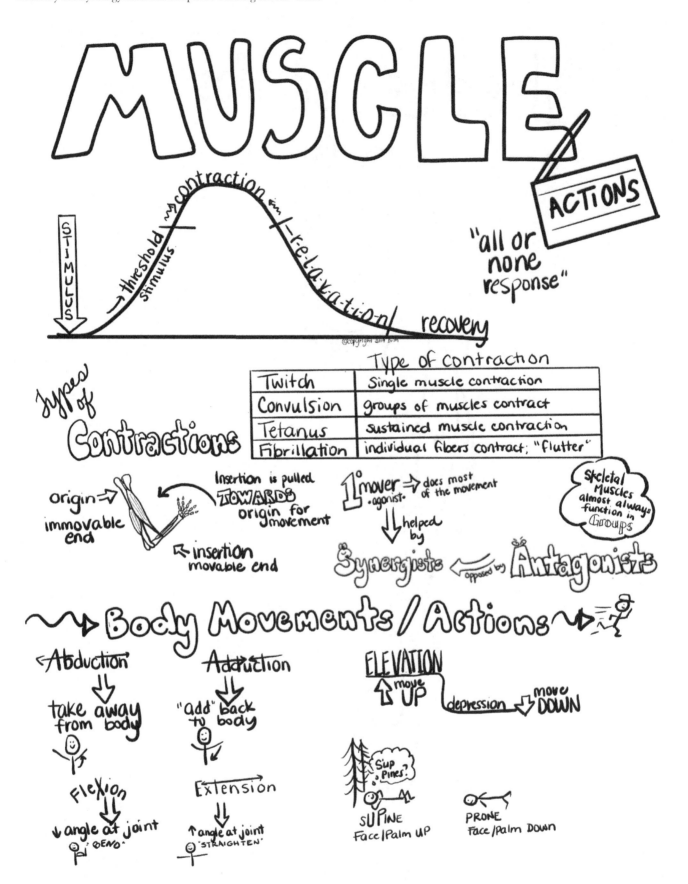

STIMULUS

→ threshold stimulus

contraction

re-l-a-x-a-t-i-o-n

recovery

©copyright 2019 b.m.

Type of contraction	
Twitch	Single muscle contraction
Convulsion	groups of muscles contract
Tetanus	sustained muscle contraction
Fibrillation	individual fibers contract; "flutter"

Types of Contractions

origin ⇒ immovable end

Insertion is pulled TOWARDS origin for movement

← insertion movable end

1° mover ·agonist· → does most of the movement

↓↓ helped by

Synergists ← opposed by Antagonists

Skeletal Muscles almost always function in Groups

Body Movements / Actions

←Abduction
⇓
take away from body

Flexion
⇓
↓ angle at joint ·BEND·

Adduction
⇓
"add" back to body

Extension
⇓
↑ angle at joint ·STRAIGHTEN·

ELEVATION
↑ move UP
depression ↘ move DOWN

Sup Pines

SUPINE Face/Palm UP

PRONE Face/Palm DOWN

Figure 4-13

CHAPTER 5. NERVOUS SYSTEM

Divisions of the Nervous System

I. The Nervous System can be divided into two major regions: the <u>Central</u> and <u>Peripheral Nervous Systems</u>.

    A. <u>Central Nervous System</u> (CNS)-brain and spinal cord.

    B. <u>Peripheral Nervous System</u> (PNS)-all the nerves (cranial and spinal) outside the brain and spinal cord. These nerves are on the "*periphery*".

II. The basic functions of the Nervous System are <u>sensation</u> (*sensory input*), <u>integration</u>, and <u>response</u> (*motor output*).

    A. <u>Sensory receptors</u> (sense organs)-gather environmental information and stimuli and convert them into nerve impulses which are transmitted over peripheral nerves to the <u>Central Nervous System</u> (CNS).

    B. In the CNS, these signals are <u>integrated</u> (brought together) to create sensations that are added to memory or translated into perceptions.

    C. Because of this integration, we make conscious or subconscious decisions and use <u>motor functions</u> to act upon them through <u>effectors</u> (*muscles* that contract or *glands* that secrete).

III. <u>Response</u>-is based on the stimuli perceived by sensory structures and involves an action by an <u>effector</u>. There are 2 types of effectors:

    A. <u>Skeletal muscles</u>-produce motion, such as withdrawing a hand from a hot stove.

    B. <u>Glands</u>-produce secretions such as sweat or hormones.

    C. Responses by effectors can be divided into:

        1. <u>Voluntary</u> (under conscious control)-governed by the <u>Somatic Nervous System</u> (SNS); Example-contraction of skeletal muscle.

        2. <u>Involuntary</u> (automatic)-governed by the <u>Autonomic Nervous System</u> (ANS); Example-contraction of smooth muscles, regulation of cardiac muscle, and activation of glands.

III. Controlling the Body (**Figure 5-1**)

    A. <u>Peripheral Nervous System</u> (PNS)-separated into 2 divisions:

- <u>Afferent</u> (Sensory) <u>Division</u>-connects the <u>body</u> (sense organs) to the <u>Central Nervous System</u> (CNS).
- <u>Efferent</u> (Motor) <u>Division</u>-connects the <u>CNS</u> to <u>muscles</u> and <u>glands</u>.

    B. <u>Afferent</u> and <u>efferent</u> neurons are the neurons *within the PNS* that travel from the body to the Central Nervous System (CNS), then back out to the effector organ in order to produce a signal transmission pathway which integrates information and coordinates functions in the body.

- <u>Afferent neurons</u> are also known as <u>sensory</u> neurons.
- <u>Efferent neurons</u> are also known as <u>motor</u> neurons.
- The main difference between afferent and efferent is that <u>afferent</u> refers to the neurons carrying signals *from sensory perceptions towards the CNS* while <u>efferent</u> refers to the neurons carrying signals *from the CNS to the effector organs*.

    C. <u>Afferent Division</u>-carries sensory information from the PNS sensory receptors to the CNS.

Receptors include:

1. <u>Osmoreceptors</u>-detect changes in osmotic pressures of body fluids.

2. <u>Chemoreceptors</u>-detect changes in chemical concentrations (CO_2, H^+, and O_2) in solution.

3. <u>Nociceptors</u>-detect pain when tissues are damaged.

4. <u>Photoreceptors</u>-sensitivity to light that strikes the retina in the eye.

5. <u>Thermoreceptors</u>-detect temperature changes.

6. <u>Mechanoreceptors</u>-detect stimuli responsible for compressing, bending, and stretching cells, as well as allowing for the sensations of touch, pressure, and vibration. Example-Pacinian (Lamellated) Corpuscles that detect deep pressure in dermis of skin, joints, tendons, pancreas, and periosteum.

C. <u>Efferent Division</u> (of the PNS)-is divided into two parts based on the difference in responses:

1. <u>Somatic Nervous System</u> (SNS)-(soma= "*body*") responsible for <u>voluntary</u> motor responses involving the *contraction of skeletal muscle*. Some somatic motor responses are reflexes and occur without a conscious decision to perform them. Other motor responses become automatic as a person learns motor skills (*procedural memory*).

2. <u>Autonomic Nervous System</u> (ANS)-("*automatic*") responsible for <u>involuntary</u> control of the body, usually for the sake of *homeostasis*. The job of the autonomic system is to regulate the organ systems of the body by controlling <u>cardiac muscle</u>, <u>smooth muscle</u>, and <u>glands</u> of the body and regulating bodily functions such as the heart rate, digestion, respiratory rate, pupillary response, and urination.

B. <u>Autonomic Nervous System</u>-two main branches are the <u>Sympathetic Nervous System</u> and the <u>Parasympathetic Nervous System</u>. In many cases, these systems have "opposite" actions where one system activates a physiological response while the other inhibits it (*dual innervation*).

1. <u>Sympathetic Nervous System</u>-"*fight or flight*" system.

2. <u>Parasympathetic Nervous System</u>-"*rest and digest*" or "*feed and breed*" system.

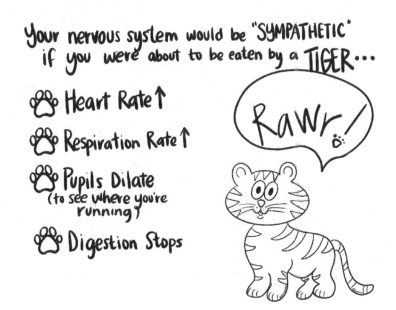

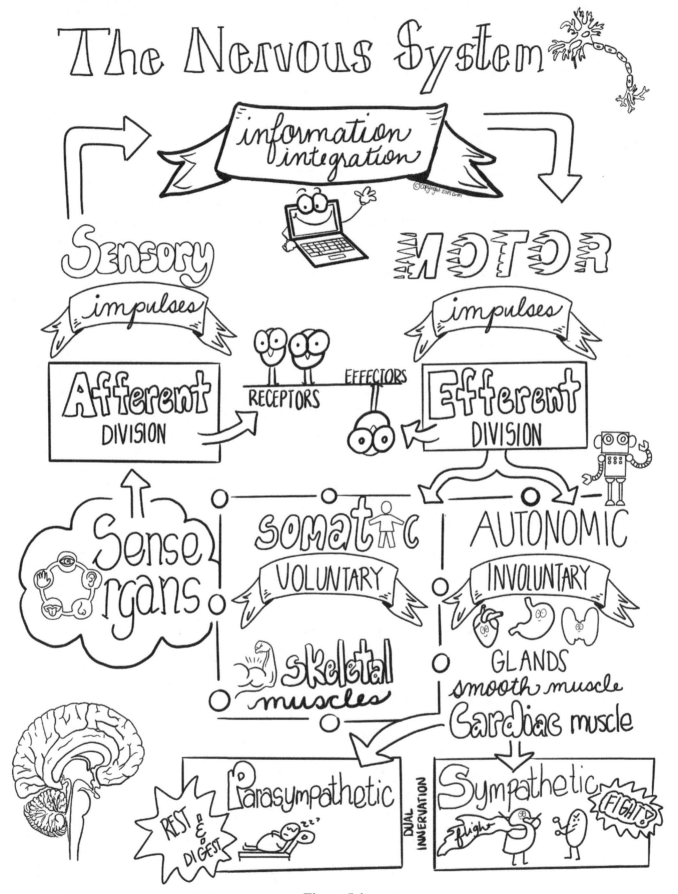

Figure 5-1

Nervous Tissue

I. Nervous Tissue is composed of 2 kinds of cells:

A. <u>Conducting</u> (neurons)-transmit electrical signals.

B. <u>Non-Conducting</u> (neuroglial or glial)-fill spaces, provide structural framework, produce myelin, carry on phagocytosis, as well as surround and support neurons.

II. Neuroglial (Non-Conducting) Cells in the Central Nervous System (CNS)-**Figure 5-2**

A. <u>Microglial Cells</u>-phagocytize bacterial cells and cellular debris.

B. <u>Oligodendrocytes</u>-align along nerve fibers and produce *myelin* (insulation).

C. <u>Astrocytes</u>-found between neurons and blood vessels; function to provide structural support, join structures with their processes, as well as help regulate nutrient and ion concentrations. They form scar tissue with damage to CNS.

D. <u>Ependymal Cells</u>-form an epithelial-like membrane that covers the fluid-filled cavities of the brain (choroid plexuses and ventricles) and the Central Canal of the spinal cord; circulate Cerebrospinal Fluid (CSF).

III. Neuroglial (Non-Conducting) Cells in the Peripheral Nervous System (PNS)

A. <u>Schwann Cells</u>-form myelin around axons.

B. <u>Satellite Cells</u>-protective cushioning cells that surround neuron cell bodies in PNS.

Multiple Sclerosis [MS] sclerosis = "hardening"

Disease in which the immune system attacks the myelin surrounding axons of conducting neurons. This demyelination causes communication problems between the brain and the rest of the body.

Symptoms Depend on amount of damage and the nerves that are affected. Some people lose the ability to walk.

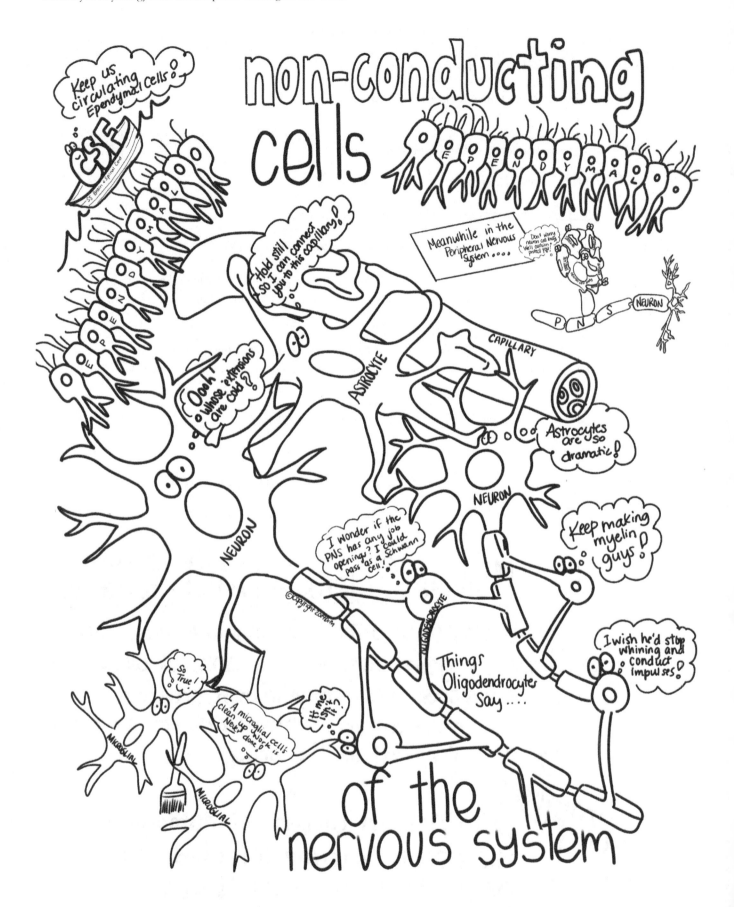

Figure 5-2

Neurons

I. <u>Neurons</u>-structural units of the Nervous System.

    A. Conducting cells.

    B. Most neuron cell bodies are located in the Central Nervous System (CNS).

        a. <u>Nuclei</u>-clusters of cell bodies in the <u>CNS</u>.

        b. <u>Ganglia</u>-clusters of cell bodies in the <u>PNS</u>.

    C. All have a <u>cell body</u> (control center) and 1 or more processes (<u>axon</u> that conducts impulse; <u>dendrite</u> that receives impulse).

        a. <u>Neuron processes</u>-arm-like projections that extend from the cell body.

        b. The CNS contains *both* neuron cell bodies and their processes.

        c. The PNS contains chiefly neuron processes.

        d. <u>Tracts</u>-bundles of neuron processes in the CNS.

        e. <u>Nerves</u>-bundles of neuron processes in the PNS.

    D. Organelles found in the cell body of neurons:

- Nucleus
- Nucleolus
- Mitochondria
- Golgi body
- Nissl bodies

    E. Path of an impulse through a neuron is always in this direction:

    Dendrite → Cell body → Axon

II. Axon

    A. Conducting region of neuron

    B. Generates impulses and transmits them along the <u>axolemma</u> (neuron cell membrane) to the <u>axonal terminal</u> where <u>neurotransmitters</u> (chemical messengers) are secreted.

III. Myelin Sheath

    A. Surrounds the axon of many neurons.

    B. Composed of myelin.

    C. <u>Myelin</u>-white protein-lipid substance that protects and insulates axon and increases speed of nerve transmission.

    D. <u>Myelinated fibers</u> have a segmented sheath that surrounds most long or large diameter axons.

E. Non-myelinated fibers-do not contain a myelin sheath therefore conduct impulses more slowly.

F. Schwann cells-form myelin in the PNS.

G. Nodes of Ranvier-gaps between adjacent cells that serve as sites where collaterals can emerge.

H. Oligodendrocytes-form myelin in the CNS.

      a. Each cell can wrap 60 axons at once.

      b. Can also contain a myelin sheath gap.

      c. White matter (in the CNS)-consists of regions in the brain and spinal cord with dense collections of myelinated fibers arranged in tracts.

      d. Grey matter-consists mostly of neuron cell bodies and non-myelinated fibers.

IV. Classification of Neurons

    A. Classified on basis of structure.

Type	Description	Example
Multipolar	3 or more processes (1 axon, multiple dendrites)	Most common type in CNS
Bipolar	2 processes (1 axon, 1 dendrite); rare	Only found in retina, ear, and olfactory mucosa
Unipolar	1 T-like process (2 axons).	Very short, found in the sensory neurons of the PNS

    B. Can also be classified on basis of function.

Type	Location of Cell Bodies	Pathway
Sensory	Ganglia in PNS	Sensory receptors to CNS
Motor	In CNS (Brain or Spinal Cord)	CNS to effectors (muscles or glands)
Interneurons (Association)	Most entirely within CNS	Shuttle signals between motor and sensory neurons

The Neuron

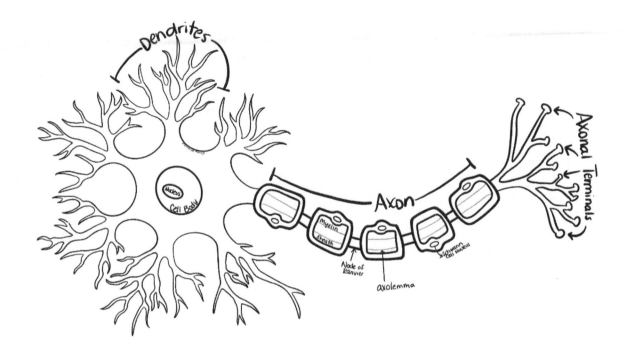

Figure 5-3

The Neuron

Structure	Description or Function	Color
Axon		
Axonal Terminals		
Cell Body		
Dendrite		
Myelin Sheath		
Node of Ranvier		
Schwann Cell		
Axolemma		

V. Synapse (means *"to clasp" or "join"*)-**Figure 5-4**

A. <u>Synapse</u>-meeting between 2 neurons; communication link.

B. Synapses turn the structure of the nervous system (isolated neurons) into a <u>system</u>. Their strength and purpose lies in their connections.

C. <u>Action potential</u>-sends <u>electrical</u> messages into the end of an axon where the <u>synapse</u> converts it into a different type of signal and passes it to another neuron.

D. Brain has <u>100 million</u> neurons and each one has <u>1000-10,000</u> synapses, so there are <u>100-1000</u> trillion synapses in the brain.

E. <u>Synapses</u> can change and adapt in response to neuron firing patterns:

- Can strengthen/weaken dependent upon use.
- Allow you to learn and remember.
- Are the root of all psychological disorders.
- Reason why illicit drugs and abused and addictions occur.

F. Nerve cells have 2 settings for communication:

1. <u>Electrical</u>-sends to all cells; immediate.

2. <u>Chemical</u>-sends to certain cells; slower, occurs more often and is easier to control.

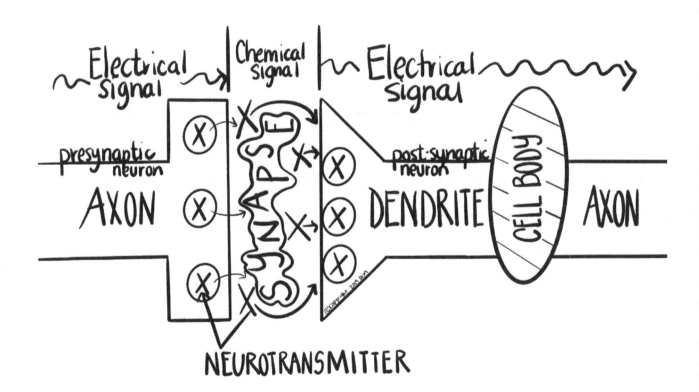

Figure 5-4

VI. Electrical Communication (to all cells)-occurs quickly. (For more information see **Figure 1-4**, p. 10)

- Ion current flows directly from the cytoplasm of one nerve cell to another through small holes called gap junctions.
- Electrical signal is *never converted* from the prime electrical state into another signal.
- One cell and one synapse can trigger many cells that act together (similar to muscle cells of the heart).
- An action potential in one neuron will generate an action potential in the all the other cells across the synapse.
    - Good-in the heart.
    - Bad-in the body (because all the muscles and nerves would be stimulated at one time).

VII. Chemical Communication (to specific cells)-occurs slowly. (For more information see **Figure 1-4**, p. 10)

- More abundant, more precise, and very selective.
- Use neurotransmitters (chemical signals) to diffuse across the synaptic gap in order to deliver message.
- Advantage is that it can convert the signal in steps:
    - Electrical → Chemical → Electrical
- This allows for different ways to control the synapse so the signal can be modified, amplified, inhibited, or split immediately or over a longer period of time.

VIII. Parts to Chemical Communication (see **Figure 5-4**)

A. Presynaptic Neuron-"*Sending*"

- Cell sends signal→ Signal moves down axon to presynaptic terminals(usually the axon terminal) → Terminals hold synaptic vesicles loaded with neurotransmitters

B. Postsynaptic Neuron-"*Receiving*"

- Accepts neurotransmitter in receptive region (usually on dendrite). The neurons don't touch directly because they are separated by synaptic gap (or cleft).

IX. Chain of events for release, diffusion, and reception of neurotransmitter in order to transmit signals:

1. Action potential activates Na^+ and K^+ channels in a wave down axon.

2. Signal travels to presynaptic terminals.

3. Voltage-gated Ca^+ channels activated at presynaptic terminals.

4. Channels open and release Ca^+ into neuron's cytoplasm.

5. Flow of Ca+ causes the synaptic vesicles to merge with cell membrane and release their neurotransmitters.

6. These neurotransmitters act as couriers and diffuse across synaptic gap.

7. Neurotransmitters bind to receptor sites on postsynaptic neuron.

8. Causes ion channels to open.

    - Depending on which neurotransmitter binds to which receptor, neurons are either excited or inhibited.
    - Excitatory neurotransmitters-*depolarize* the postsynaptic neuron; make it more positive (+) and bring it closer to the action potential threshold of -55mV.

      o   Inhibitory neurotransmitters-*hyperpolarize* the postsynaptic neuron; make it more negative (-) and bring it farther from the action potential threshold of -70mv. This also makes it harder to excite this portion of the neuron.

X. Actions at the Synapse

    A. 1st neuron (presynaptic neuron) converts <u>electrical</u> signals into <u>chemical</u> (steps #1-7).

    B. 2nd neuron (postsynaptic neuron) converts it <u>back into electrical</u> in order for it to become an action potential again. (step #8).

    C. Any region of a single neuron may have hundreds of synapses, each with a different inhibitory or excitatory neurotransmitter.

    D. The likelihood of the postsynaptic neuron developing an action potential depends on the sum of <u>all excitations and inhibitions</u> in that area.

    E. There are over <u>100</u> different kinds of naturally occurring neurotransmitters in the body. Each one has a different function.

    F. Neurotransmitters don't stay bonded to receptors for longer than a few milliseconds. Then, they are released and will either degrade or are recycled.

    G. <u>Reuptake</u>-some neurotransmitters diffuse back across the synapse and are reabsorbed by the presynaptic neuron. Others are broken down by <u>enzymes</u> in the synaptic cleft or are sent away from the synapse by diffusion.

XI. Drugs

    A. Drugs either <u>inhibit</u> or <u>excite</u> the production, release, and reuptake of neurotransmitters. Some can also <u>mimic</u> neurotransmitters.

    B. <u>Cocaine</u>-targets 3 major neurotransmitters <u>serotonin</u>, <u>dopamine</u>, and <u>norepinephrine</u>.

    C. <u>Serotonin</u>-inhibitory, regulates mood, appetite, circadian rhythm, and sleep. Antidepressants stabilize moods by stabilizing serotonin release.

    D. <u>Dopamine</u>-influences emotion and attention and makes you "feel good".

    E. <u>Norepinephrine</u>-triggers fight or flight response, increases heart rate, and primes muscles to run.

    F. Cocaine and other opiates <u>block reuptake</u> by binding to receptors, especially targeting <u>dopamine</u>. Chemicals accumulate so person feels euphoric, paranoid, and jittery. This flooding of synapses with the neurotransmitters will eventually deplete the body's natural supply. (see **Figure 5-5**)

    G. These types of drugs trick the brain so, eventually, the brain will adapt and synapses will accept how all the extra chemicals feel and the number of receptors will <u>decrease</u>. This will mean that it will require more dopamine (or cocaine) to function normally.

    H. The nasal spray Naloxone (Narcan) counteracts the effects of opiate binding by blocking the opiate receptors.

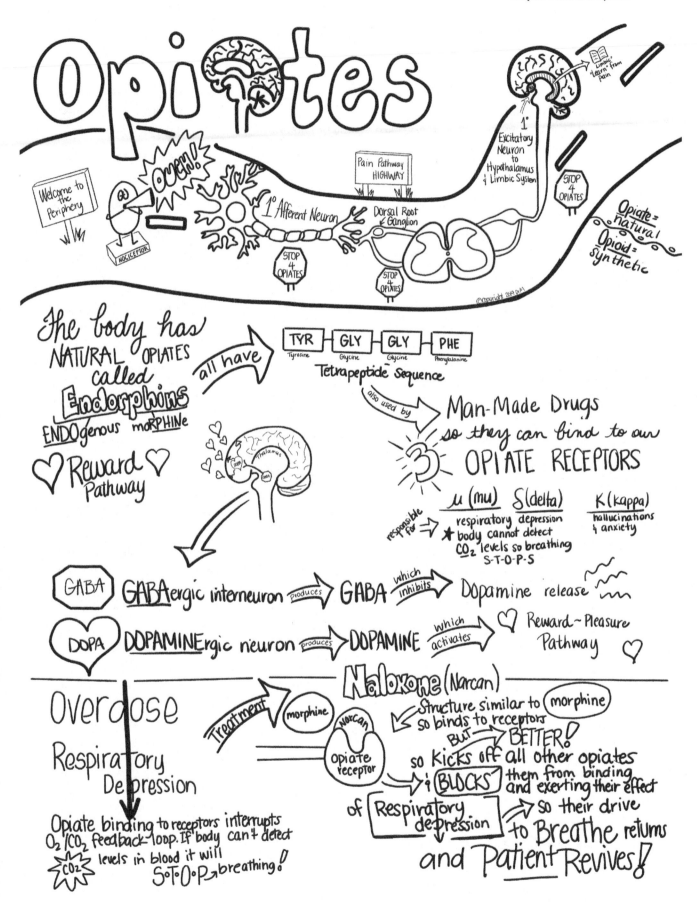

Figure 5-5

The Spinal Cord

I. Characteristics (see **Figure 5-6**)

    A. <u>Description</u>-cylindrical structure composed of <u>white matter</u> (myelinated fiber tracts) surrounded by an H-shaped area of <u>grey matter</u> (unmyelinated neurons). The two posterior projections (called dorsal or <u>posterior horns</u>) and the two anterior projections (called ventral or <u>anterior horns</u>) surround the Central Canal containing Cerebrospinal Fluid (CSF).

        1. <u>Dorsal horns</u>-contain interneurons

        2. <u>Dorsal root ganglion</u>-enlarged area of dorsal horn that contains cell bodies of sensory neurons.

        3. <u>Ventral horns</u>-contain cell bodies of motor neurons. Axons of these neurons exit the ventral root and fuse to form spinal nerves.

    B. <u>Diameter</u>-1.8 cm (3/4 in) thick.

    C. <u>Length</u>-42cm (17in) long. Extends from Foramen Magnum where it is continuous with the Medulla to the level of the 1st or 2nd lumbar vertebrae.

    D. Enlargements (2)

        1. <u>Cervical</u>-nerves for upper limbs.

        2. <u>Lumbar</u>-nerves for lower limbs.

    E. <u>Segments</u>-segmented like spinal column; each segment has 1 pair spinal nerves that exit.

    F. <u>Cauda equina</u> ("*horse's tail*")-end where nerves exit through holes in sacrum.

    G. Protections

        1. <u>Bone</u>-vertebrae; each area of the vertebral column has a different structure.

        2. <u>Meninges</u>-membranes that are continuous with the membranes surrounding the brain. An easy way to remember is that the meninges **PAD** the spinal cord/brain → **P**ia; **A**rachnoid; **D**ura

            a. <u>Pia mater</u> (inner)-delicate.

            b. <u>Arachnoid mater</u> (middle)-loose, "*spider web-like*".

            c. <u>Dura mater</u> (outer)-tough, leathery, "*durable*".

        3. <u>Cerebrospinal Fluid</u> (CSF)-circulates through the ventricles of the brain and the Central Canal of the spinal cord.

II. Spinal nerves

    A. All spinal nerves are classified as *mixed* (contain both sensory and motor fibers) and named according to the area of the spinal cord from which they *leave*.

    B. Areas:

        1. <u>Cervical</u> (C1-C8)-8 pair

        2. <u>Thoracic</u> (T1-T12)-12 pair

        3. <u>Lumbar</u> (L1-L5)-5 pair

4. <u>Sacral</u> (S1-S5)-5 pair

5. <u>Coccygeal</u> (terminal end of spinal cord)-1pair

B. <u>Rami</u> (singular=*ramus*)-a *branch* of a nerve. Spinal nerves are only about ½ inches long because they divide almost immediately into dorsal and ventral rami containing both sensory and motor fibers.

C. <u>Plexus</u>- a *network* of nerves in a particular area.

    1. <u>Cervical</u>-serves the head, neck, and shoulders.

    2. <u>Brachial</u>-serves the chest, shoulders, arms, and hands.

    3. <u>Lumbar</u>-serves the back, abdomen, groin, thighs, knees, and calves.

    4. <u>Sacral</u>-serves the pelvis, buttocks, genitals, thighs, calves, and feet.

    5. <u>Coccygeal</u>-serves a small region over the coccyx.

D. Roots (see **Figure 5-8**)

1. Ventral root (motor root)-made of axons from motor neurons whose cell bodies are found within the grey matter; emerges from anterior side of spinal cord.

2. Dorsal root (sensory root)-transmits sensory information; emerges from posterior part of spinal cord.

3. A ventral root and a dorsal root join for form a <u>spinal nerve</u> which exits the vertebral canal through an opening in the bone called the <u>vertebral foramen</u>.

    a. The posterior branch (called the posterior ramus) of each spinal nerve innervates the muscles and skin of the back.

    b. The main portion of the nerve, the anterior branch (called the anterior ramus) innervates the muscle and skin of the front and sides of the trunk and limbs.

    c. The spinal nerves found in the thoracic and lumbar regions have an additional branch (called the visceral branch) that is part of the Autonomic Nervous System (ANS).

VI. Grey Matter vs White Matter

A. <u>Grey matter</u>-is for sensory and motor functions.

B. <u>White matter</u>-is for communication between parts of the spinal cord, as well as between the spinal cord and brain.

C. Anterior and Posterior Horns
    1. <u>Anterior horns</u>-are *motor.*
    2. <u>Posterior horns</u>-are *sensory* and also contain *interneurons.*

VII. Spinal Cord Injury

Type of Paralysis	Damage	Effect
Flaccid paralysis	Damage to anterior horn	Muscles atrophy
Spastic paralysis	Cut or crushed cord	Irregular nerve impulses
Paraplegia	Cut between T1- L1	Lower limbs only
Quadriplegia	Damage in cervical region	All 4 limbs

VIII. Diagnostic Test

    A. Lumbar puncture (spinal tap)-CSF is drawn out for examination.

    B. It is performed around L3 because it is past the length of the spinal cord.

The Spinal Cord (Figure 5-6)

Structure	Description or Function	Color
Dorsal (Sensory) Root		
Dorsal Root Ganglion		
Ventral (Motor) Root		
Spinal Nerve		
Anterior Horn		
Posterior Horn		
Grey Matter		
White Matter		
Central Canal		
Pia Mater		
Arachnoid Mater		
Dura Mater		

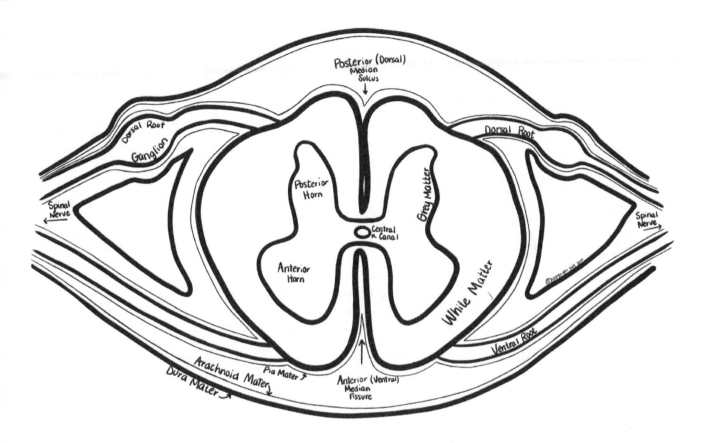

Figure 5-6

The Reflex Arc

VII. Reflex Arc (see **Figure 5-7**)

A. Reflexes

1. Purpose-to detect a change in the environment (a *stimulus*) and react to the change (a *response*) in a way that maintains homeostasis. When this is performed without thinking, it is called a reflex.

2. Reflex-rapid, predictable, involuntary, always goes in the same direction.

3. Autonomic reflexes-"*automatic*"; regulate the action of smooth muscle, heart, and glands. Example: secretion of saliva, pupil changes.

4. Somatic reflexes-reflexes that stimulate skeletal muscles.

B. Reflex Arcs

1. All have 4 elements:

a. Sensory receptor-reacts to stimulus.

b. Afferent (sensory) neuron-sends information to spinal cord via the dorsal root. Cell bodies of these neurons are located outside the spinal cord in a mass called a dorsal root ganglion.

c. Efferent (motor) neuron-leaves spinal cord with information about response via the ventral root.

d. Effector organ-muscle/gland that is stimulated to either contract or secrete.

2. Reflex Arc-how the message travels from the receptor to the effector

a. Nerve cells (neurons)-carry the message from the stimulated receptors to the correct effectors.

b. Sensory neuron-carries the message from the receptor to the Central Nervous System (spinal cord and brain).

c. Motor neuron-carries the message from the Central Nervous System to the effector.

d. In most reflex arcs the sensory neuron connects to motor neurons through association neurons (interneurons) in the Central Nervous System (CNS).

C. Common Reflexes

Stimulus	Response
Increased body temperature	Sweating
Decreased body temperature	Goosebumps or shivering
Aroma of your favorite food	Salivation
Foul odor	Nausea
Bright light shining in your eye	Decreased pupil size
Insect flying towards your eye	Blinking

D. Knee-jerk Reflex

   1. <u>Sensory receptor</u>-receptors in muscle stretched in knee.

   2. <u>Afferent</u> (sensory) <u>neuron</u>-impulse travels from leg to spinal cord.

   3. Efferent (motor) <u>neuron</u>-impulse leaves spinal cord and travels to muscle of leg.

   4. <u>Effector organ</u>-muscle of leg moves.

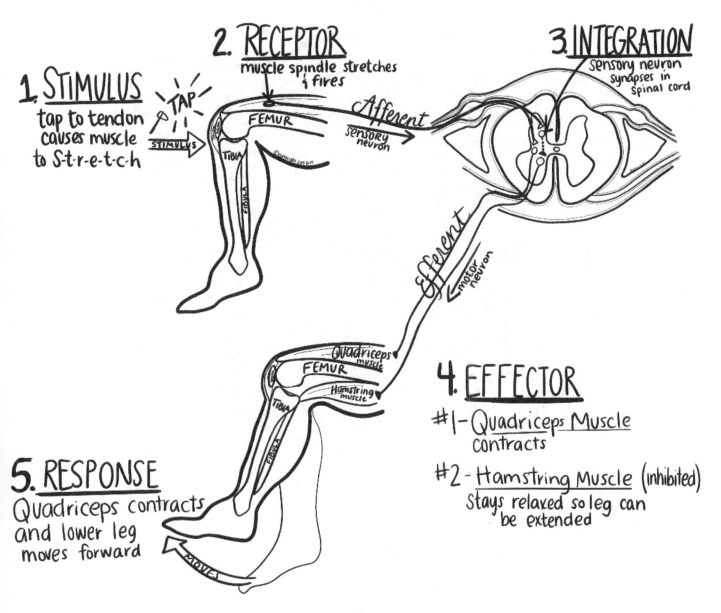

Figure 5-7

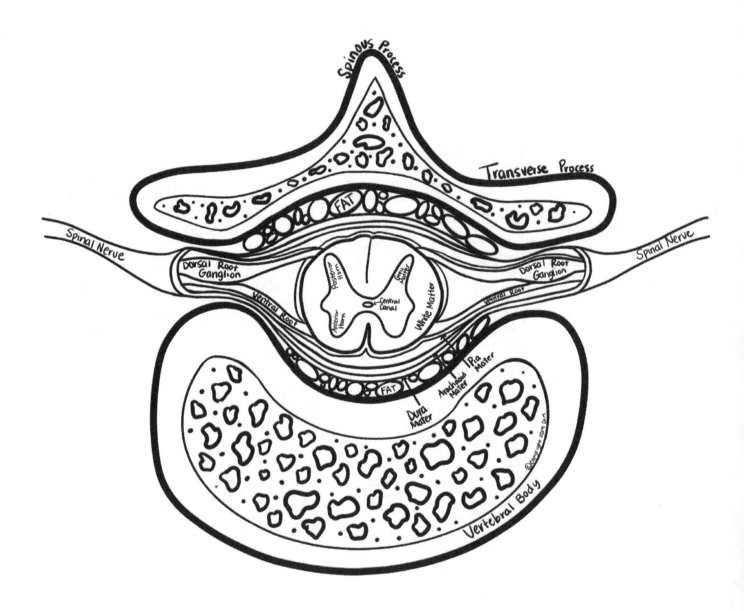

Figure 5-8

The Brain

I. Major Areas of the Brain (see **Figure 5-10**)

A. The brain is divided into 2 hemispheres connected by the corpus callosum (large nerve tract made of white matter) that are part of the forebrain which is made up of the cerebral cortex and structures beneath it (like the thalamus and limbic system). The cerebral cortex is associated with higher level processes such as consciousness and thought.

B. Each cerebral hemisphere can be divided into 4 lobes (frontal, parietal, temporal, and occipital), each with different functions.

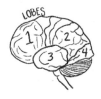

    1. Frontal lobe-responsible for cognitive functions and control of voluntary movement.

    2. Parietal lobe-processes information about temperature, taste, touch, and movement.

    3. Temporal lobe-processes memories and integrates them with sensations of, sight, sound, and touch.

    4. Occipital lobe-responsible for vision.

C. The brain as a whole is composed of 4 major regions:

    1. Brain Stem-connects brain to spinal cord.

    2. Diencephalon-the interbrain (inner part); located deep in the brain underneath the cerebrum and serves as the link between the Nervous System and the Endocrine System. It includes the thalamus and hypothalamus.

    3. Cerebrum-"*cerebral hemispheres*"; makes up 3/4 of the brain; located in the upper part of the cranial cavity and divided into a right hemisphere and a left hemisphere by a deep groove known as the longitudinal fissure.

    4. Cerebellum-"*small brain*"; 2nd largest area of brain; located behind the top part of the brain stem (where the spinal cord meets the brain); made of two hemispheres

II. Brain Stem-composed of *grey matter surrounded by* white matter (like spinal cord).

A. About 1 inch long.

B. Most cranial nerves (all except 2) arise from this area.

C. Composed of:

    1. Medulla-*Cranial nerves 9, 10, 11, 12*; responsible for vital functions such as:

        • Heart rate
        • Blood vessel diameter
        • Breathing
        • Reflex center (vomiting, coughing, sneezing, swallowing, gagging)

    2. Pons-"*bridge*"; *Cranial nerves 5, 6, 7, 8*; less than 1 inch long.

- Relay center between cerebrum and cerebellum.
- Contains ascending/descending nerve tracts.

3. Midbrain-*Cranial nerves 3, 4;* highest part of brain stem.

Responsible for:

- Movement of head to respond to light/sound.
- Change shape of lens in eye.

4. Reticular Formation-responsible for keeping brain alert.

III. Diencephalon (Interbrain)

A. Interbrain-composed of primarily *grey matter*; source of only 2 cranial nerves.

1. Thalamus-*Cranial nerves 1 and 2;* largest, 80% of diencephalon; held together by *"intermediate mass"*; called *"gateway to cerebral cortex"* (all impulses go through this area). Functions:

- Influences mood
- Registers pain
- Relay center to cerebrum
- Memory processing/learning

2. Hypothalamus-small, contains Pituitary gland connected by a stalk (infundibulum); responsible for maintaining *"homeostasis"*; is part of limbic system and the main visceral (organ) control center of body. Functions include regulation of:

- Temperature
- Hunger
- Thirst
- Pleasure/displeasure
- Growth
- Secretion and control of hormones
- Odor (mammillary body)
- Appetite
- Rage/anger

3. Epithalamus-forms the roof of the 3rd ventricle; contains pineal body (endocrine gland responsible for sexual maturity as well as regulation of the sleep/wake cycle (with the secretion of melatonin) and choroid plexus (forms CSF).

4. Limbic System- *"emotional"* brain; supports a variety of functions including: emotion, behavior, motivation, long-term memory, and olfaction. Emotional life is largely housed in the limbic system, and it critically aids the formation of memories.

5. Pineal Gland-endocrine gland responsible for biological rhythms; also regulates sleep-wake cycle by secreting melatonin.

6. Pituitary Gland-endocrine gland whose major function is to secrete hormones into the bloodstream. These hormones can affect other organs and glands.

IV. Cerebrum-3/4 of brain; "*cerebral hemispheres*"; composed of *grey matter outside* and *white matter inside*. It performs higher functions like interpreting touch, vision and hearing, as well as speech, reasoning, emotions, learning, and fine control of movement. These functions fall into 3 major categories:

1. Motor

2. Sensory

3. Association (integrate information)

V. Cerebellum-"*small brain*"; 2nd largest part; composed of *grey matter outside* and *white matter inside*; contains arbor vitae ("*white tree*"); responsible for:

1. Coordination

2. Tone

3. Balance

VI. Cerebrospinal Fluid (CSF)-125 mL in the ventricles and subarachnoid spaces of the CNS; produced by *choroid plexus* (in roof of each ventricle); function include acting as a shock absorber and circulating nutrients filtered from blood.

VII. Circulation of Cerebrospinal Fluid (CSF)

    A. Ventricles (4) in the brain circulate CSF.

    B. Path of CSF:

        1. Secreted by 1st and 2nd lateral ventricles.

        2. Flows to 3rd ventricle (in middle).

        3. Through Cerebral Aqueduct (of Sylvius).

        4. Through 4th ventricle (joins spinal cord as central canal).

        5. Through subarachnoid space around brain.

        6. Pass back into venous blood through arachnoid granulations (villi).

    C. CSF is secreted by the lateral ventricles and reabsorbed by the blood in the subarachnoid space.

    D. Hydrocephalus-a blockage in the 4th ventricles so that CSF stays around the brain.

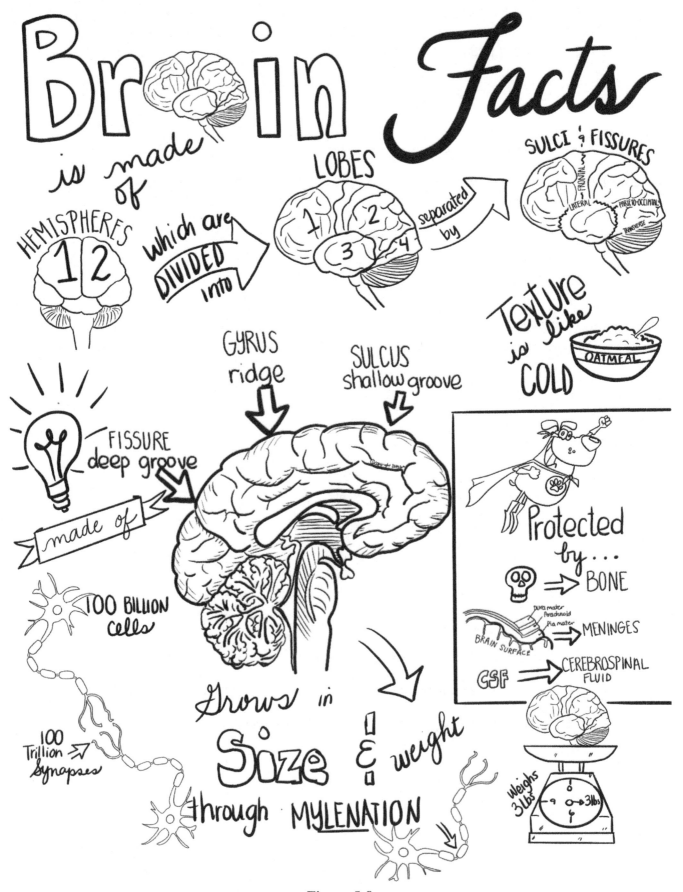

Figure 5-9

Areas of the Brain and Associated Functions

	Region	Functions	Arrangement of Grey / White Matter
	I. BRAINSTEM		
Composed of:			
Cranial Nerve #s	(1) Medulla	1. 2. 3. 4.	
	(2) Pons	1. 2.	
	(3) Midbrain	1. 2.	
	(4) Reticular Formation		

	Region	Functions	Arrangement of Grey / White Matter
	II. INTERBRAIN (DIENCEPHALON)		
Composed of:			
Cranial Nerve #s	(1) Thalamus	1. 2. 3. 4.	
	(2) Hypothalamus	1. 2. 3. 4. 5. 6. 7. 8. 9.	
	(3) Pineal Body	1. 2.	
	(4) Limbic System		

	Region	Functions	Arrangement of Grey / White Matter
	III. CEREBRUM	1. 2. 3.	
	IV. CEREBELLUM	1. 2. 3.	

Nervous System (Figures 5-6 and 5-10)

Structure	Function	Color
Spinal Cord		
Brain Lobes		
Frontal		
Temporal		
Parietal		
Occipital		
Cerebellum		
Brain Interior		
Arbor Vitae		
Corpus Callosum		
Pineal Gland		
Thalamus		
Hypothalamus		
Pituitary Gland		
Midbrain		
Pons		
Medulla		

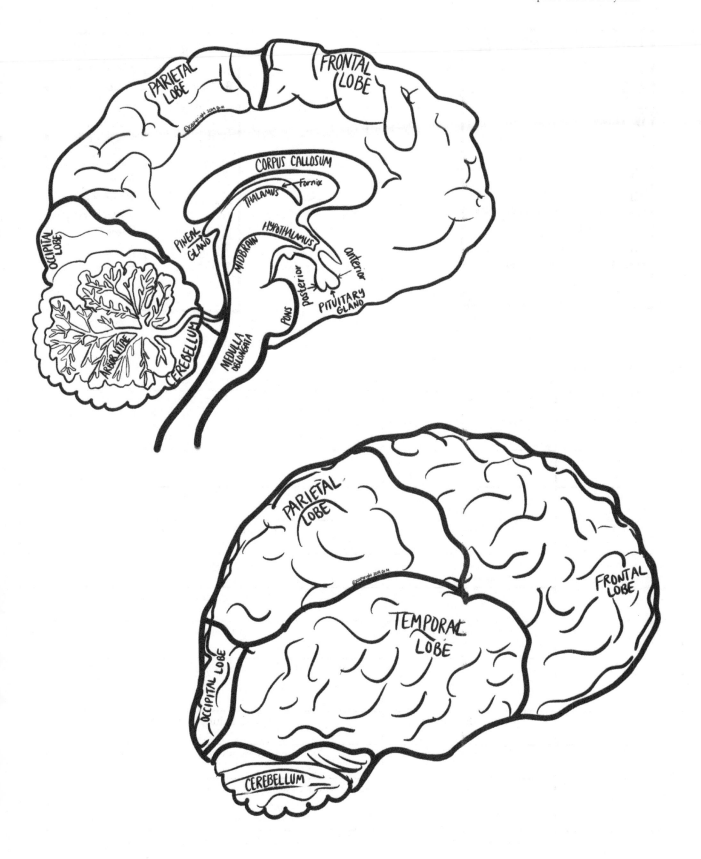

Figure 5-10

Cranial Nerves I-XII

I	Oh	Olfactory
II	Once	Optic
III	One	Oculomotor
IV	Takes	Trochlear
V	The	Trigeminal
VI	Anatomy	Abducens
VII	Final,	Facial
VIII	Very	Vestibulocochlear
IX	Good	Glossopharyngeal
X	Vacations	Vagus
XI	Are	Accessory
XII	Heavenly	Hypoglossal

Sensory? Motor? & Both?

I	Some	Olfactory
II	Say	Optic
III	Marry	Oculomotor
IV	Money	Trochlear
V	But	Trigeminal
VI	My	Abducens
VII	Brother	Facial
VIII	Says	Vestibulocochlear
IX	Big	Glossopharyngeal
X	Brains	Vagus
XI	Matter	Accessory
XII	Most	Hypoglossal

Cranial Nerves

Cranial Nerve Number	Cranial Nerve Name	Function
I	Olfactory	Smell
II	Optic	Vision
III	Oculomotor	Eyelid & eyeball movement
IV	Trochlear	Turns eye downward & laterally
V	Trigeminal	Chewing, Face & mouth touch and pain
VI	Abducens	Turns eye laterally
VII	Facial	Controls most facial expression, Secretion of tears & saliva, Taste
VIII	Vestibulocochlear	Hearing, Equilibrium sensation
IX	Glossopharyngeal	Taste, Senses carotid blood pressure
X	Vagus	Senses aortic blood pressure, Slows heart rate, Stimulates digestive organs, Taste
XI	Accessory	Controls trapezius & sternocleidomastoid muscles, Controls swallowing movements
XII	Hypoglossal	Controls tongue movements

CHAPTER 6. SPECIAL SENSES

Special Senses

I. <u>Special Senses</u>-allow humans to detect certain changes in the environment; include: smell, taste, vision, hearing, and equilibrium.

II. Olfactory Sensations (Smell)

A. Smell is a *chemical* sense; chemicals react with smell receptors to produce a sensation.

B. <u>Olfactory Epithelium</u>-specialized epithelium that *lines the nasal cavity*, the air-filled cavity behind the nose.

Types of Cells in the Olfactory Epithelium:

1. <u>Olfactory Receptors</u>-*neurons* that respond to chemicals by *producing smell impulses* that are created by the <u>olfactory bulbs</u> and carried to the brain over the <u>olfactory tracts</u>.

2. <u>Supporting</u> (Sustentacular) <u>Cells</u>-columnar epithelial cells that make up the *mucous membrane* lining the nasal cavity and can *produce new olfactory receptor cells*.

3. <u>Bowman's Glands</u>-*produce mucus* which moistens the nasal cavity.

C. Humans can develop <u>adaptations</u> to smells as well as a decreased sensitivity to smells as one ages.

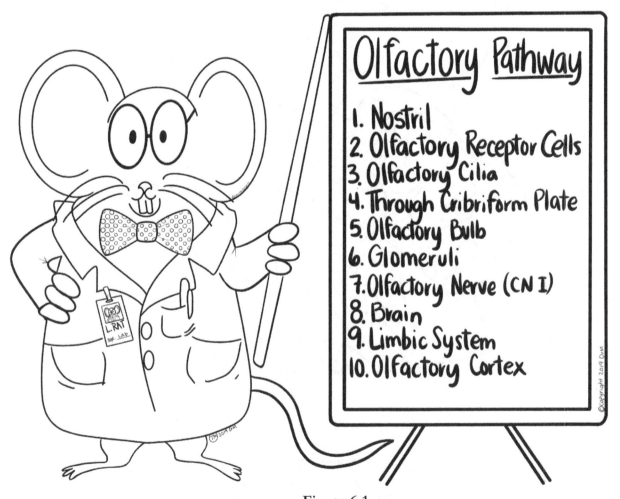

Figure 6-1

Olfactory (Smell) Pathway (Figures 6-1 and 6-2)

The olfactory nerve (Cranial Nerve I or CNI) is made up of multiple nerve fibers/rootlets coming from the receptor cells and is one of the few cranial nerves that carries <u>only</u> sensory information. The pathway can be summarized as follows:

1. Vaporized odor molecules (chemicals) floating in the air reach the nostrils and dissolve in the mucus located on the roof of each nostril.

2. Odor is detected by millions of specialized <u>olfactory nerve fibers</u> (called olfactory receptor neurons) located in the mucosa of the nasal cavity. These olfactory nerve fibers have thin threadlike projections (<u>olfactory cilia</u>), which float in the nasal mucus. Olfactory cilia contain the molecular machinery for detecting the arrival of odorants and then generating an electrical signal to be sent to the brain. The basal surface of olfactory nerve fibers is located directly inferior to the <u>cribriform plate</u> of the ethmoid bone that makes up the bony roof of the nasal cavity. These neurons can detect thousands of different odors. Olfactory receptor cells are unique because:

   a. They are <u>nerve cells</u> so they are directly connected to the brain.

   b. They <u>can regenerate</u> throughout their lifespan (unlike other nerve cells) from cells arising from the underlying basal (stem) cells. This process likely occurs over a period of weeks.

3. The axons from these receptors can collectively be thought of as the <u>olfactory nerve</u> (CNI). These bundles of nerve fibers transmit impulses to the olfactory bulbs by passing through the foramina (small holes) in the cribriform plate of the ethmoid bone. Unlike many other nerves, CNI does not possess two trunks. Rather, its sensory fibers extend through the ethmoid bone's cribriform plate, a part of the skull located behind the nose. While part of the nervous system, the CNI, along with the optic nerve (CN II), does not join the brainstem and is the shortest cranial nerve within the human head.

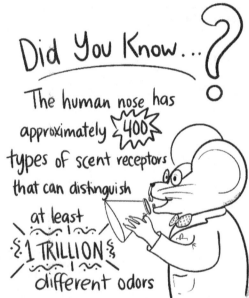

Did You Know...?
The human nose has approximately 400 types of scent receptors that can distinguish at least 1 TRILLION different odors

4. When an odorant molecule binds with a receptor, it triggers a biochemical chain reaction inside the receptor cell resulting in a *shift of the cell's electrical charge*. This shift causes the receptor cell to fire off a series of electrical pulses, which are sent to the brain along a thin nerve fiber known as an <u>axon</u>. When this process reaches a critical level, the receptor cell sends an electrical signal to the next cell, which is located in the olfactory bulb.

5. The <u>olfactory bulb</u> serves as the main relay station within the olfactory pathway and is the brain's first processing station for odor information. Information from millions of receptor cells is passed to cells whose projections make up the olfactory tract that travels to the brain. Each receptor cell is believed to contain *only one type* of olfactory receptor of the hundreds which are scattered randomly throughout the nose. Nerve axons from these cells reorganize into those containing the same type of olfactory receptor as they travel to the olfactory bulb. Here, these nerve endings gather and form tiny spheres called <u>glomeruli</u>.

The hundreds of glomeruli resemble an electronic switchboard. A particular odorant may activate several different receptors, causing the switchboard to "'light up'" in unique patterns. These complex patterns provide the raw information for the brain to interpret. The olfactory bulb processes these patterns and distributes the information to the rest of the brain, where additional coding takes place.

6. The olfactory bulbs have sensory receptors that are part of the brain and send messages directly to 2 areas:

a. Limbic system-most primitive brain center that is involved in influencing emotions and memories.

b. Olfactory cortex-area where conscious awareness of an odor takes place.

Cross-connections between cortex and the limbic system may be essential in forming lifelong, emotionally-laden, olfactory memories. These brain centers perceive odors and access memories to remind us about people, places, or events associated with these olfactory sensations.

Anatomy of Smell (Figure 6-2)

Structure	Function/Description	Color
Cribriform Plate		
Nasal Cavity		
Olfactory Bulb		
Olfactory Nerve Fibers		

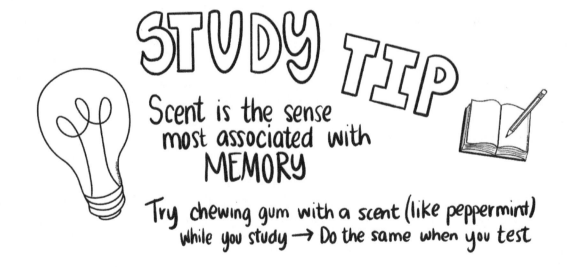

STUDY TIP
Scent is the sense most associated with MEMORY

Try chewing gum with a scent (like peppermint) while you study → Do the same when you test

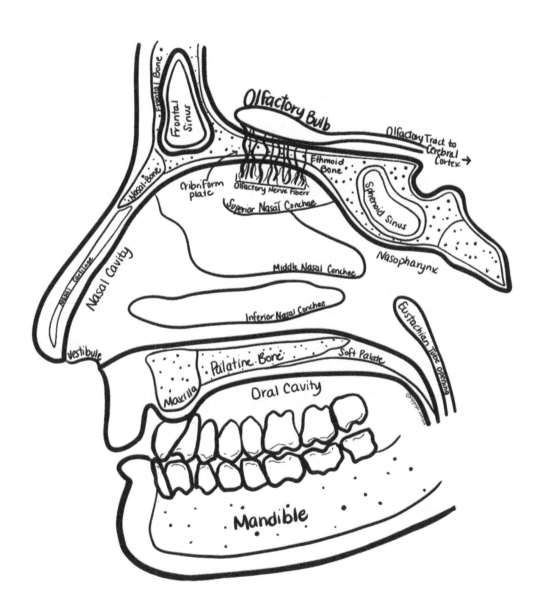

Figure 6-2

Gustatory (Taste)

III. Gustatory Sensations (Taste)

    A. Taste is a *chemical* sense.

    B. Receptors are located in taste buds.

    C. Taste Buds (See **Figures 6-3** and **6-5**)

        1. Humans have about 10,000 taste buds located on the *tongue*, the *larynx*, the *pharynx*, and the *soft palate*.

        2. Papillae-rough elevations on the tongue that *contain the taste buds*.

        Types of Papillae include: (**Figure 6-3**)

            a. Circumvallate Papillae-located in an inverted V region on the *back of the tongue*.

            b. Fungiform Papillae-mushroom-shaped; *scattered all over* the tongue.

            c. Filiform Papillae-pointed in shape and found in large numbers across the surface of the tongue.

            d. Foliate Papillae-clustered in two groups on each side of the tongue.

        3. Types of Cells in Taste Buds: (**Figure 6-5**)

            a. Support Cells-*surround* gustatory receptor cells.

            b. Gustatory Taste Receptor Cells-*detect chemicals in food* and may contain small hairs known as microvilli.

            c. Basal Cells-*produce new support cells* that can further develop into new gustatory receptor cells.

        4. Primary Taste Sensations: (**Figure 6-5**)

            a. Sour-detected along the *sides* of the tongue.

            b. Salty-detected near the *tip* of the tongue.

            c. Sweet-detected at the *tip* of the tongue.

            d. Bitter-detected at the *posterior portion* of the tongue.

            e. All other taste sensations are combinations of the above 4 tastes.

The Tongue (Figure 6-3)

Structure	Function/Description	Color
Circumvallate Papillae		
Filiform Papilla		
Foliate Papillae		
Fungiform Papillae		
Lingual Tonsil		
Palatine Tonsil		

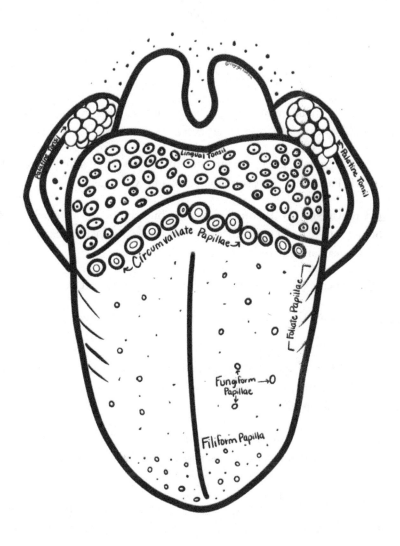

Figure 6-3

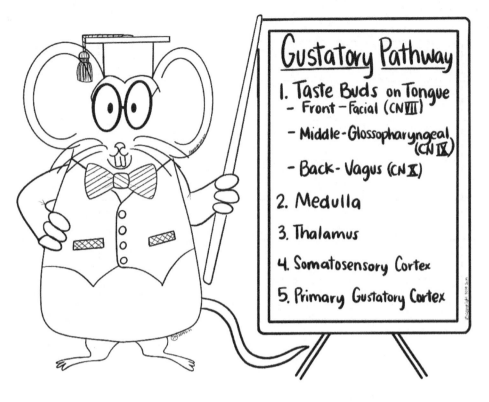

Gustatory (Taste) Pathway

1. The tongue contains small bumps (papillae) near the location of the taste buds. In the tongue's taste buds, the taste receptors receive sensory input and release neurotransmitters onto the dendrites of sensory neurons. This occurs via 2 mechanisms:

a. The intake of *salty foods* leads to more *sodium ions* entering the receptor and triggers depolarization, then neurotransmitter release.

Figure 6-4

b. This also occurs with the intake of *sour foods* (hydrogen ions) and *sweet foods* (sugar molecules), both of which result in the *closing of K⁺ channels* upon their entry.

2. From the axons of the taste receptors, the sensory information is transferred along three taste pathways via the branches of Cranial Nerves VII (Facial), IX (Glossopharyngeal), and X (Vagus).

a. The facial nerve (Cranial Nerve VII) connects to taste buds in the *anterior third of the tongue* through the chorda tympani (branch of the facial nerve that originates from the taste buds in the front of the tongue, runs through the middle ear, and carries taste messages to the brain).

b. The glossopharyngeal nerve (Cranial Nerve IX) connects to taste buds in the *posterior two thirds of the tongue*.

c. The vagus nerve (Cranial Nerve X) connects to taste buds in the *extreme posterior of the tongue*, along the edge of the pharynx.

3. Axons from the three cranial nerves carrying taste information travel to the medulla. Specifically, it is received via the solitary tract (a series of purely sensory nuclei {clusters of nerve cell bodies} that forms a vertical column of grey matter embedded in the medulla oblongata).

4. From the medulla, much of the information is carried to the thalamus. More precisely, it is the ventral posteromedial nucleus of the thalamus that receives the sensory information from the face and head and relays it to the somatosensory cortex.

5. The thalamus relays the information to the primary gustatory cortex located in the somatosensory cortex near the inferior margin of the post-central gyrus. The primary gustatory cortex is where the perception of a particular taste is processed.

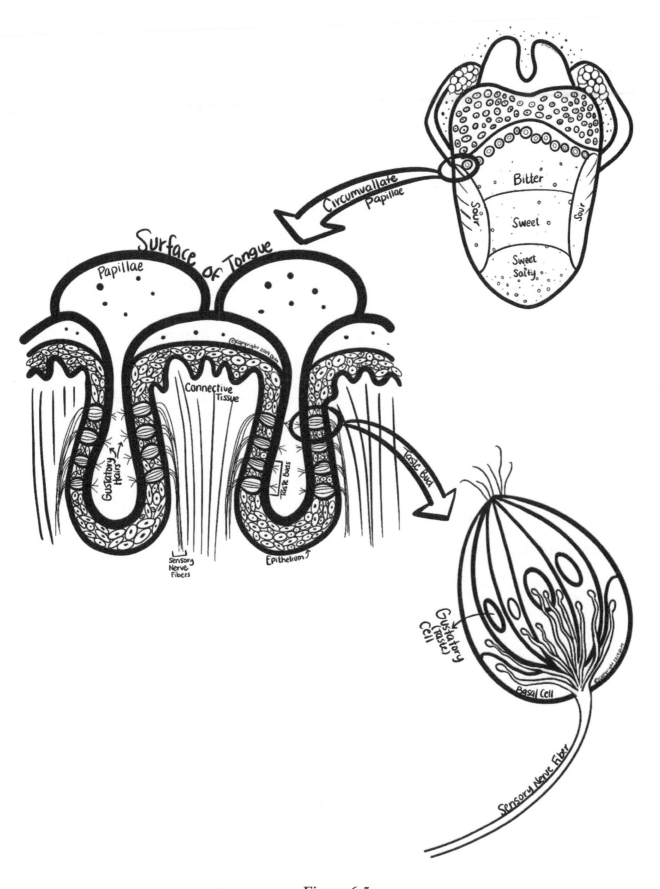

Figure 6-5

Visual (Sight)

IV. Visual Sensations (Sight)

    A. External Structures of the Eye (**Figure 6-6**)

        1. Eyelids (palpebrae)-shade the eyes during sleep.

            a. Spread lubricating fluid over the surface of the eye and *protect* the eyes from sunlight.

            b. Conjunctiva-thin mucous membrane associated with the eyelids; contains goblet cells that *secrete mucus.*

        2. Eyelashes-protect the eyes from dust and foreign debris.

        3. Lacrimal Apparatus-collection of structures involved in producing lacrimal fluid (tears). Includes:

            a. Lacrimal Glands-*secrete lacrimal fluid* through the lacrimal ducts onto the eyeball surface.

            b. Lacrimal fluid (tears)-fluid that lubricates, moistens, and protects the eyeball; composed of water, salts, mucus, and lysozyme (an enzyme that kills bacteria).

    B. External Eyeball

        1. Cornea-nonvascular covering that surrounds the iris (colored part) of the eye that is involved in focusing light on the lens.

        2. Sclera-white covering of the eye.

        3. Pupil-hole in the center of the iris that allows light to pass into the eye.

    C. External Muscles Controlling the Eyeball

        1. Lateral Rectus (LR)-moves eye outwards away from nose (abduction).

        2. Medial Rectus (MR)-moves eye inwards towards nose (adduction).

        3. Superior Rectus (SR)-moves eye up and in.

        4. Inferior Rectus (IR)-moves eye down and in.

        5. Superior Oblique (SO)-moves eye down and out.

        6. Inferior Oblique (IO)- moves eye up and out.

    C. Internal Eyeball

        1. Choroid-lines the internal surface of the sclera and provides nutrients to the posterior surface of the retina.

        2. Ciliary body-consists of:

            a. Ciliary Processes-which *secrete a fluid* known as aqueous humor.

            b. Ciliary Muscle-smooth muscle that *alters the shape of the lens* for near/far vision.

3. Retina-highly vascular inner lining of the posterior portion of the eyeball.

    b. Structures associated with the retina:

        1) Optic disk (blind spot)-portion of the retina that lacks rods and cones; location where optic nerve exits.

        2) Rods-photoreceptors that detect black and white light and allow us to see shape and movement.

        3) Cones-allow for color vision.

        4) Macula Lutea-center of the posterior portion of the retina.

        5) Fovea Centralis-small depression in the center of the Macula Lutea containing cones only; location where sharpest image is formed.

    c. Detached Retina-usually caused by trauma and can lead to blindness.

4. Lens-located posterior to the pupil and iris; primarily composed of protein.

    a. Held in place by the suspensory ligaments and is *involved in focusing*.

    b. Cataracts-disease in which lens *loses transparency* due to aging, trauma, exposure to UV light, certain medications; can be repaired via surgery.

5. Chambers of the Eyeball

    a. Anterior-small space *anterior* to the lens filled with aqueous humor (watery fluid).

    b. Posterior-large space *posterior* to the lens filled with vitreous humor (transparent gel).

The Eye (Figure 6-6)

Structure	Function/Description	Color
Anterior Chamber		
Aqueous Humor		
Choroid Coat		
Ciliary Body		
Cornea		
Fovea Centralis		
Iris		
Lens		
Macula		
Optic Disk		
Optic Nerve		
Posterior Chamber		
Pupil		
Retina		
Sclera		
Vitreous Humor		

Chapter 6 Special Senses

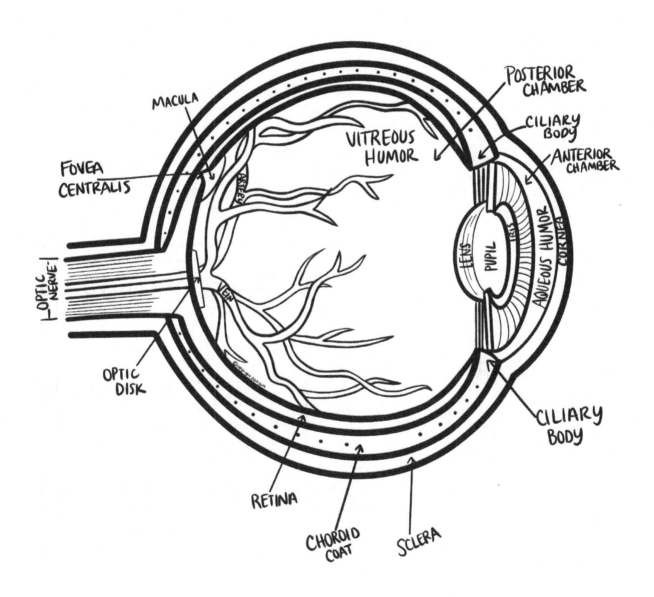

Figure 6-6

163

Visual (Sight) Pathway (Figure 6-7)

1. Light passes through the <u>cornea</u>, the clear, dome-shaped surface that covers the front of the eye. The cornea refracts (bends) this incoming light.

2. The <u>pupil</u> controls the amount of light that enters the eye. The size of the pupil is regulated by the <u>iris</u>.

3. Light travels through the pupil to the <u>lens</u>, a clear part of the eye that further focuses light, or an image, onto the <u>retina</u>. Ciliary muscles surround the lens and hold it in place as well as adjust the lens to allow vision at different distances. The interior chamber of the eyeball is filled with a jelly-like tissue called the <u>vitreous humor</u>. After passing through the lens, light must travel through this humor before striking the sensitive layer of cells of the <u>retina</u>.

4. When light strikes the <u>retina</u>, special photoreceptor cells convert this light into *electrical signals*.

5. These electrical signals are further processed and travel from the retina of the eye to the brain through the <u>optic nerve</u> (Cranial Nerve II), a bundle of about one million nerve fibers.

6. As the two optic nerves enter the brain, they cross over, coming together at a point known as the <u>optic chiasma</u>. Here, signals from the left side of both eyes are diverted to the left side of the brain, and vice versa, allowing the images from both eyes to be combined and compared.

7. The signals travel through <u>optic tracts</u> and enter the brain synapsing in the <u>thalamus</u>, which separates the incoming information into two parts, one containing color and detail, and the other movement and contrast. The messages then move through the <u>optic radiation</u> to the back of the brain, and into the <u>primary visual cortex of the occipital lobe</u>. The cortex is laid out so that it mirrors the back of the retina, allowing a detailed image to be reconstructed.

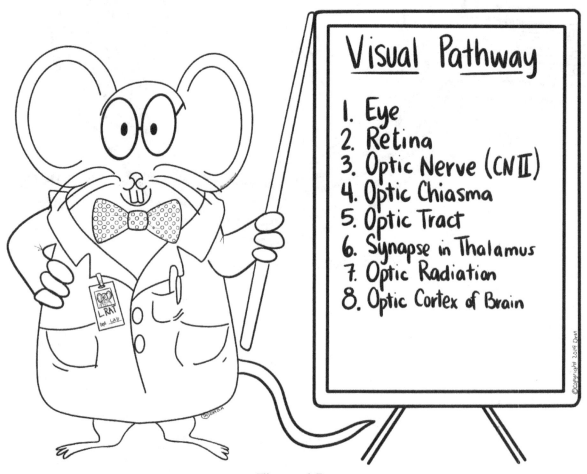

Figure 6-7

Auditory (Hearing and Equilibrium)

V. <u>Auditory Sensations</u> (Hearing and Equilibrium)-**Figure 6-8**

A. The ear plays a major role in providing auditory sensations as well as allowing us to maintain our balance (<u>equilibrium</u>).

B. External Ear

1. <u>Auricle</u> (pinna)-outer ear composed of elastic cartilage; divided into two sections: the <u>helix</u> (upper) and <u>lobule</u> (lobe).

2. <u>External Acoustic Meatus</u>-tube that extends from the <u>auricle</u> to the <u>tympanum</u> (eardrum) through the <u>temporal bone</u>; lined with <u>ceruminous glands</u> which secrete <u>cerumen</u> (earwax) to prevent dust and debris from collecting in the canal.

C. Internal Ear

1. <u>Tympanic Membrane</u> (eardrum)-thin layer of tissue between the external acoustic meatus and the inner ear; helps to move sound waves deep into the ear.

2. <u>Eustachian</u> (Auditory) <u>Tube</u>-connects the middle ear with the nasopharynx; opens during swallowing and yawning to regulate pressure in the middle ear.

3. <u>Auditory Ossicles</u>-3 bones (<u>malleus</u>, <u>incus</u> and <u>stapes</u>) within the middle ear held in place by ligaments; involved in moving sound waves into the inner ear.

4. <u>Semicircular Canals</u>-contain <u>otoliths</u> that are involved in providing humans with balance and equilibrium; each ear has three.

5. <u>Cochlea</u> (the Organ of Hearing)-contains the <u>Spiral Organ</u> (*"snail's shell"*). It is named from the Greek word for *'snail'* because of its distinctive coiled shape. The cochlea contains receptors and is filled with special fluids which are important to the process of hearing.

D. The anatomy of our hearing is very complex but can be broadly divided into two parts: the <u>peripheral hearing system</u> and the <u>central hearing system.</u>

1. The <u>peripheral hearing system</u> is composed of three parts: the outer ear, the middle ear and the inner ear.

   a). The <u>outer ear</u> consists of the pinna (also called the <u>auricle</u>), ear canal, and eardrum.

   b). The <u>middle ear</u> is a small, air-filled space that contains three small bones (the <u>ossicles</u>-malleus, incus and stapes). The malleus connects to the eardrum and links it to the outer ear. The stapes (smallest bone in the body) connects to the inner ear.

   c). The <u>inner ear</u> consists of both hearing and balance organs. The hearing part of the inner ear and is the <u>cochlea</u>, which contains many thousands of sensory cells (called *'hair cells'*). It is connected to the central hearing system by the hearing or auditory nerve (Cranial Nerve VIII).

2. The <u>central hearing system</u> consists of the <u>auditory nerve</u> (Cranial Nerve VIII) and an incredibly complex pathway through the brain stem and onward to the auditory cortex of the brain.

The Ear (Figure 6-8)

Structure	Function/Description	Color
Cochlea		
External Acoustic Meatus		
Incus (Anvil)		
Internal Acoustic Meatus		
Malleus (Hammer)		
Oval Window		
Pinna (Auricle)		
Round Window		
Semicircular Canals		
Stapes (Stirrup)		
Tympanic Membrane (Eardrum)		

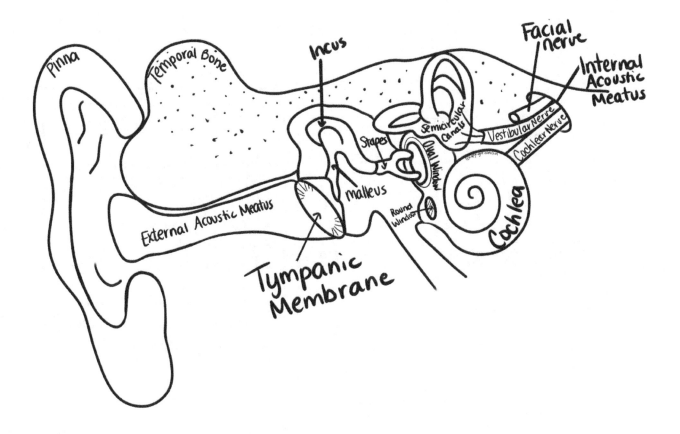

Figure 6-8

Auditory (Hearing) Pathway (Figure 6-9)

1. Sound waves enter the outer ear and travel through the narrow ear canal that leads to the eardrum.

2. The eardrum vibrates from the incoming sound waves and transfers these vibrations to the ossicles in the middle ear.

3. These three bones in the middle ear amplify the sound vibrations and send them to the cochlea in the inner ear. The cochlea is divided into an upper and lower part with an elastic partition called the basilar membrane that serves as the base on which key hearing structures sit.

4. The vibrations from the sound waves cause the fluid inside the cochlea to ripple, producing a traveling wave along the basilar membrane. Hair cells near the wide end of the snail-shaped cochlea detect high-pitched sounds, while those closer to the center detect lower-pitched sounds.

5. As the hair cells move up and down, stereocilia (microscopic hair-like projections) on top of these hair cells bump against an overlying structure and bend, causing pore-like channels at the tips of the stereocilia to open allowing chemicals to rush into the cells creating an electrical signal.

6. The auditory nerve (cranial nerve VIII) carries this electrical signal to the primary auditory cortex located in the temporal area of the brain, which turns it into a sound that we recognize and understand.

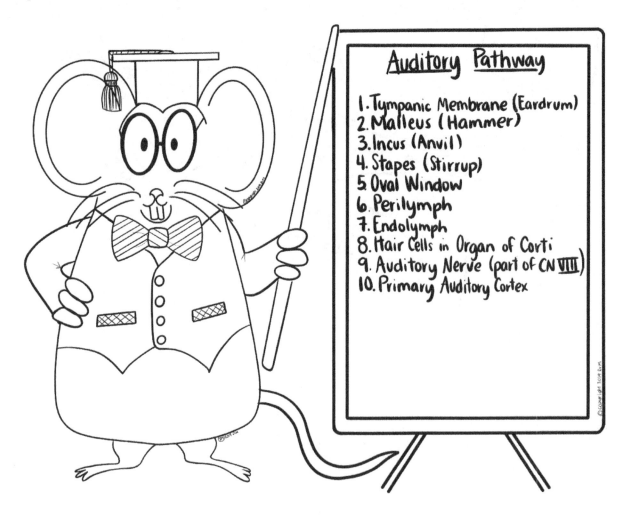

Figure 6-9

CHAPTER 7. ENDOCRINE SYSTEM

The Endocrine System

I. Endocrine System

    A. Works with the Nervous System to maintain homeostasis in the human body.

    B. Composed of glands that secrete chemical messengers known as hormones.

    C. Secretes hormones *directly into the bloodstream* allowing them to travel all over the body in order to stimulate specific cells or organs (known as target cells or target organs). Target cells have special proteins receptors that essentially functions as "hands" which enable them to bind *only* to specific molecules that fit.

    D. Regulates metabolism, reproduction, growth, and development.

II. Relationship Between the Endocrine System and Nervous System

    A. Nervous System-*produces impulses* that regulate muscle and gland activities. These impulses are generally *quick responses* to a stimulus.

    B. Endocrine System-*responds to a stimulus* by releasing *hormones*. Hormones usually have *widespread effects* on the body, but they are *slower responding* than impulses created in the Nervous System.

    C. Hypothalamus-link between the Endocrine and Nervous Systems. The Hypothalamus produces releasing and inhibiting hormones which stop and start the production of other hormones throughout the body.

III. Hormones-chemical substances secreted by glands to regulate the metabolic functioning of cells and organs.

    A. Hormones are classified based on their *chemical structure*.

    Major types of hormones include:

        1. Amino acid-based hormones-vary in size from small amino acids to large protein-based hormones. Most human hormones are composed of amino acids.

        2. Steroid-based hormones-composed of compounds synthesized from cholesterol. The gonadal and adrenocortical hormones are steroid-based.

        3. Eicosanoids-typically released by cell membranes and are often involved in inflammation and allergic reactions. Examples of eicosanoids include leukotrienes and prostaglandins.

    B. Parts of the Hormonal System of Communication:

        1. Exocrine-hormone substance is excreted *into a duct or tube* to travel to another part of the body.

        2. Endocrine-hormone substance is excreted directly *into the blood* to travel to another part of the body.

        3. Neurosecretory-hormones released by neurons (such as the Pituitary Gland and Hypothalamus).

    C. Hormones are *specific* for certain target cells or target organs in the body.

    D. Hormonal secretion is *regulated by the Autonomic Nervous System* (ANS) via negative feedback.

E. Hormonal control mechanisms:

    1. <u>Negative feedback loop</u>-reactions that *stop* a process already occurring and reverse it to go in the *opposite direction.*

    2. <u>Positive feedback loop</u>-reactions that *enhance* a process that is already occurring.

F. <u>Hormones influence activities in the body by</u>:

    1. Altering cell membrane permeability to certain molecules.

    2. Stimulating the production of proteins or enzymes.

    3. Activating or deactivating enzymes.

    4. Inducing secretions of other materials in the body.

    5. Stimulating cell division.

Major Endocrine Glands (Figure 7-10, p.185)

Endocrine Gland	Primary Function	Hormone(s) Secreted
Pituitary	Water Retention, Milk Production, Stimulate Reproductive Cell Formation	o Anterior- 2 hormones (Ex. ADH anti-diuretic hormone) o Posterior- 6 hormones (Ex. Growth)
Thyroid	Metabolism	T3 & T4 hormones
Parathyroid	Increase Blood Calcium	Parathyroid hormone (PTH)
Adrenal	Increase Blood Glucose	Epinephrine & Norepinephrine
Thymus	Programs T-lymphocytes	Thymosin
Pancreas	Blood Glucose	Insulin & Glucagon
Pineal	Biological Rhythms, Sleep/Wake	Melatonin
Ovary	Female Sex Characteristics	Estrogen & Progesterone
Testes	Male Sex Characteristics	Androgens

IV. Major Endocrine Glands

    A. <u>Pineal Gland</u>-located in the brain, attached to the thalamus; secretes the hormone <u>melatonin</u> that regulates <u>diurnal rhythms</u> and <u>sleep patterns</u>. (see **Figure 7-1**)

    B. <u>Pituitary gland</u> (hypophysis)-located in the brain between the Hypothalamus and Pineal Gland; sits in the Sella turcica (*"Turk's saddle"*) of the sphenoid bone. (see **Figure 7-1**)

        1. Composed of two major lobes:

a. <u>Neurohypophysis</u>-posterior lobe

b. <u>Adenohypophysis</u>-anterior lobe

2. <u>Neurohypophysis</u> (posterior lobe)-only <u>stores</u> hormones that have been synthesized by <u>neurons</u> in the <u>Hypothalamus</u> of the brain. Hormones stored by the neurohypophysis are:

a. <u>Oxytocin</u> (OT)-regulates blood pressure and stimulates contractions of the uterine muscles during childbirth; also plays a role in regulating the release of prolactin during milk ejection.

b. <u>Antidiuretic Hormone</u> (ADH)-regulates water balance in the kidney by preventing dehydration and water overload. Drinking alcoholic beverages inhibits ADH secretion and leads to the formation of large supplies of urine.

3. <u>Adenohypophysis</u> (anterior lobe)-often called the "Master Gland". It secretes the following hormones:

a. <u>Somatotropic Hormone</u> (STH)-also known as <u>Human Growth Hormone</u> (hGH); regulates the growth of the skeleton and is regulated by the hypothalamus via Growth Hormone Releasing Factor and Growth Hormone Inhibiting Factor.

b. <u>Thyrotropin Hormone</u> (TSH)-stimulates secretions from the thyroid gland and is regulated by the hypothalamus.

c. <u>Adrenocorticotrophic Hormone</u> (ACTH)-stimulates hormonal secretions of the adrenal glands.

d. <u>Gonadotrophins</u>-includes <u>Follicle-Stimulating Hormone</u> (FSH) and <u>Luteinizing Hormone</u> (LH) which regulate the growth and development of the sex organs and can act to regulate the female menstrual cycle.

e. <u>Prolactin</u> (PRL)-stimulates breast development and milk secretion from the mammary glands; release is stimulated by estrogen.

1). In pregnant women, PRL levels increase dramatically. After birth, the infant's nursing stimulates PRL release in the mother to encourage additional milk production. (see **Figure 13-6**, p. 317)

2). Males also secrete prolactin but the function of this hormone in men is not understood.

f. <u>Follicle Stimulating Hormone</u> (FSH)-gonadotrophic hormone released by the pituitary gland.

1). One of the hormones essential to pubertal development and the function of women's ovaries and men's testes.

2). In women, this hormone stimulates the growth of ovarian follicles in the ovary before the release of an egg from one follicle at ovulation. It also increases estradiol production.

3). In men, acts on the Sertoli cells of the testes to stimulate sperm production.

g. <u>Luteinizing Hormone</u> (LH)-gonadotrophic hormone produced and released by cells in the anterior pituitary gland; crucial in regulating the function of the testes in men and ovaries in women.

1). In men, LH stimulates Leydig cells in the testes to produce <u>testosterone</u>, which acts locally to support sperm production.

2). In women, LH carries out different roles in the two halves of the menstrual cycle. (see **Figure 7-4**, p. 177)

a). Weeks one to two of the cycle, LH is required to stimulate the ovarian follicles in the ovary to produce the female sex hormone, <u>estradiol</u>.

b). Around day 14 of the cycle, a surge in LH levels causes the ovarian follicle to release a mature oocyte (egg) from the ovary in a process called <u>ovulation</u>.

c). Weeks three to four (the remainder of the cycle), the remnants of the ovarian follicle form a corpus luteum. LH stimulates the corpus luteum to produce progesterone, which is required to support the early stages of pregnancy, if fertilization occurs.

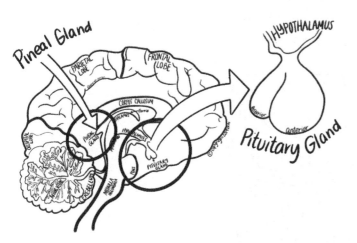

Figure 7-1

Endocrine Glands in the Brain (Figure 7-1)

Structure	Function/Description	Color
Hypothalamus		
Pineal Gland		
Pituitary Gland		
Anterior Lobe of Pituitary		
Posterior Lobe of Pituitary		

C. <u>Gonads</u> (ovaries and testes)-produce *steroid sex hormones*. (see **Figures 7-2** and **7-3**)

1. <u>Ovaries</u>-located in the pelvis of the female; also a *dual organ* (serves as an endocrine organ and a reproductive organ). Hormones secreted by the ovaries include:

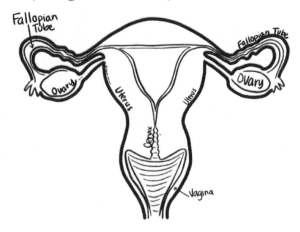

Figure 7-2

a. <u>Estrogen</u>-stimulates the development of *secondary sex characteristics* of females and regulates the growth of the endometrium.

b. <u>Progesterone</u>-maintains the growth of the endometrium of the uterus.

2. <u>Testes</u>-located below the pelvis inside the male scrotum; also a *dual organ* (serves as a reproductive structure and as an endocrine gland). The testes produce only one hormone (<u>testosterone</u>) which stimulates the development of the male *secondary sex characteristics*.

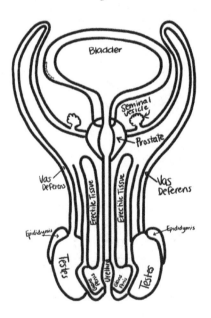

Figure 7-3

Ovaries and Testes (Figures 7-2 and 7-3)

Structure	Function/Description	Color
Ovary		
Testes		

Feedback Mechanism of the Menstrual Cycle (Figure 7-4)

I. <u>Menstrual Cycle</u>-recurring changes that occur within the female reproductive system to make pregnancy possible; lasts roughly one month (around 28 days) and begins at puberty (<u>menarche</u>) before ending with menopause.

II. Hormone Control

    A. <u>Pituitary hormones</u> (FSH and LH)-released from the *anterior pituitary gland* and act on the *ovaries* to develop follicles.

        1. Follicular Stimulating Hormone (FSH)-stimulates follicular growth in ovaries and stimulates estrogen secretion from developing follicles.

        2. Luteinizing Hormone (LH)-causes <u>ovulation</u> when levels surge and results in the formation of a <u>corpus luteum</u>.

    B. <u>Ovarian hormones</u> (estrogen and progesterone)-released from the *ovaries* and act on the *uterus* to prepare for pregnancy.

        1. Estrogen

            a. Thickens endometrium (uterine lining).

            b. Inhibits FHS and LH for most of the menstrual cycle.

            c. *Stimulates* FSH and LH release pre-ovulation.

        2. Progesterone

            a. Thickens endometrium (uterine lining).

            b. *Inhibits* FSH and LH.

III. <u>Key Events</u>-characterized by changes in *hormonal levels, follicular development*, and status of *endometrium*.

    A. Follicular Phase

        1. <u>Follicle Stimulating Hormone</u> (FSH)-secreted from the anterior pituitary; stimulates growth of ovarian follicles.

        2. <u>Estrogen</u>-produced by the dominant follicle; inhibits FSH secretion (negative feedback) to prevent other follicles growing.

        3. <u>Endometrial layer</u>-stimulated to thicken as estrogen acts on the uterus.

    B. Ovulation

        1. <u>Estrogen</u>-stimulates the anterior pituitary to secrete hormones; occurs midway through the cycle (around day 12); occurs as a result of <u>positive feedback</u>.

        2. <u>Positive feedback</u>-results in a large surge of luteinizing hormone (LH) and a lesser surge of FSH; LH causes ovulation when the dominant follicle will rupture and release an egg (secondary oocyte).

C. Luteal Phase

1. <u>Ruptured follicle</u>-develops into a slowly degenerating <u>corpus luteum</u> that secretes high levels of progesterone, as well as lower levels of estrogen.

2. <u>Estrogen and progesterone</u>-act on the uterus to thicken the endometrial lining (in preparation for pregnancy) as well inhibit secretion of FSH and LH, preventing any follicles from developing.

D. Menstruation

1. <u>If fertilization occurs</u>-developing embryo will *implant* in the endometrium and release hormones to sustain the corpus luteum.

2. <u>If fertilization does not occur</u>-corpus luteum eventually degenerates.

   a. When the corpus luteum degenerates, *estrogen and progesterone levels drop* and the endometrium can no longer be maintained so is sloughed away and eliminated from the body as menstrual blood.

   b. As this occurs, estrogen and progesterone levels are now too low to inhibit the anterior pituitary so the cycle can begin again.

IV. Hormonal Feedback Mechanisms

A. <u>Estrogen</u>, <u>LH</u>, and <u>FSH</u>-same hormones that control female puberty and oogenesis also control the menstrual cycle. <u>Estrogen</u>-controls the secretion of the two pituitary hormones by acting on the *Hypothalamus* (which controls the *Pituitary Gland*). When the estrogen level rises in the blood, the Pituitary (via the Hypothalamus) is stimulated to secrete *more or less LH and FSH*.

B. Types of feedback

1. <u>Negative feedback</u>-rising levels of hormones feed back to the Hypothalamus and Pituitary Gland to *decrease the production of the hormones*. During most of the menstrual cycle, estrogen and progesterone provide negative feedback to the Hypothalamus and Pituitary Gland to keep their levels fairly constant.

2. <u>Positive feedback</u>-rising levels of hormones feed back to *increase hormone production*. During days 12–14 of the cycle, estrogen provides positive feedback to the Hypothalamus and Pituitary Gland, causing *a rapid rise in the production of estrogen* by the ovaries and leads to <u>ovulation</u>.

C. Summary of Feedback Mechanisms in the Menstrual Cycle

1. <u>First half of the cycle</u>-*negative* feedback keeps levels of FSH, LH, estrogen, and progesterone relatively stable.

2. <u>Ovulation</u>-*positive* feedback causes a burst of FSH, LH, and estrogen.

3. <u>Second half of the cycle</u>-progesterone rises as the corpus luteum in the ovary matures and produces this hormone. *Negative* feedback helps keep levels of the other three hormones fairly constant.

Menstrual Cycle

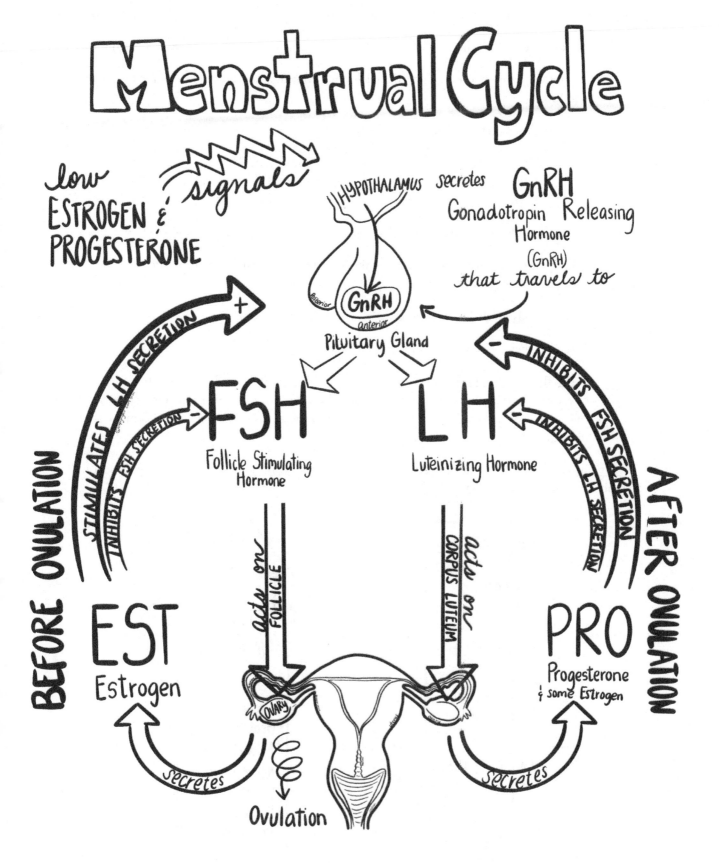

low ESTROGEN & PROGESTERONE

signals

HYPOTHALAMUS secretes GnRH Gonadotropin Releasing Hormone (GnRH) that travels to

GnRH

Posterior Anterior

Pituitary Gland

BEFORE OVULATION

STIMULATES LH SECRETION +

INHIBITS FSH SECRETION

AFTER OVULATION

INHIBITS FSH SECRETION −

INHIBITS LH SECRETION

FSH
Follicle Stimulating Hormone

LH
Luteinizing Hormone

acts on FOLLICLE

acts on CORPUS LUTEUM

EST
Estrogen

OVARY

PRO
Progesterone & some Estrogen

secretes

Ovulation

secretes

Figure 7-4

D. <u>Thyroid Gland</u>-located in the neck just below the larynx on either side of the trachea. (see **Figure 7-6**)

    1. Two lobes of the Thyroid Gland are connected by a mass of tissue known as the <u>isthmus</u>.

    2. Internally, is composed of hollow follicles that contain cells which are capable of secreting hormones.

    3. Hormones secreted by the Thyroid Gland:

        a. <u>Thyroid Hormone</u> (TH) {Triiodothyronine/T_3 and Thyroxine/T_4}-play a critical role in *metabolism* and in *regulating heat production* in the body by stimulating the release of enzymes that regulate glucose oxidation.

        b. <u>Calcitonin</u> (CT)-removes *calcium from the blood* and relocates it into the bones.

    4. Increase or decrease in the activity of the Thyroid Gland can result in specific imbalances within the body. (see **Figure 7-5**)

E. <u>Parathyroid Glands</u>-located on the *posterior surface* of the thyroid gland.

    1. Usually there are four, but numbers can vary.

    2. <u>Parathyroid Hormone</u> (PTH)- increases *calcium* levels in the bloodstream when needed (opposite effect of calcitonin) by breaking down bone (where most of the body's calcium is stored) and causing calcium release; also regulates the use of calcium by body tissues. It is the only hormone secreted by these glands.

F. <u>Thymus Gland</u>-located in the upper mediastinum, secretes <u>thymosin</u> that regulates the production of lymphocytes (T cells), an extremely important type of WBC.

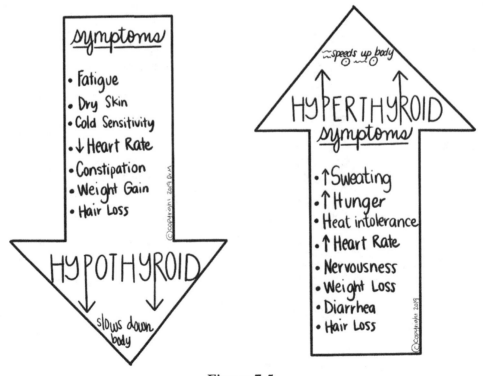

Figure 7-5

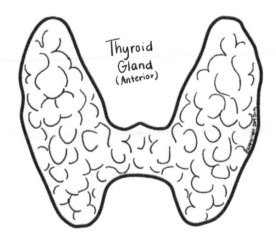

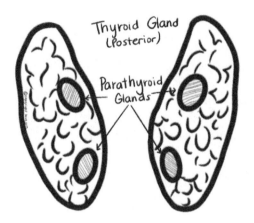

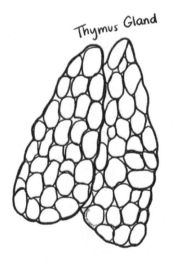

Figure 7-6

Thyroid and Thymus Glands Figure 7-6

Structure	Function/Description	Color
Parathyroid		
Thymus		
Thyroid		

Blood Calcium Feedback Mechanism (Figure 7-7)

I. Body functions, such as regulation of the heartbeat, contraction of muscles, activation of enzymes, and cellular communication require tightly regulated calcium levels. As a rule, most calcium comes from our diet when the small intestine absorbs calcium from digested food.

II. Endocrine System-control center for regulating blood calcium homeostasis via the parathyroid and thyroid glands which contain receptors that respond to levels of calcium in the blood. In this negative feedback system, *blood calcium level is the variable*, because it changes in response to the environment.

    A. Low Blood Calcium-parathyroid glands secrete Parathyroid Hormone (PTH), a hormone that causes the effector organs (kidneys and bones) to respond.

        a. Kidneys-prevent calcium from being excreted in the urine.

        b. Bones-osteoclasts in bones break down bone tissue and release stored calcium into the bloodstream in a process known as resorption.

    B. High Blood Calcium-parafollicular cells of the Thyroid Gland increase calcitonin secretion into the blood (and decrease the amount of parathyroid hormone) stimulating the osteoblasts in bones to remove calcium from the blood plasma and deposit it as bone in a process known as ossification. Calcitonin also reduces the absorption of dietary calcium in the intestines, and signals the kidneys to reabsorb less calcium, resulting in larger amounts of calcium excreted in the urine.

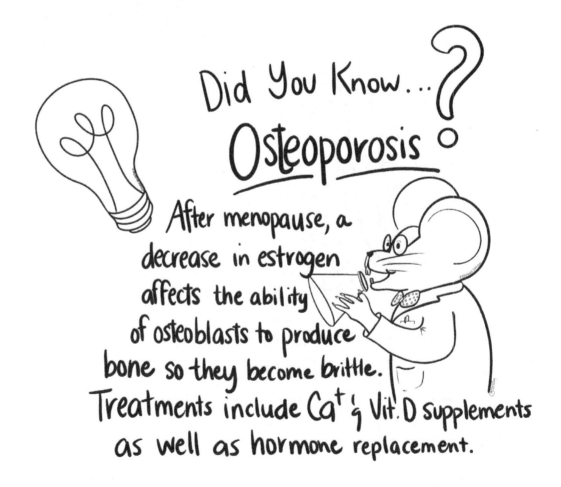

Did You Know...?

Osteoporosis

After menopause, a decrease in estrogen affects the ability of osteoblasts to produce bone so they become brittle. Treatments include Ca^+ & Vit. D supplements as well as hormone replacement.

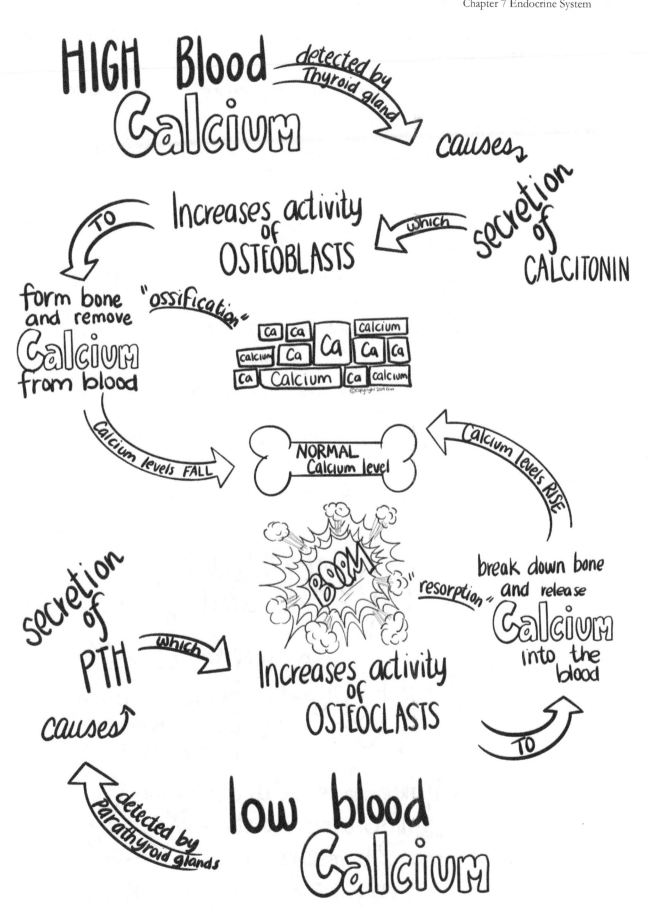

Figure 7-7

D. Adrenal (Suprarenal) Glands-pyramid-shaped glands that sit atop each *kidney*; controlled by the Pituitary Gland. (see **Figure 7-8**)

1. Have an outer region known as the cortex and an inner portion known as the medulla.

2. Hormones secreted by the Adrenal Cortex (all are steroids):

a. Mineralocorticoids-regulate *electrolyte concentrations* (especially Na⁺ and K⁺ ions) in extracellular fluid; most abundant mineralocorticoid aldosterone which regulates sodium levels in the body.

b. Glucocorticoids-regulate the *energy metabolism* of most body cells and help humans resist stressors; secretion is *regulated by ACTH* from the *Pituitary Gland.*

c. Gonadocorticoids (sex hormones)-may supplement the true sex hormones produced by the gonads.

3. Hormones secreted by the Adrenal Medulla (both are amines):

a. Epinephrine (E)and Norepinephrine (NE)-sometimes referred to as *adrenaline.*

1) Involved in *"Fight or Flight"* responses associated with the Autonomic Nervous System (ANS).

2) Secretion of epinephrine typically accounts for about 80% of the total secretion into the blood.

3) Typically increase (or *"excite"*) activity of an organ.

Epinephrine and Norepinephrine used as medications to treat ↑heart rate & ↑blood pressure

✴Epinephrine is used as a drug for cardiac arrest to stimulate the ♡ to restart from asystole → NO electrical activity = Ø heart rate

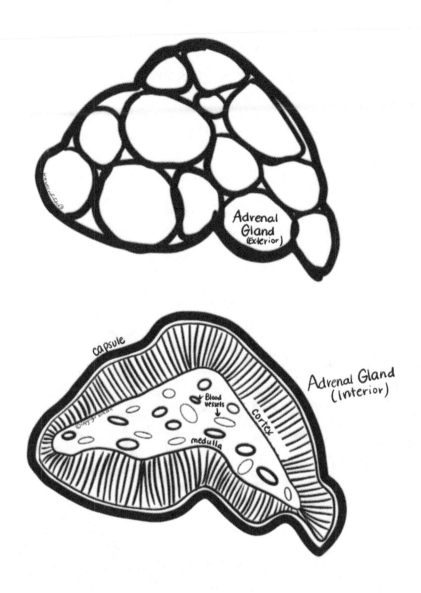

Figure 7-8

Adrenal Gland (Figure 7-8)

Structure	Function/Description	Color
Adrenal Gland Cortex (outside)		
Adrenal Gland Medulla (inside)		

H. <u>Pancreas</u>-located below and behind the stomach.

    1. Considered a *dual organ* (has both digestive and glandular functions).

    2. Composed of cells that *can act as exocrine glands* (Acini) and cells that *can act as endocrine cells* (alpha and beta cells of the Islets of Langerhans).

    3. <u>Hormones Secreted by the Pancreas</u> (see **Figure 1-3**, p. 6)

        a. <u>Glucagon</u>-amino acid hormone produced in the *alpha cells* of the Islets of Langerhans that stimulates the liver to *convert glycogen into glucose* (<u>glycogenolysis</u>).

        b. <u>Insulin</u>-protein hormone produced in the *beta cells* of the Islets of Langerhans; causes a decrease in blood sugar level by stimulating the *conversion of glucose into glycogen* (<u>glycogenesis</u>).

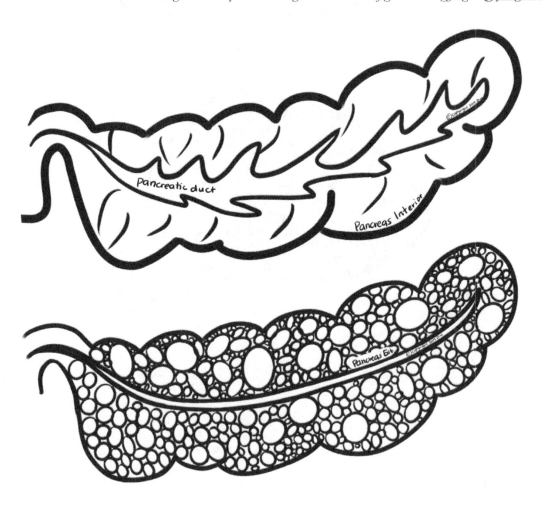

Figure 7-9

Pancreas (Figure 7-9)

Structure	Function/Description	Color
Pancreas		

I. Other Structures that Serve as Endocrine Glands:

    1. <u>GI Tract</u>-contains *digestive glands* that regulate the digestive process.

    2. <u>Placenta</u>-secretes hormones that influence the course of *pregnancy*.

    3. <u>Kidneys</u>-release *erythropoietin* that stimulates erythrocyte production in red bone marrow.

    4. <u>Skin</u>-secretes hormones that are involved in *vitamin D* production.

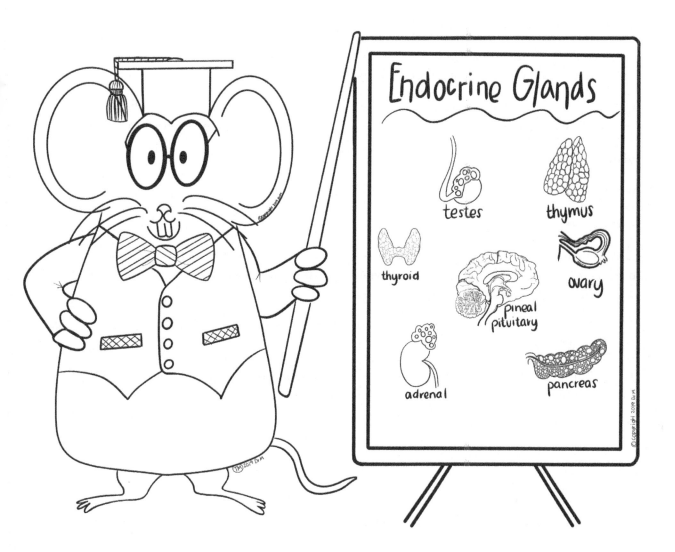

Figure 7-10

Cellular Communication and Hormone Reception by Cells

I. Communication Within the Body (see **Figure 1-4**, p. 10)

    A. Process where a sender (a *gland*) transmits signals (*ligands/hormones*) to one or more receivers (*target cells or glands*) to control and coordinate actions.

    B. Can occur over a <u>short distance</u> with specific, immediate results.

    C. Can also occur over a <u>long distance</u> with broader, slower results.

    D. Occurs between the Nervous System and the Endocrine System to maintain homeostasis in the body.

II. Long Distance Communication Between Cells

    A. Involves cells *far apart* or for *large audiences* of cells (like posting on social media so that anyone who is your "friend" can see it). A signal is sent to many cells, but few cells act upon it.

    B. <u>Hormone example</u>-Pituitary Gland in brain releases Human Growth Hormone (hGH) which travels through bloodstream to *all types* of cells, but acted upon mainly by bone and muscle cells (by growing).

III. Ligand (the signal molecule)

    A. Often a *hormone*.

    B. Specific to a receptor.

    C. Binds to its specific receptor and causes a *change in shape* that initiates a response pathway. Attachment of the ligand to the receptor protein causes the receptor to change shape (called a "*conformational shape change*") and activates a series of events known as the <u>*signal transduction pathway*</u>.

        1. The receptor protein can be located *on the cell membrane* or *inside the cell* and act like "hands" to hold specific ligands.

        2. The receptor "hands" and ligands must fit for activation; different ligands can initiate different responses.

IV. Receptors

    A. Intracellular

        1. Located <u>inside</u> cell.

        2. Examples include thyroid and steroid hormones.

    B. Extracellular

        1. Located <u>outside</u> cell on surface of plasma membrane.

        2. Types:

            a. <u>Ligand-gated ion channels</u>-open/close in response to ligand binding. For example, neurons have ligand-gated ion channels bound by neurotransmitters.

b. G protein-coupled receptors (GPCRs)-have 7 different protein segments that transport through specific G proteins. For example, scent receptors are G proteins (humans have 800).

c. Receptor tyrosine kinase (RTKs)-transfer phosphate groups to amino acid tyrosine forming a complex that serves as a docking station for other proteins. For example, growth factors which promote cell division and survival such as platelet-derived growth factor (for wound healing) and nerve growth factor. Growth factors are essential to body but must be kept in balance because overgrowth can lead to some types of cancer.

IV. Signal Transduction Pathway (STP)

A. Parts to the pathway:

1. Reception-signal molecule binds to its corresponding receptor protein. For example, if someone dials your phone number and calls your specific phone, you hear the ring and know someone is calling but will not know what the caller wants until you answer it and change the ringing into words you can understand.

Receptors are of 2 types:

a. Intracellular (intra= "*within*")-inside cell cytoplasm or nucleus.

b. Extracellular (extra= "*outside*")-outside cell on surface of plasma membrane.

2. Transduction-"*to change or carry through*"

a. Series of actions to change the signal to something the cell can understand.

b. Response involves making something or turning on/off an enzymatic process.

c. The "signal" is passed from one receptor molecule to another using enzymes.

1). Kinase-adds a phosphorous molecule to turn the process ON (phosphorylation).

2). Phosphatase-removes a phosphorus molecule to turn the process OFF.

d. Each interaction modifies the signal in some way, until it reaches the target gland or organ. Signal can be amplified to turn small signal into a large response, or stop the response entirely

e. For example, when you answer your phone, you must put your phone to your ear, say "hello", listen to the other person's words, answer them, and then you can either continue the conversation {amplify} or hang up {stop}. All of these are a series of steps to transform the "ringing" of the phone into words that you can understand.

3. Response

a. Involves either changing the *activity of enzymes* or *altering gene expression* at the DNA level inside the nucleus.

b. Response can occur at a *molecular level* (as an increase in transcription of certain genes or activation of particular enzymes) and at a *macroscopic level* (as a change in appearance of the cell as in cell growth or cell death).

c. For example, once you have heard why the person was calling, you hang up and do what the caller asked you to do, thus completing the pathway with the action you performed as the response.

V. Pathways

   A. Intracellular-receptors inside cell; pathway ends in *nucleus*.

      1. Turns on/off transcription in cell to activate or deactivate genes.

      2. Steps:

         a. Hormone binds to receptor inside cell. The receptor changes shape to allow entry into nucleus.

         b. Enters nucleus and attaches to a specific sequence of DNA.

         c. Regulates gene activity (turns genes on/off) by altering transcription when it directly attaches to DNA.

      3. Examples include:

         a. Steroid hormones (sex hormones)-testosterone and estradiol

         b. Nitric oxide (NO)-gas that activates signal pathway in the smooth muscle surrounding blood vessels to cause this muscle to relax and allow these blood vessels to dilate. This is how nitroglycerine treats heart disease as well as the mechanism by which erectile dysfunction medications work.

   B. Extracellular-receptors outside on plasma membrane; pathway ends in *cytoplasm*.

      1. Turned on/off by enzymes; can also involve secondary messengers.

      2. Steps:

         a. Hormone binds to receptor on surface of plasma membrane.

         b. Signal is passed through ("*relayed*") a chain of chemical messengers (often proteins) until a cellular response occurs.

            1). Proteins in this chain are activated/inactivated by adding a phosphate group on 1 of 3 amino acids (tyrosine, threonine, or serine) in a process called phosphorylation.

            2). Phosphorylation is catalyzed by the enzyme kinase and reversed by the enzyme phosphatase.

            3). Secondary messengers (such as Ca^{+2} and cyclic AMP) are often used to transmit the signal to the target cells.

      3. Examples-secondary messenger Ca^{+2} signaling of beta cells of the pancreas leads to the release of insulin and Ca^{+2} signaling in muscle cells leads to muscle contraction.

CHAPTER 8. CARDIOVASCULAR SYSTEM

The Cardiovascular System

I. <u>Cardiovascular System</u>-consists of the heart, blood vessels and blood.

II. Blood Vessels (see **Figure 8-1**)

    A. Types of Blood Vessels

        1. <u>Arteries</u>-transport blood *away* from the heart.

           a. Carry *oxygenated* blood (with the exception of the pulmonary artery).

           b. Always maintain a circular shape.

           c. Walls are *thick* and strong (made of smooth muscle).

           d. Walls must be *strong* because the blood in the arteries is under <u>pressure</u>.

           e. Blood is pumped in the arteries when the heart muscle contracts.

           f. Arterial wounds spurt blood.

        2. <u>Veins</u>-transport blood *toward* the heart.

           a. Carry *deoxygenated* blood (with the exception of the pulmonary vein).

           b. Walls are *thin* (no smooth muscle).

           c. Lay flat when not carrying blood.

           d. Blood moves through veins when skeletal muscle contracts.

           e. Contain one-way *valves* that prevent the blood from flowing backwards when the skeletal muscle relaxes.

           f. Venous wounds ooze blood.

        3. <u>Capillaries</u>-beds of very small, thin walled vessels that *connect the arterial and venous systems.*

           a. Walls are only *one cell layer* thick.

           b. Diameter is only large enough to accommodate *one blood cell at a time.*

           c. Location where <u>diffusion</u> occurs in the circulatory system (oxygen and nutrients diffuse *into* blood; carbon dioxide and other wastes diffuse *out*).

           d. *Smallest* and *most numerous* of the blood vessels.

    B. Generalized path of blood through the vessels: (**Figure 8-1**)

Heart → Artery → Arteriole → Capillaries → Venule → Vein → Heart

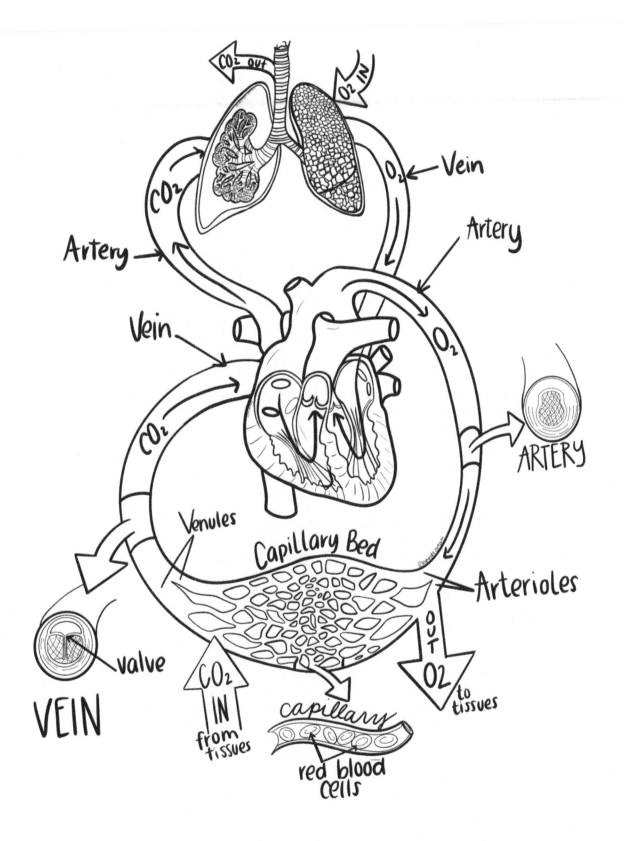

Figure 8-1

Major Arteries and Veins

Arteries	Veins
Aorta/Aortic Arch-main artery that carries blood away from your heart to the rest of your body; largest artery in the body. Ascending aorta begins at the heart's left ventricle and extends to the aortic arch, (the bend in the aorta). Arch of the aorta gives off branches to the head and arms.	External Jugular-more superficial of the two jugular veins (other is the internal jugular vein) situated on each side of the neck; drains blood from the head, brain, face and neck and conveys it toward the heart.
Common Carotid Artery-main blood supply to the head and neck.	Subclavian Vein-responsible for draining blood from the upper extremities and returning this blood to the heart.
Brachiocephalic Artery-supplies blood to the right arm and the head and neck.	Superior Vena Cava Vein-returns deoxygenated blood from the systemic circulation (upper half of the body) to the right atrium of the heart.
Subclavian Artery-supplies the arms with blood.	Brachiocephalic Vein-returns oxygen-depleted blood from the upper limbs, neck, and head to the heart.
Axillary Artery-large blood vessel that conveys oxygenated blood to the lateral aspect of the thorax, the axilla (armpit) and the upper limb.	Axillary Vein-large blood vessel that conveys blood from the lateral aspect of the thorax, axilla (armpit) and upper limb toward the heart.
Brachial Artery-major blood vessel located in the upper arm that serves as the main supplier of blood to the arm and hand.	Brachial Vein-deep vein that joins the basilic vein to form the axillary vein; has small tributaries that drain the muscles of the upper arm (such as *biceps brachii* and *triceps brachii* muscles).
Thoracic Aorta-travels through the chest. Its small branches supply blood to the ribs and some chest structures.	Median Cubital Vein-superficial vein of the arm commonly used to draw blood (venipuncture).
Radial Artery-major artery in the forearm; supplies the arm and hand with oxygenated blood from the lung	Renal Vein-carries the blood filtered by the kidney and drains the kidney by connecting it to the inferior vena cava.
Ulnar Artery-main blood vessel of the medial aspect of the forearm; supplies the forearm, wrist, and hand with oxygenated blood.	Inferior Vena Cava-large vein that carries deoxygenated blood from the lower and middle body into the right atrium of the heart.
Palmar Arch-arterial network found in the palm of the hand.	Radial Vein-one of a pair of veins that accompany the radial artery through the back of the hand and the lateral aspect of the forearm; joins the ulnar veins to form the brachial veins.
Renal Artery-branches directly from the aorta and carries blood from the heart to the kidneys.	Ulnar Vein-located in the forearm, next to the ulna bone; drains oxygen-depleted blood from the forearm.

Common Iliac Artery-supplies blood to the pelvic organs, gluteal region, and legs; abdominal aorta divides to form the "common iliac arteries" in the lower abdomen.	Common Iliac Vein-receives blood from the reproductive organs; both internal & external iliac veins join to form the inferior vena cava.
Femoral Artery-large artery in the thigh that is the main arterial supply to the thigh and leg.	Femoral Vein-located in the upper thigh and pelvic region of the human body; drains deoxygenated blood to the leg and pelvic region and transports it to the inferior vena cava.
Popliteal Artery-primary distributor of oxygenated blood to regions around the knee; branches off from the femoral artery and into other significant blood vessels.	Great Saphenous Vein-large, subcutaneous, superficial vein of the leg; longest vein in the body; returns blood from the foot, leg and thigh to the deep femoral vein at the femoral triangle; sometimes stripped out of the leg to eliminate varicose veins; also used as the source of grafts in coronary bypass surgery.
Tibial Artery (anterior & posterior)-posterior tibial artery of the lower limb carries blood to the posterior compartment of the leg and plantar surface of the foot; anterior tibial artery of the leg carries blood to the anterior compartment of the leg and dorsal surface of the foot.	Popliteal Vein-carries blood from the knee (as well as the thigh and calf muscles) back to the heart.
Abdominal Aorta-largest artery in the abdominal cavity that reaches from the chest into the abdomen; supplies blood to the stomach, pelvis, and legs.	Tibial Vein-deep vein of the calf that carry oxygen-depleted blood away from the foot and lower leg, and back toward the heart.

Major Arteries (Figure 8-2)

Arteries	Destination	Color
Aorta/ Aortic Arch		
Common Carotid Artery		
Brachiocephalic Artery		
Subclavian Artery		
Axillary Artery		
Brachial Artery		
Thoracic Aorta		
Radial Artery		
Ulnar Artery		
Palmar Arch		
Renal Artery		
Common Iliac Artery		
Femoral Artery		
Popliteal Artery		
Tibial Artery		
Abdominal Aorta		

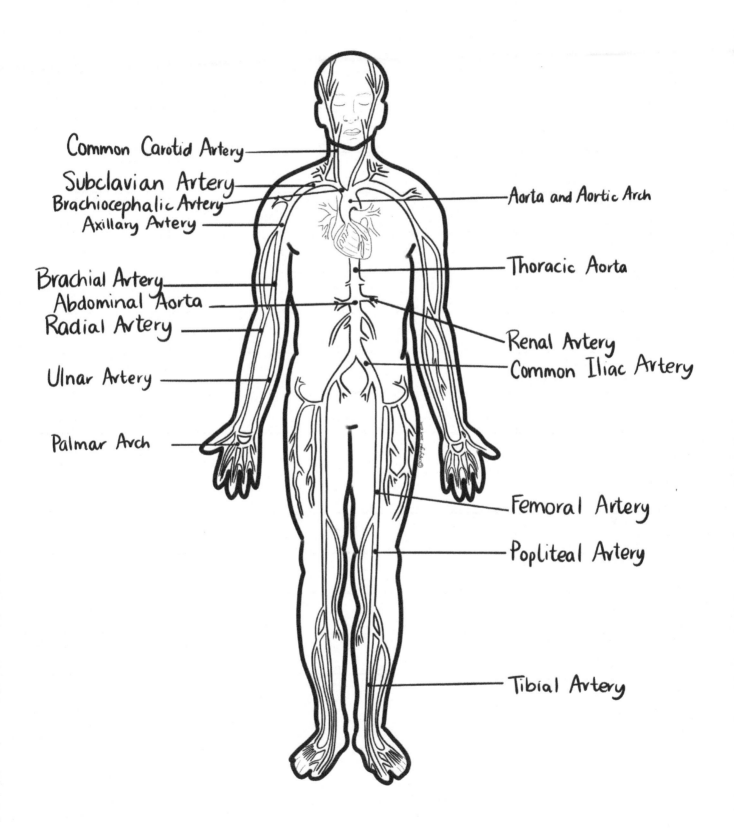

Common Carotid Artery

Subclavian Artery
Brachiocephalic Artery
Axillary Artery

Brachial Artery
Abdominal Aorta
Radial Artery

Ulnar Artery

Palmar Arch

Aorta and Aortic Arch

Thoracic Aorta

Renal Artery
Common Iliac Artery

Femoral Artery

Popliteal Artery

Tibial Artery

Figure 8-2

Major Veins (Figure 8-3)

Veins	Destination	Color
External Jugular		
Subclavian Vein		
Superior Vena Cava Vein		
Brachiocephalic Vein		
Axillary Vein		
Brachial Vein		
Median Cubital Vein		
Renal Vein		
Inferior Vena Cava		
Radial Vein		
Ulnar Vein		
Common Iliac Vein		
Femoral Vein		
Great Saphenous Vein		
Popliteal Vein		
Tibial Vein		

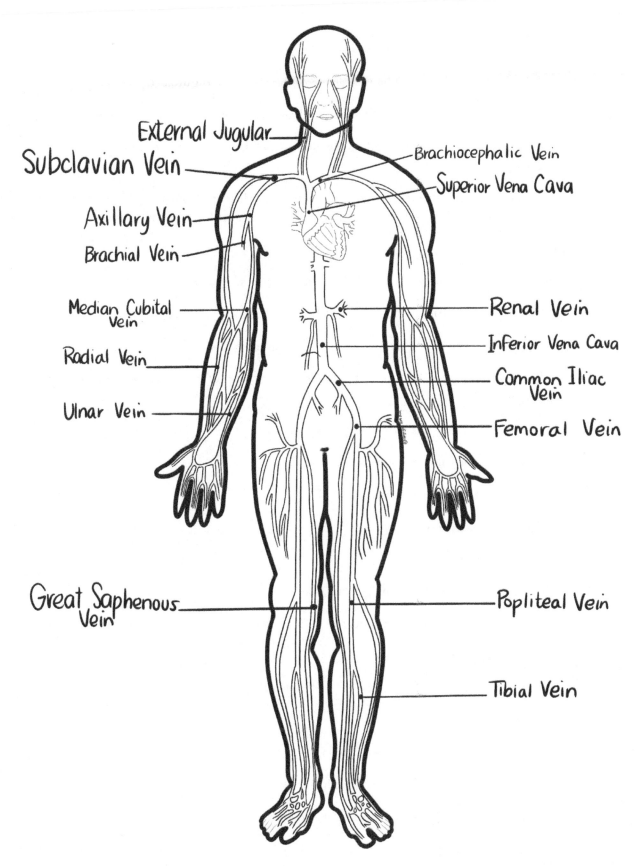

External Jugular

Subclavian Vein

Brachiocephalic Vein

Superior Vena Cava

Axillary Vein

Brachial Vein

Median Cubital Vein

Renal Vein

Inferior Vena Cava

Radial Vein

Common Iliac Vein

Ulnar Vein

Femoral Vein

Great Saphenous Vein

Popliteal Vein

Tibial Vein

Figure 8-3

Blood

I. Blood

A. Only fluid tissue in the human body (contains living cells and fluid).

B. Pushed through the body by the pumping action of the heart. (see **Figure 8-1**)

    1. Arteries-carry blood away from the heart; branch until they become microscopic capillaries.

    2. Capillaries-carry carbon dioxide and wastes, as well as nutrients; materials pass into and out of capillaries by diffusion.

    3. Veins-carry deoxygenated blood back to the heart where it is then pumped to the lungs to pick up oxygen. This oxygenated blood is then returned to the heart for dispersal to the body.

II. Characteristics of Blood

A. Classified as a type of connective tissue because it shares these 3 elements:

    1. Cells-blood contains red blood cells (RBCs), white blood cells (WBCs), and platelets.

    2. Matrix-the liquid portion of blood; this is the serum in blood.

    3. Fibers-mostly protein fibers such as fibrin; provide support to blood and play a role in blood clotting.

B. Salty, metallic taste of blood is due to the presence of iron.

C. Color depends on the amount of oxygen it is carrying.

    1. Scarlet red blood-oxygen rich.

    2. Dark red blood-low in oxygen.

D. Has a greater density than water.

E. Slightly alkaline, with a pH between 7.35 and 7.45.

F. Maintains a temperature around 100.4 degrees F (38 degrees C), slightly higher normal body temperature.

G. Makes up about 8% of total body weight.

H. Average blood volume is 5-6L in males and 4-5L in females.

III. Functions

A. Distribution

    1. Carries oxygen from the lungs to body tissues.

    2. Delivers nutrients, hormones, and water to body tissues.

    3. Transports metabolic wastes from body tissues to sites of elimination. For example, CO_2 to the lungs and nitrogenous wastes to the kidneys.

B. Regulation

    1. Maintains normal body temperature by absorbing and distributing heat throughout the body and skin where heat loss can occur.

    2. Maintains normal pH in body tissues

        a. Many blood proteins and solutes act as buffers that prevent sudden pH changes.

        b. Blood stores bicarbonate ions, which serve as the primary buffer in body tissues.

C. Protection

    1. <u>Prevents blood loss</u>-platelets and blood proteins aid in clot formation which stops blood loss.

    2. <u>Fights and prevents infection</u>-antibodies and leukocytes (white blood cells) are involved in fighting and preventing infection.

IV. Composition of Blood

    A. <u>Plasma</u>-liquid matrix of blood.

    B. <u>Formed Elements</u>-blood cells and cell fragments which are suspended in plasma.

        1. <u>Erythrocytes</u> (RBC)-red blood cells.

        2. <u>Leukocytes</u> (WBC)-white blood cells.

        3. <u>Thrombocytes</u>-platelets.

V. Erythrocytes (RBC)

    A. Small (7.5 micrometers in diameter) biconcave discs with depressed centers.

    B. Cellular Structure

        1. Bound by a true cellular membrane.

        2. Lack a nucleus (<u>anucleate</u>) and do not contain cellular organelles.

        3. Contain Hemoglobin (Hb) which transports most of the oxygen through the body

        4. Greatly contribute to blood viscosity.

            a. <u>Women</u>-have 4.3-5.2 million cells per mm^3 of blood.

            b. <u>Men</u>-have 5.1-5.8 cells per mm^3 of blood.

            c. Healthy adult has about 2.5 trillion erythrocytes.

        5. Transport oxygen and carbon dioxide through the body.

        6. <u>Hemopoiesis/Hematopoiesis</u>-blood cell formation.

VI. Leukocytes (WBC) **Mnemonic to remember the types of white blood cells**: **N**ever **L**et **M**onkeys **E**at **B**ananas (neutrophils, lymphocytes, monocytes, eosinophils, basophils). (see **Figure 8-4**)

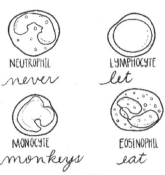

A. General Features of Leukocytes:

    1. They are complete cells that contain a nucleus and organelles.

    2. On average, there are 4000-11,000 leukocytes per mm³ of blood. They account for less than 1% of total blood volume.

    3. They help fight disease and protect the body from damage by bacteria, viruses, parasites, toxins, and tumor cells.

        a. To carry out this function, leukocytes can leave capillaries and enter tissues (a process known as <u>diapedesis</u>).   **Figure 8-4**

        b. Can follow chemical trails secreted by damaged cells (known as <u>positive chemotaxis</u>).

        c. Body increases its leukocyte production whenever an infection occurs. A leukocyte count greater than 11,000 cells per mm³ is common during bacterial and viral infection.

    5. <u>Leukopoiesis</u>-production of leukocytes.

B. Major Categories

    1. <u>Granulocytes</u>-contain membrane-bound cytoplasmic granules.

    2. <u>Agranulocytes</u>-do not contain membrane-bound cytoplasmic granules.

C. Granulocytes (contain granules in cytoplasm)

    1. Characteristics:

        a. Are spherical in shape and contain lobed nuclei.

        b. Stained with Wright's Stain.

        c. All granulocytes are phagocytic.

    2. Types of Granulocytes:

        a. <u>Neutrophils</u>-most numerous leukocytes in the body. 60-70% of all WBCs.

            1). Are twice as large as erythrocytes.

            2). Produced in the bone marrow.

            3). Granules in nuclei take up basic (blue) and acidic (red) dyes are lilac in color.

            4). Granules contain <u>defensins</u> (antibiotic type proteins and <u>enzymes</u>).

            5). Nuclei contain 3 to 6 lobes.

6). Are chemically attracted to sites of inflammation.

7). Are involved in:

a). Attacking bacteria and fungi via phagocytosis.

b). Producing defensins which "spear" bacteria.

c). Using oxygen to produce hydrogen peroxide which kills bacteria.

8). Numbers increase greatly during bacterial infection.

b. Eosinophils-account for 2-4% of all leukocytes; similar in size to neutrophils.

1). Nuclei stain red and contain 2 lobes that are connected by a thin band of nuclear material.

2). Contain large granules that are filled with a variety of digestive enzymes.

3). Functions of Eosinophils:

a). Fight parasitic worms (roundworms, flatworms) by secreting enzymes that digest the covering around the worm.

b). Destroy antigen/antibody complex and inactivate/phagocytize chemicals or molecules that lead to allergies.

c. Basophils-account for 0.5-1.0% of all leukocytes (are the rarest of all leukocytes); similar in size to neutrophils.

1). Contain numerous large granules that stain dark purple to black.

2). Granules contain histamine which acts as a vasodilator during an inflammatory response. Histamine also attracts leukocytes to an inflamed site.

3). Nucleus is generally U or S-shaped with two or three constrictions but is hard to detect because of the abundance of granules.

4). Contain anticoagulant heparin which prevents blood from clotting too quickly.

D. Agranulocytes (no granules in cytoplasm)

1. Characteristics

a. Lack visible cytoplasmic granules.

b. Nuclei are spherical or kidney shaped.

2. Types of Agranulocytes

a. Lymphocytes-2nd most abundant type of leukocyte. 20-25% of all WBCs.

1). Have a large, spherical nucleus that almost fills the entire cell and stains deep purple. They are slightly larger than RBCs.

2). Most are found in lymphoid tissues (such as the spleen and lymph nodes). Only a few are actually in the bloodstream.

3). Part of the immune response and defend against viruses and bacteria.

4). Types of Lymphocytes:

a. T Lymphocytes (T cells)-involved in immune responses and act directly against viruses and tumor cells.

b. B Lymphocytes (B cells)-give rise to plasma cells which can produce antibodies that are released into the blood.

b. Monocytes-largest WBC; account for 4-8% of all WBCs in body.

1). Nucleus takes up about half the cell volume, stains dark purple, and has a distinct U or kidney shape.

2). Can differentiate into macrophages that are phagocytic to viruses and bacteria.

VII. Thrombocytes (platelets)-are cell fragments, not true cells so have no nucleus.

1. Contain many small, purple-staining granules containing chemicals involved in blood clotting including serotonin, epinephrine, histamine, and thromboxane.

2. Begin forming clots when blood vessels are broken; stick to the damaged site to form a plug which stops blood loss.

3. Live for only about 10 days if not involved in clot formation.

4. Platelet formation is regulated by the hormone thrombopoietin.

VIII. In one drop of blood, there are:

Type of Cell	Estimated Number
Erythrocyte (RBC)	4-6 million
Leukocyte (WBC)	7,000-25,000
• Neutrophil	4500- 11,000
• Eosinophil	100-400
• Basophil	20-50
• Lymphocyte	1500-3000
• Monocyte	100-700
Thrombocyte (platelets)	250,000-500,000

Blood Cells

Use pgs. 199-202 if you need additional assistance.

Cell	Shape	Nucleation/ shape of nucleus / presence of granules in cytoplasm	Estimated Number in 1 drop of blood	Functions
Erythrocyte				
Leukocyte				
• *Neutrophil*				
• *Eosinophil*				
• *Basophil*				
• *Lymphocyte*				
• *Monocyte*				
Thrombocyte				

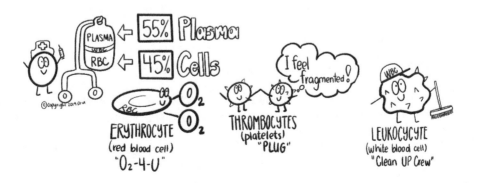

Blood Clotting (Hemostasis)-Figure 8-5

I. Hemostasis ("*hemo*"= blood; "*stasis*"= stop)

    A. Process by which the body seals a ruptured (broken) blood vessel and prevents further loss of blood; begins when cells in the endothelial lining secrete specific chemicals to initiate the process of hemostasis.

    B. Very effective in dealing with small, simple wounds, but rupture of larger vessels will result in <u>hemorrhage</u> (excessive bleeding) and usually requires medical attention.

    C. Steps in hemostasis:

        1. Vascular spasm (<u>vasoconstriction</u>)

        2. Formation of a platelet plug

        3. Coagulation (blood clotting)

II. Steps in Hemostasis

    A. Vascular Spasm (Vasoconstriction)

        1. Occurs when a vessel is severed, punctured, or when the wall of a vessel is damaged.

        2. Smooth muscle in the walls of the vessel contracts dramatically.

            a. This smooth muscle has both circular layers and longitudinal layers if the blood vessel is large enough.

            b. Circular layers tend to constrict the flow of blood.

            c. Longitudinal layers pull the vessel back into the surrounding tissue.

        3. Is designed to slow blood flow; typically lasts for up to 30 minutes, although it can last for hours.

    B. Formation of the Platelet Plug

        1. Platelets, which normally float free in the plasma, come into contact with collagen fibers that have become exposed due to the rupture of the blood vessel.

        2. Collagen fibers become "sticky" and react with the platelets to clump together.

        3. A platelet plug seals a small opening in a blood vessel until more permanent repairs can be made.

    C. Coagulation (Blood Clotting)

        1. Formation of a blood clot (<u>coagulation</u>) is a *more permanent* and *durable* repair.

        2. Process is sometimes called a <u>cascade</u> because one event prompts the next until a clot is formed from a mesh of fibrin. This is also an example of <u>positive feedback</u>.

    3. <u>Fibrin</u> (insoluble filamentous protein)-comes from the protein fibrinogen that traps platelets blood cells.

HEMOSTASIS

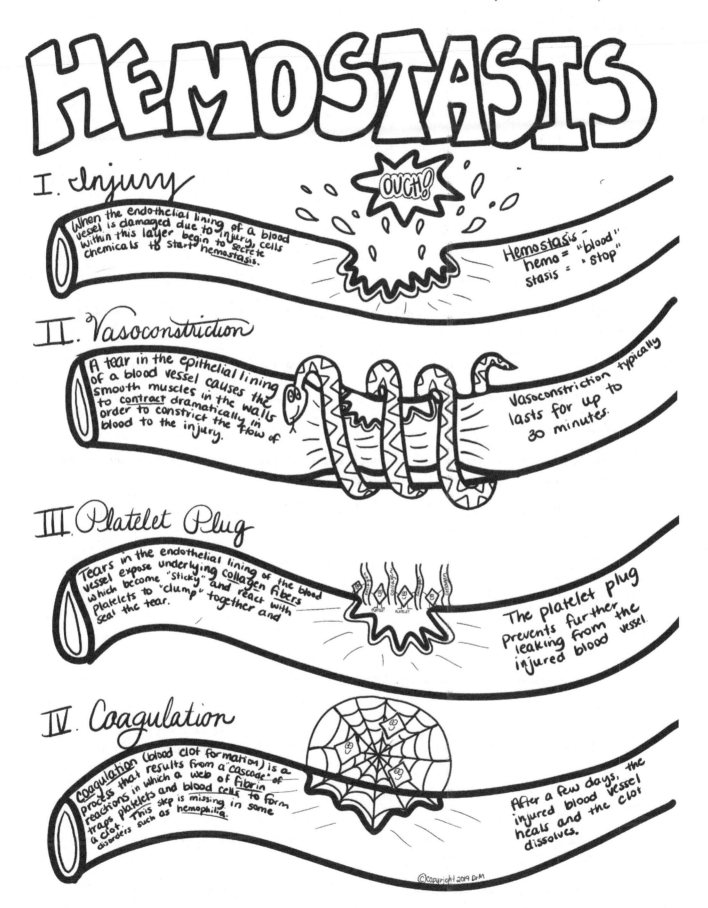

I. Injury

When the endothelial lining of a blood vessel is damaged due to injury, cells within this layer begin to secrete chemicals to start hemostasis.

OUCH!

Hemostasis -
hemo = "blood"
stasis = "stop"

II. Vasoconstriction

A tear in the epithelial lining of a blood vessel causes the smooth muscles in the walls to contract dramatically in order to constrict the flow of blood to the injury.

Vasoconstriction typically lasts for up to 30 minutes.

III. Platelet Plug

Tears in the endothelial lining of the blood vessel expose underlying collagen fibers which become "sticky" and react with platelets to "clump" together and seal the tear.

The platelet plug prevents further leaking from the injured blood vessel.

IV. Coagulation

Coagulation (blood clot formation) is a process that results from a "cascade" of reactions in which a web of fibrin traps platelets and blood cells to form a clot. This step is missing in some disorders such as hemophilia.

After a few days, the injured blood vessel heals and the clot dissolves.

©copyright 2019 DrM

Figure 8-5

III. Clotting Factors Involved in Coagulation

    A. In the coagulation cascade, chemicals called <u>clotting factors</u> (or coagulation factors) begin reactions that activate additional coagulation factors.

    B. The complex process is initiated along two basic pathways:

        1. <u>Extrinsic pathway</u>-normally is triggered by *trauma*.

        2. <u>Intrinsic pathway</u>-begins in the bloodstream and is triggered by *internal damage* to the wall of the vessel.

    C. Both pathways merge into a third pathway (referred to as the <u>common pathway</u>) in which <u>fibrin</u> is produced to seal off the vessel.

    D. All three pathways depend upon the *12 known clotting factors* which include Ca^{2+} and vitamin K.

    E. Clotting factors are secreted primarily by the *liver* and the *platelets*. The *liver* requires the fat-soluble *vitamin K* to produce many of them.

    F. Calcium ions, considered to be factor IV, come from the diet and from the breakdown of bone.

    G. The 12 clotting factors are numbered I through XIII according to the order of their discovery.

IV. Fibrinolysis

    A. Stabilized clot is acted upon by *contractile proteins* within the platelets. As these proteins contract, they pull on the fibrin threads, bringing the edges of the clot more tightly together.

    B. Process also causes a small amount of fluid (called <u>serum</u>) to be squeezed out of the clot. <u>Serum</u> is blood plasma without its clotting factors.

    C. Clot must eventually be removed to restore normal blood flow as the vessel heals.

    D. <u>Fibrinolysis</u>-gradual degradation of the clot.

V. Plasma Anticoagulants

    A. <u>Anticoagulant</u>-any substance that keeps blood from coagulating; several different types circulate in the blood.

    B. <u>Example</u>-Basophils release <u>heparin</u> (a short-acting anticoagulant found on the surfaces of cells lining the blood vessels). A pharmaceutical form of heparin is often administered to surgical patients at risk for blood clots.

VI. Disorders of Clotting

    A. <u>Clotting disorders</u>-can result from either too many, or not enough platelets produced by the body which can lead to severe disease or death.

    B. <u>Thrombocytopenia</u>-disorder caused by *too few platelets* that typically results in the *inability of blood to form clots* which can lead to excessive bleeding, even from minor wounds.

C. <u>Hemophilia</u>-genetic disorder that can lead to a failure of blood to clot due to an inability to produce sufficient quantities of factor VIII. This disorder is linked to the X chromosome and is typically passed from a healthy mother (carrier) to her male offspring. Patients with hemophilia bleed from even minor internal and external wounds but can be treated with regular infusions of clotting factors.

D. <u>Thrombosis</u> (excessive clot formation)-often results from production of excessive numbers of platelets.

    1. <u>Thrombus</u> (plural=*thrombi*)-stationary blood clot in a vessel.

    2. <u>Embolus</u>-moving blood clot formed when a portion of a thrombus breaks free from the vessel wall and enters the circulation; can be large enough to block a vessel critical to a major organ.

    3. <u>Embolism</u>-when an embolus becomes trapped; may cause a heart attack, stroke, or pulmonary embolism if it becomes trapped in the heart, brain, or lungs.

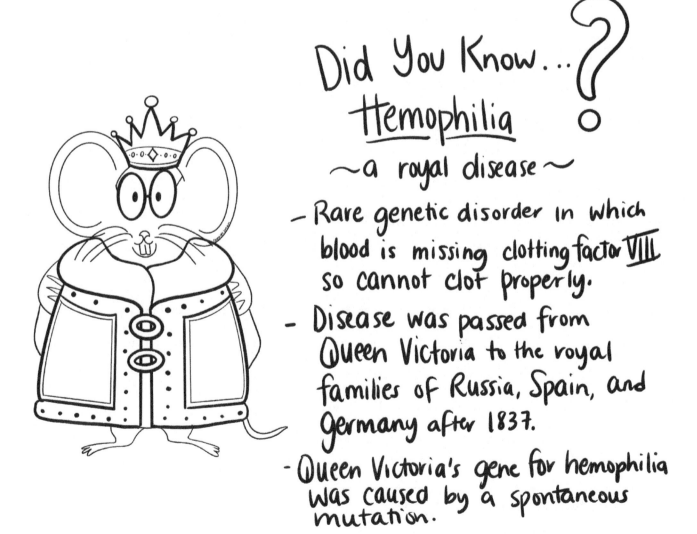

Did You Know...?
Hemophilia
~a royal disease~
- Rare genetic disorder in which blood is missing clotting factor VIII so cannot clot properly.
- Disease was passed from Queen Victoria to the royal families of Russia, Spain, and Germany after 1837.
- Queen Victoria's gene for hemophilia was caused by a spontaneous mutation.

Blood Types

I. Discovery of Blood Types

    A. <u>Landsteiner</u> (1900)-discovered there are *4 types of blood groups* (A, B, AB, and O) based on the surface antigens of RBC (red blood cells).

        1. <u>Type O</u>-45% of population

        2. <u>Type A</u>-40% of population

        3. <u>Type B</u>-11% of population

        4. <u>Type AB</u>-4% of population

    B. <u>Landsteiner and Weiner</u> (1940)-discovered the <u>Rhesus factor</u> (Rh factor) antigen that is either present (+) or absent (-) on the surface of RBC. It was called "rhesus" because it was first identified in the blood of rhesus monkeys.

        1. <u>Rh$^+$</u>-85% of population

        2. <u>Rh$^-$</u>-15% of population

II. Blood Antigens and Antibodies

    A. <u>Antigen</u>-protein on membrane of RBCs.

        1. The antigen(s) on the surface of the RBC determines your blood type.

            a. <u>Type A</u> blood has <u>A antigens</u> on RBC surface.

            b. <u>Type B</u> blood has <u>B antigens</u> on RBC surface.

            c. <u>Type AB</u> blood has **both** <u>A and B antigens</u> on RBC surface.

            d. <u>Type O</u> blood has **neither** <u>A nor B antigens</u> on RBC surface.

        2. Antigens are inherited.

            a. A and B are dominant over O (For example, AA and AO are both type A blood).

            b. This allows blood typing to be used to exclude people in paternity tests.

        3. There are 30 common RBC antigens.

            a. Most common are A, B, AB, and O.

            b. M, N, S are also important antigens.

            c. Before a blood transfusion, antigens must be closely matched.

    B. <u>Antibody</u>-a Y-shaped protein found in blood plasma.

        1. *Specifically* shaped to correspond to different blood surface antigens.

2. Each blood group contains antibodies for antigens found <u>only</u> in other blood groups, and *not its own* antigens. (Example-<u>Type A</u> blood contains <u>A antigens</u> on the *surface* of its RBCs and *makes* <u>anti-B antibodies</u> that circulate in the *plasma* of the individual).

       a. <u>Type A</u> blood has <u>anti-B antibodies</u>.

       b. <u>Type B</u> blood has <u>anti-A antibodies</u>.

       c. <u>Type AB</u> blood has **neither** <u>anti-A</u> nor <u>anti-B antibodies</u> so is called the *"universal recipient"* and can <u>receive</u> all blood types.

       d. <u>Type O</u> blood has **both** <u>anti-A</u> and <u>anti-B antibodies</u> so is called the *"universal donor"* and can <u>donate</u> blood to all blood types.

C. Agglutination

    1. <u>Agglutination</u>- *"clumping"*

    2. When antibodies in blood encounter foreign *"antigens"* of another blood type, the interaction will cause the blood to clump (or <u>agglutinate</u>).

Determination of Blood Type Through Inheritance

The presence of antigens on red blood cells is genetically determined. Humans inherit two alleles for ABO blood type antigens—1 from the mother and 1 from the father. Type A and B are dominant to type O. Therefore, individuals who are blood type A can be AA (homozygous for A, receiving both dominant type A from both mother and father), or AO (heterozygous, receiving dominant type A from 1 parent and recessive type O from the other.

Possible combinations of alleles and their blood types:

Allele Combination	Blood Type
AA, AO	Type A
BB, BO	Type B
AB	Type AB
OO	Type O

A Punnett square is often used to show the probable genes for the blood type of an offspring of two individuals. The father's alleles are typically written down the left side of the Punnett square. The mother's alleles are written across the top of the Punnett square. Each box shows the *possible* combinations of alleles their resulting offspring might possess.

<u>Example problem</u>-If both parents have blood type AB, what is the chance that their offspring will inherit the blood type AB?

	Alleles of Mother		
		A	B
A	A	AA	AB
B	B	AB	BB

Alleles of Father

Answer: <u>50% chance</u>

Why Type Blood?

Blood typing is useful because it can show that two blood samples did not have the same origin (come from the same source). This is called <u>exclusion</u>. It is also useful in excluding people in paternity cases. Even though it might not be able to prove that a man is *definitely* the father, it <u>can</u> show that a man with a certain blood type could definitely <u>not</u> have fathered the child in question. Blood typing can also provide information that narrows down the list of possible suspects in a crime based upon the percentage of people in the population who possess a certain blood type.

Percentage of people with A, B, AB, and O blood types.

Blood Type	% of Population With This Antigen
O	45
A	40
B	11
AB	4

Percentage of people with M, N, and S blood types.

Blood Type	% of Population With This Antigen
M	30
N	22
S	48

Percentage of people with Rh+ and Rh- blood types.

Blood Type	% of Population With This Antigen
Rh+	85
Rh-	15

Using the information in the charts above, you can calculate the probability that a person would have a particular combination of blood types.

Example problem: What is the likelihood that a person has the blood combination that is types A, N, and Rh-?

Solution: First, look up the percentages of each antigen occurring in the population. Convert the percentage to a ratio by considering the ratio as *people to blood type*. Then, multiply the ratios together. The number that you get will mean that 1 out of that number would have type A, N, Rh- blood.

	A	N	Rh-
Percentage	40%	22%	15%
Ratio **people: blood type** **Answer**	100:40 100/40 = 2.50	100:22 100/22 = 4.55	100:15 100/15 = 6.67
Solution:	(2.50) x (4.55) x (6.67) = 75.9 → <u>76</u> 1 out of 76 people will have type A, N, Rh- blood.		

211

Heart Structure

A. <u>Membrane</u> (pericardium)-loose-fitting double serous membrane that encloses the heart and attaches to the major vessels of the heart, inside surface of the sternum, and to the diaphragm.

Functions:

    1. Prevents over distension of the heart.

    2. Protection for the heart.

    3. Anchors heart to body wall.

B. <u>Heart wall</u>-composed of three layers:

    1. <u>Epicardium</u> (outer layer)-thin and transparent. The space between epicardium and heart tissue (called <u>pericardial cavity</u>) contains <u>pericardial fluid</u> which prevents friction when the heart moves.

    2. <u>Myocardium</u>-cardiac muscle tissue that makes up bulk of heart. The <u>interventricular septum</u> is the muscular wall that separates the ventricles.

    3. <u>Endocardium</u>-lines *inside* of the myocardium and covers the valves of the heart; contains *smooth* muscle and blood vessels.

      • <u>Myocarditis</u>-inflammation of heart muscle.
      • <u>Pericarditis</u> or <u>Endocarditis</u>-inflammation of the membranous tissues of heart.

C. <u>Heart valves</u>-composed of flaps of tough connective tissue attached to the endocardium that prevents blood from flowing backwards. (see **Figure 8-6**)

    1. <u>Atrioventricular Valves</u> (AV valves)-lie *between the atria and the ventricles.*

      a. <u>Tricuspid Valve</u>-between right atrium and right ventricle.

      b. <u>Bicuspid</u> (Mitral) <u>Valve</u>-between left atrium and left ventricle.

    2. <u>Chordae Tendineae</u>-cords of connective tissue that connect <u>cusps</u> (flaps) of valves to the muscles of the ventricle; often known as the "heart strings".

    3. <u>Semilunar Valves</u>-valves attached to the inside surface of the artery wall; allows blood to flow *only* into the arteries and prevents blood in the arteries leaving the heart from flowing back into the heart.

      a. <u>Pulmonary Semilunar Valve</u>-lies between where the pulmonary trunk of the pulmonary artery leaves the right ventricle. It has 3 cusps.

      b. <u>Aortic Semilunar Valve</u>-lies between the left ventricle and the aorta, normally has 3 cusps.

D. <u>Heart muscle</u>-pumps blood through the body. The heart does not pump right to left, it pumps from top to bottom.

    1. <u>Double pump</u>-the heart is a double pump that consists of a right and a left side separated by a muscular septum.

      a. <u>Right side</u>-pumps *deoxygenated* blood to the <u>lungs</u>.

b. <u>Left side</u>-pumps *oxygenated* blood to the <u>body</u>.

2. <u>Chambers</u>-consists of four chambers which *separate* the oxygenated and deoxygenated blood, never allowing them to mix. The four chambers of the heart are:

a. <u>Right</u> and <u>Left Atria</u> (singular=*atrium*)-small, thin-walled chambers located at the <u>top</u> of the heart. They <u>receive blood from the body</u>. The atria are separated by a muscular wall (<u>interatrial septum</u>). The <u>Fossa Ovalis</u>, a remnant of the thin, fibrous sheet that covered the Foramen Ovale during fetal development, is a depression located on the right atrium side of the interatrial septum.

1). <u>Right Atrium</u>-right, upper chamber that receives <u>deoxygenated</u> blood from the body through the Superior and Inferior Vena Cava.

2). <u>Left Atrium</u>-left, upper posterior chamber that receives <u>oxygenated</u> blood from the lungs and acts as a holding chamber for blood until it passes into the ventricle.

b. <u>Right</u> and <u>Left Ventricles</u>-*large, thick walled* chambers located in the <u>lower</u> portion of the heart. They *pump blood to the body*.

1). <u>Right Ventricle</u>-right, lower chamber that sends <u>deoxygenated</u> blood to the <u>lungs</u> through the pulmonary arteries; slightly larger than left atrium.

2). <u>Left Ventricle</u>-left, lower chamber that sends <u>oxygenated</u> blood to the <u>body</u>; walls composed of thick layer of myocardium; separated from the left atrium by the Mitral (Bicuspid) Valve. It is responsible for pumping oxygenated blood to tissues all over the body.

3). <u>Apex</u>-most inferior tip of the heart.

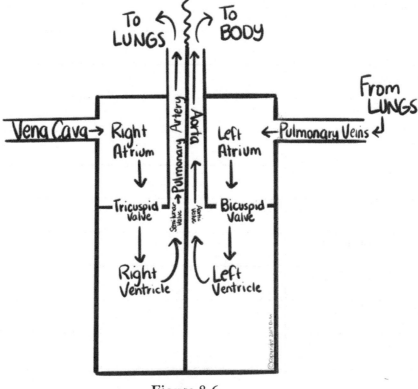

Figure 8-6

Several important arteries and veins can be seen on the anterior surface of the heart. These include:

1. <u>Right Coronary Artery</u>-supplies blood to the right ventricle and right atrium as well as the sinoatrial (SA) and atrioventricular (AV) to regulate the heart rhythm,

2. <u>Circumflex Artery</u>-branch of the left main coronary artery that supplies blood to the left atrium and to the back and side of the left ventricle.

3. Aorta and its branches:

     a. <u>Brachiocephalic Trunk</u>-supplies blood to head, neck, and right arm.

     b. <u>Left Common Carotid Artery</u>-main blood supply to the head and neck.

     c. <u>Left Subclavian Artery</u>-supplies blood to arms.

4. <u>Pulmonary Trunk and its branches</u> (right and left pulmonary arteries)-carry deoxygenated blood from right side of heart to lungs.

5. <u>Pulmonary Veins</u>-carry oxygenated blood from the lungs back to the heart.

6. Superior and Inferior Vena Cava-carry blood from upper half of body (via Superior Vena Cava) and lower half of body (via Inferior Vena Cava) back to the heart.

Heart (Anterior)-Figure 8-7

Please see pgs. 192-193 if you need additional assistance.

Structure	Function	Color
Superior Vena Cava		
Inferior Vena Cava		
Brachiocephalic Trunk		
Left Common Carotid Artery		
Left Subclavian Artery		
Aortic Arch		
Aorta		
Right & Left Pulmonary Arteries		
Right & Left Pulmonary Veins		
Pulmonary Trunk		
Right Coronary Artery		

Circumflex Artery		
Right Atrium		
Right Ventricle		
Left Atrium		
Left Ventricle		
Apex		

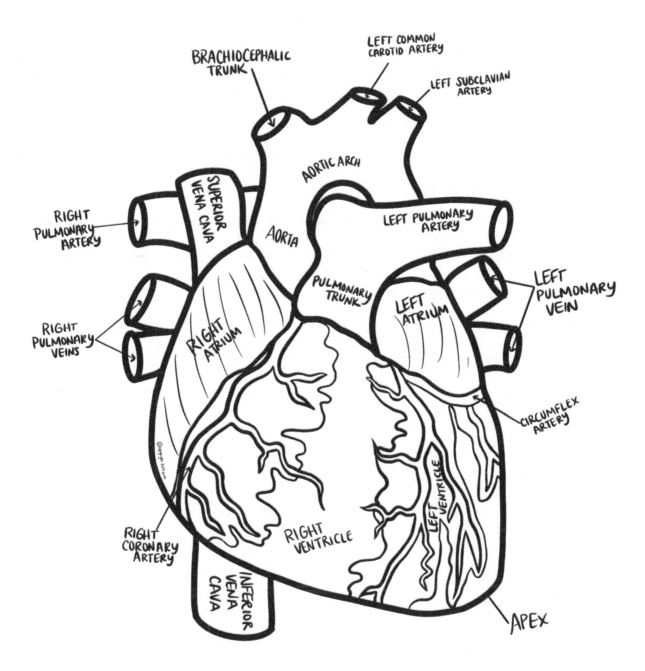

Figure 8-7

Several important arteries and veins can be seen on the posterior surface of the heart that were no seen on the anterior surface. These include:

1. <u>Great Cardiac Vein</u>-returns deoxygenated blood from the anterior surfaces of the left ventricle.

2. <u>Middle Cardiac Vein</u>-drains part of the right and left ventricles into the coronary sinus at the junction of the interventricular and atrioventricular grooves on the posterior surface of the heart.

3. <u>Posterior Interventricular Artery</u>-supplies the posterior third of the interventricular septum; most commonly a branch of the Right Coronary Artery but can be a branch of the Circumflex Coronary Artery. It is often called the Post Descending Artery (PDA).

Heart (Posterior)-Figure 8-8

Please see pgs. 192, 193, and 214 if you need additional assistance.

Structure	Function	Color
Superior Vena Cava		
Pulmonary Arteries		
Right & Left Pulmonary Veins		
Inferior Vena Cava		
Left Atrium		
Great Cardiac Vein		
Right Coronary Artery		
Left Ventricle		
Middle Cardiac Vein		
Posterior Interventricular Artery		

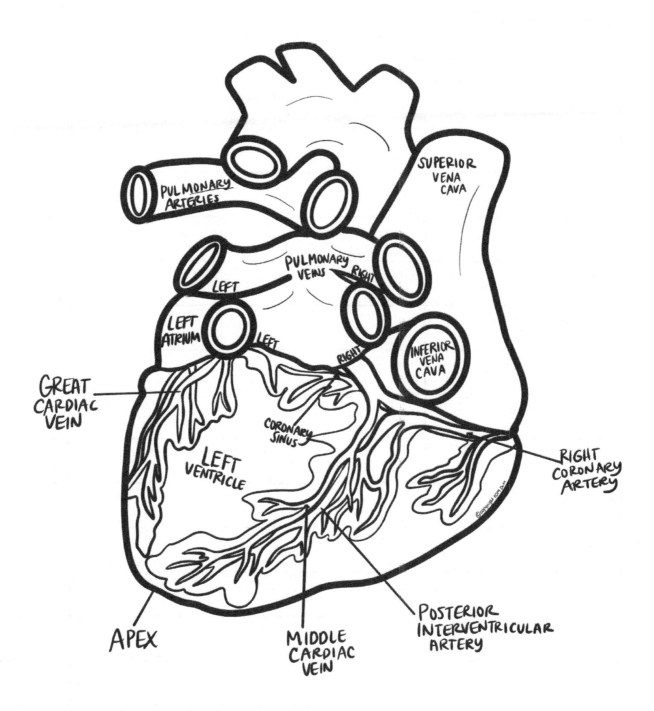

Figure 8-8

Heart (Interior)-Figure 8-9

Please see pgs. 212-213 if you need additional assistance.

Structure	Function	Color
Right Atrium		
Right Ventricle		
Left Atrium		
Left Ventricle		
Myocardium		
Interventricular Septum		
Bicuspid (Mitral) Valve		
Tricuspid valve		
Pulmonary Semilunar Valve		
Aortic Semilunar Valve		
Right & Left Pulmonary Arteries		
Right & Left Pulmonary Veins		
Aorta		
Fossa Ovalis		
Chordae Tendineae		
Superior Vena Cava		
Inferior Vena Cava		

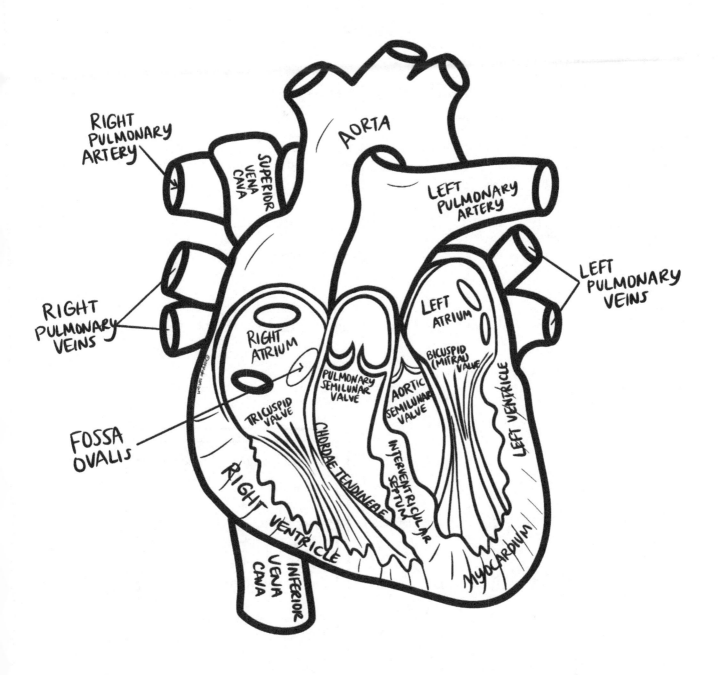

RIGHT PULMONARY ARTERY

SUPERIOR VENA CAVA

AORTA

LEFT PULMONARY ARTERY

RIGHT PULMONARY VEINS

LEFT PULMONARY VEINS

RIGHT ATRIUM

LEFT ATRIUM

PULMONARY SEMILUNAR VALVE

BICUSPID (MITRAL) VALVE

AORTIC SEMILUNAR VALVE

FOSSA OVALIS

TRICUSPID VALVE

CHORDAE TENDINEAE

INTERVENTRICULAR SEPTUM

LEFT VENTRICLE

RIGHT VENTRICLE

INFERIOR VENA CAVA

MYOCARDIUM

Figure 8-9

219

Path of Blood through the Heart (Figures 8-6, 8-10, and 8-11)

Right Side	Left Side
1. <u>Deoxygenated blood</u> enters the <u>right atrium</u> through the <u>Superior</u> and <u>Inferior Vena Cava</u>.	1. <u>Oxygenated blood</u> enters the <u>left atrium</u> through the <u>Pulmonary Veins</u>.
2. Blood passes from the <u>right atrium</u> through the <u>Tricuspid Valve</u> to reach the <u>right ventricle</u>.	2. Blood passes from the <u>left atrium</u> through the <u>Mitral Valve</u> (Bicuspid Valve) to reach the <u>left ventricle</u>.
3. <u>Right ventricle</u> contracts, causing the <u>Pulmonary Semilunar Valve</u> to open. Blood moves through the pulmonary semilunar valve into the <u>Pulmonary Trunk and arteries</u>.	3. <u>Left ventricle</u> contracts, causing the <u>Aortic Valve</u> to open. Blood moves through the aortic valve and into the <u>Aorta</u>.
4. Blood moves through the <u>Pulmonary Artery</u> to the <u>lungs</u>, where it picks up oxygen and releases carbon dioxide.	4. Blood moves through the <u>Aorta</u> to <u>the body</u>, where oxygen is delivered to cells and carbon dioxide is picked up.
5. <u>Oxygenated blood</u> returns to the heart through the <u>Pulmonary Veins</u>, which enters the heart through the <u>left atrium</u>.	5. <u>Deoxygenated blood</u> returns to the heart through the <u>Superior Vena Cava</u> (upper body) and the <u>Inferior Vena Cava</u> (lower body), which enter the heart through the <u>right atrium</u>.

***This process is repeated about once every second.

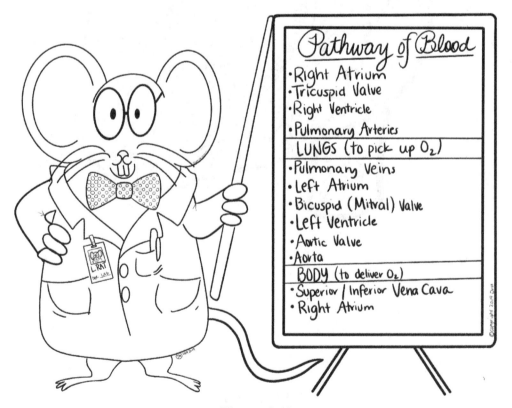

Figure 8-10

Figure 8-11

Cardiac Conduction System

I. <u>Cardiac Conduction System</u>-regulates the heartbeat via special cardiac muscle cells (in the "*pacemaker*") and a tract of conducting <u>Purkinje fibers</u> located throughout the <u>myocardium</u> (heart muscle) to ensure heart contractions (beats) are well-coordinated.

    A. <u>Autorhythmic Cells</u>-compose the Cardiac Conduction System; localized in these areas of the heart:

        1. Sinoatrial node (SA Node)-"*pacemaker*"

        2. Atrioventricular node (AV Node)-"*gatekeeper*"

        3. Atrioventricular Bundle (Bundle of His)

        4. Right and Left Bundle Branches

        5. Purkinje Fibers

    B. Nerve impulses travel over the heart through the structures 1-5 in the exact order listed above.

    C. Events in the Cardiac Conduction System:

        1. <u>Sinoatrial Node</u> (SA Node)-located in the wall of the right atrium near the point where the Superior Vena Cava enters. This structure <u>initiates the Cardiac Cycle</u>, generates action potentials that cause the atria to contract, and sets the basic rhythm for the heartbeat.

            a. Called the "*pacemaker*" of the heart but is influenced by hormones and impulses from the ANS in response to body activity. It generates about 75 impulses per minute in a resting individual.

            b. Produces impulses that spread to both atria.

            c. Releases electrical stimuli at regular rates as determined by the needs of the body; recharges while atria refill.

        2. <u>Atrioventricular Node</u> (AV Node)

            a. Called the "*gatekeeper*" of the heart.

            b. Located at the base of the right atrium in the lower portion of the <u>interatrial septum</u>.

            c. Briefly <u>delays impulses</u> so atria will have time to finish contracting before ventricles contract. This delay recharges AV Node while ventricles refill.

        3. <u>Atrioventricular Bundle</u> (Bundle of His)

            a. Located in the medial wall of right ventricle in the inferior portion of the <u>interatrial septum</u>.

            b. Composed of a tract of conducting Purkinje fibers that transmits impulses and distributes action potentials across the ventricles and causes them to contract. This is the <u>only</u> connection between the atria and ventricles.

        4. Right and Left Bundle Branches

a. Located throughout the <u>interventricular septum</u> between the right and left ventricles.

b. Transmits impulses between the ventricles to the <u>apex</u> (inferior point of heart) before dividing to innervate the lateral walls of both ventricles.

5. <u>Purkinje Fibers</u>-carry impulses completely through the <u>interventricular septum</u>, the <u>apex</u> of the heart, and up through myocardium of both ventricles.

D. Issues/Disorders Associated with the Cardiac Conduction System

1. <u>Arrhythmias</u>-abnormal heart rhythms; includes:

a. <u>Tachycardia</u>-abnormally fast heart rate; greater than 100 beats/minute.

b. <u>Bradycardia</u>-slow heart rate; less than 60 beats/minute.

c. Can be treated with artificial pacemakers when abnormalities are extreme.

2. <u>Fibrillation</u>-rapid, irregular, and uncoordinated heart contractions that interrupt blood flow out of the heart; treated with electrical shock. Example-Ventricular fibrillation

3. <u>Ectopic focus</u>-abnormal pacemaker that occurs in cases where the AV Node assumes control of the heart. Example-Atrial fibrillation, Premature Ventricular Contraction

4. <u>Heart block</u>-occurs when impulse conduction in the heart is blocked due to damage to the AV Node and the AV Bundle.

II. <u>Medulla Oblongata</u>-controls and regulates much of the heart's activity; contains the cardiovascular center and the cardio-accelerating center.

III. <u>Cardiac Cycle</u>-events that occur during one complete heartbeat.

A. <u>Normal heartbeat</u>-contraction of the 2 upper atria (while the 2 ventricles relax), then contraction of the 2 ventricles (while the 2 atria relax). At the end of the cycle, all the chambers relax, then begin a new cardiac cycle.

B. On average, the heart beats <u>72 times per minute</u>.

1. <u>Systole</u>-contraction and emptying of heart chambers.

2. <u>Diastole</u>-relaxing and filling of heart chambers. This is the part of the Cardiac Cycle where the coronary arteries fill.

IV. Heart Sounds

A. Result from the closing of the heart valves; 2 distinct heart sounds-*Lub* and *Dub*.

B. Production of sounds:

1. <u>Lub</u>-produced by the closing of the <u>Atrioventricular Valves</u> (Tricuspid and Bicuspid/Mitral Valves) during ventricular systole. Ventricular pressure is greater than atrial pressure at this point.

2. <u>Dub</u>-2nd heart sound; occurs at the end of ventricular systole with the closing of the <u>Semilunar</u>

Valves (Pulmonary and Aortic Valves).

C. Heart murmur-abnormal heart sounds caused by incomplete closing of the valves; sometimes caused by stenosis (change in valve shape) or insufficiency (leaky valve).

V. Electrocardiogram (ECG or EKG)-measurement of the electrical impulses through the heart. (see **Figures 8-12** and **8-13**)

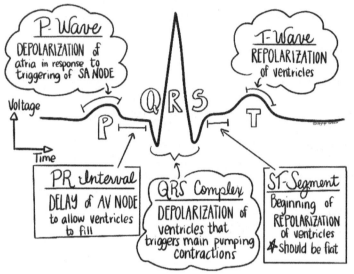

A. Consists of three distinct waves:

1. P Wave (1st wave)-very small; results from atrial depolarization. The P wave represents *atrial contraction*.

2. QRS Complex-large; results from ventricular depolarization. This complex represents *ventricular contraction*.

3. T Wave (3rd wave)-represents ventricular repolarization.

B. Waves in a normal EKG are very consistent, any changes indicate heart problems.

Figure 8-12

VI. Cardiac Output (CO)-amount of blood pumped out by each ventricle in one minute.

A. Product of heart rate (HR) and stroke volume (SV).

B. Stroke Volume (SV)-volume of blood pumped out by a ventricle with each beat; related to the force of ventricular contraction.

C. CO= SV x HR

1. For a normal functioning heart:

CO = HR (75 beats/min) x SV (70 ml/beat)=5250 mL or 5.25 L per minute

2. Normal heart volume for an individual is about 5L, so the *entire blood supply passes through the heart once every minute.*

D. Cardiac Reserve-difference between resting CO and maximal CO. In trained athletes, CO may increase as much as 7x above normal.

VII. Regulation of Heart Rate

A. Autonomic Nervous System (ANS)

1. Nerves innervate the SA and AV Nodes.

2. Divisions of the ANS:

a. Sympathetic Division-causes release of norepinephrine and epinephrine from the adrenal glands when under stress or fear. These hormones increase SA Node activity so overall heart activity will increase.

      b. <u>Parasympathetic Division</u>-reduces heart rate following stress.

3. <u>Sensory neurons</u>-play major role in determining which division is most active in regulating the heart.

4. <u>Baroreceptors</u>-can respond to blood pressure changes, forcing the brain to adjust SA Node activity as needed; only found in some blood vessels.

B. Chemical Regulation

    1. Hormones

        a. <u>Norepinephrine/Epinephrine</u>-from adrenal glands, increase heart activity.

        b. <u>Thyroxine</u>-from thyroid gland, regulates overall body metabolism.

    2. Ions

        a. <u>Calcium Ions</u>-depress heart activity when levels are reduced and increase heart activity when levels are increased.

        b. <u>Sodium and Potassium Ions</u>-needed for proper heart functioning.

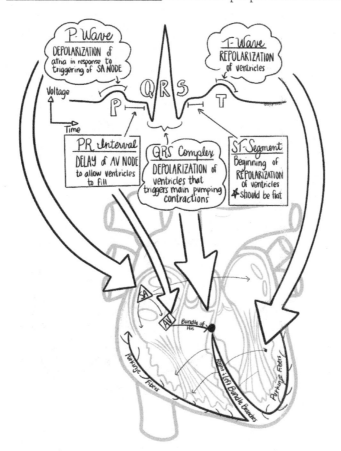

Figure 8-13

Heart Conduction System (Figure 8-14)

Please see pgs. 222-223 if you need additional assistance.

Structure	Function	Color
Sinoatrial (SA) Node		
Atrioventricular (AV) Node		
Atrioventricular (AV) Bundle (Bundle of His)		
Right & Left Bundle Branches		
Purkinje Fibers		

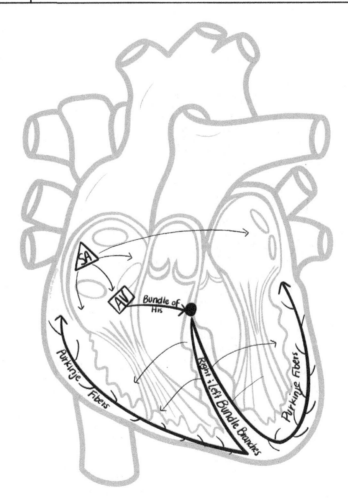

Figure 8-14

CHAPTER 9. LYMPHATIC SYSTEM AND BODY DEFENSES

The Lymphatic System

I. Lymphatic System

    A. Composed of two primary parts:

        1. <u>Lymphatic vessels</u>-transport fluids back into the blood that have escaped from the blood.

        2. <u>Lymphatic organs</u>-scattered throughout the body.

    B. Functions of the Lymphatic System

        1. Drain excess interstitial fluid.

        2. Transport lipids and lipid-soluble vitamins (A, D, E, and K) absorbed in the gastrointestinal tract throughout the body.

        3. Immune response.

II. Types of Lymphoid Cells

    A. <u>Lymphocytes</u>-serve as the primary cells of the immune system; develop in *red bone marrow* and mature into one of two types of immunocompetent cells:

        1. <u>T Cells</u> (T Lymphocytes)-manage immune response; some will directly attack and destroy foreign cells.

        2. <u>B Cells</u> (B Lymphocytes)-protect the body by producing <u>plasma cells</u> which secrete *antibodies* into the blood. <u>Antibodies</u> attach to and immobilize antigens until they can be destroyed.

    B. <u>Lymphatic macrophages</u>-protect the body by <u>phagocytizing</u> (ingesting) foreign substances and by <u>activating</u> T Cells.

    C. <u>Dendritic cells</u>-phagocytize foreign substances.

    D. <u>Reticular cells</u>-produce a network of protein fibers that support cells in the lymphoid organs.

III. Lymphatic Vessels

    A. Remove interstitial fluid and proteins and return them to the bloodstream. This material is known as <u>lymph</u> once the interstitial fluid enters lymphatic vessels.

    B. Lack a pump to push fluids into and through lymphatic vessels, so moves fluid via:

        1. Pulsations of nearby arteries.

        2. Pressure changes in the thorax during breathing.

        3. Numerous valves in lymphatic vessels.

        4. Milking action of skeletal muscles.

C. Begin as <u>lymphatic capillaries</u> (small vessels located in the spaces between cells). Lymphatic capillaries are:

    1. Typically closed at one end (unlike blood capillaries).

    2. Not found in bone marrow or nervous tissue.

    3. Composed of very thin endothelial cells whose ends overlap.

        a). The ends of these cells are easily pushed *open* when fluid pressure is great on their *external surfaces* so fluid is allowed to enter the lymphatic capillary.

        b). When fluid pressure is greatest on the *inside* of the lymphatic capillary, the ends of the endothelial cells are forced *shut* so fluid is prevented from leaking back into tissue spaces.

    4. Proteins, as well as cell debris and pathogens, found in the spaces surrounding tissues can easily enter lymphatic capillaries for transport through the body.

    5. Lymph flows from lymphatic capillaries into <u>lymphatic collecting vessels</u>.

D. Lymphatic Collecting Vessels

    1. Are *larger* than lymphatic capillaries.

    2. Will travel beside superficial veins in the skin, while the deep lymphatic vessels of the body travel with deep arteries.

E. Lymphatic Trunks

    1. Are formed by the union of the *largest* lymphatic collecting vessels.

    2. Drain large areas of the body.

    3. Are named for the area of the body they drain:

        a. <u>Lumbar Trunk</u>-lower limbs and pelvis.

        b. <u>Subclavian Trunk</u>-axilla (armpits) and arms.

        c. <u>Intestinal Trunk</u>-pancreas, spleen, and liver.

F. Lymphatic Ducts

    1. Receive lymph from lymphatic trunks.

    2. Major lymphatic ducts:

        a. <u>Right Lymphatic Duct</u>-drains lymph from the right upper arm and the right side of the head and thorax.

        b. <u>Thoracic Duct</u>-large, receives lymph from the rest of the body.

Structures and Organs of the Lymphatic System

IV. Lymphatic Organs

    A. <u>Lymph nodes</u>-cluster along the major lymphatic vessels of the body. (see **Figure 9-1**)

        1. Act to <u>filter lymph</u> as it moves through the lymphatic system.

        2. Located throughout the body, but cluster in the <u>inguinal</u> (groin), <u>axillary</u> (underarm), and <u>cervical</u> (neck) regions of the body where lymphatic collecting vessels converge to form lymphatic trunks.

        3. Primary functions:

            a. <u>Filter lymph</u>-*macrophages* in the nodes <u>destroy</u> and <u>remove</u> microbes and foreign debris carried by lymph.

            b. <u>Activate the Immune System</u>-*lymphocytes* in the nodes <u>monitor</u> the lymphatic system for foreign invaders so they can attack and destroy any that are found.

        4. Structure of a Lymph Node

            a. Small and <u>bean-shaped</u>.

            b. Surrounded by a thick <u>capsule</u>.

            c. Divided into chambers or compartments by <u>trabeculae</u> (connective tissue strands that extend inward).

            d. <u>Cortex</u>-outer portion containing <u>follicles</u> with high concentrations of *dividing B cells*.

            e. <u>Medulla</u>-contains <u>medullary cords</u> (inward extensions of lymphatic tissue) where antibody-secreting *plasma cells* are found.

            f. <u>Lymph sinuses</u>-fill the *central portion* of the node and contain the *lymphocytes* and *macrophages* which provide protection to the body.

        5. Circulation in the Lymph Nodes

            a. Lymph enters lymph nodes via <u>afferent lymphatic vessels</u>.

            b. It moves into a baglike structure known as the <u>subcapsular sinus</u>.

            c. Next, lymph flows through a series of <u>smaller sinuses</u>, finally exiting the lymph node at its <u>hilum</u> (an indention) via <u>efferent lymphatic vessels</u>.

            d. Generally, there are *fewer* efferent lymphatic vessels than afferent lymphatic vessels; therefore, lymph flow *slows substantially* allowing time for <u>macrophages</u> and <u>lymphocytes</u> to cleanse and filter lymph of foreign debris and bacteria.

            e. Lymph must pass through several lymph nodes before it is completely cleansed.

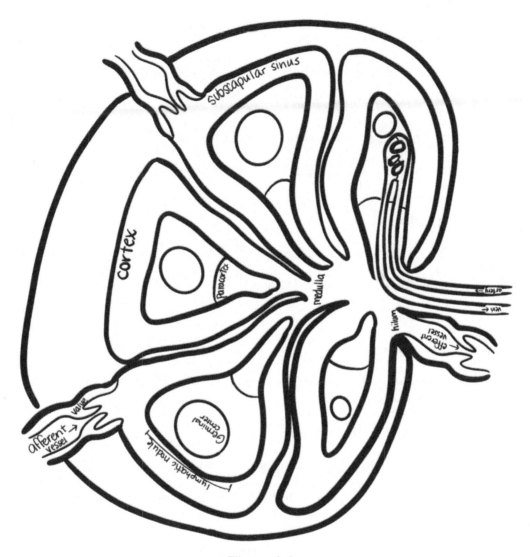

Figure 9-1

Lymph Node (Figure 9-1)

Structure	Function/Description	Color
Afferent Lymph Vessel		
Efferent Lymph Vessel		
Cortex		
Medulla		
Hilum		

B. Spleen (see **Figure 9-2**)

1. Largest lymphoid structure in the body.

2. Located in the left side of the abdominal cavity beneath the diaphragm.

3. Served by the <u>splenic artery</u> (supplies oxygenated blood) and <u>vein</u> (drains deoxygenated blood).

4. Site of <u>lymphocyte</u> proliferation and <u>immune response</u>.

5. Plays a role in <u>cleansing the blood</u> by removing old and worn blood cells and platelets from the body.

6. Other functions include:

   a. Storage of red blood cell breakdown products for future use and processing.

   b. Site of red blood cell production in the fetus (this function ends after birth).

   c. Storage of blood platelets.

7. Structure of the spleen

   a. Surrounded by a <u>capsule</u> that extends inward to divide spleen internally into smaller sections called <u>lobules</u>.

   b. Contains 2 types of tissues:

      1. <u>White Pulp</u>-stores large numbers of <u>macrophages</u> and <u>lymphocytes</u>.

      2. <u>Red Pulp</u>-filters the blood of antigens, microorganisms, and defective or worn-out red blood cells.

   c. The <u>Red Pulp</u> is composed of <u>splenic cords</u> that contain macrophages which aid in the breakdown of red blood cells.

Spleen (Figure 9-2)

Structure	Function/Description	Color
Splenic Artery & Vein		
Capsule		
White Pulp		
Red Pulp		

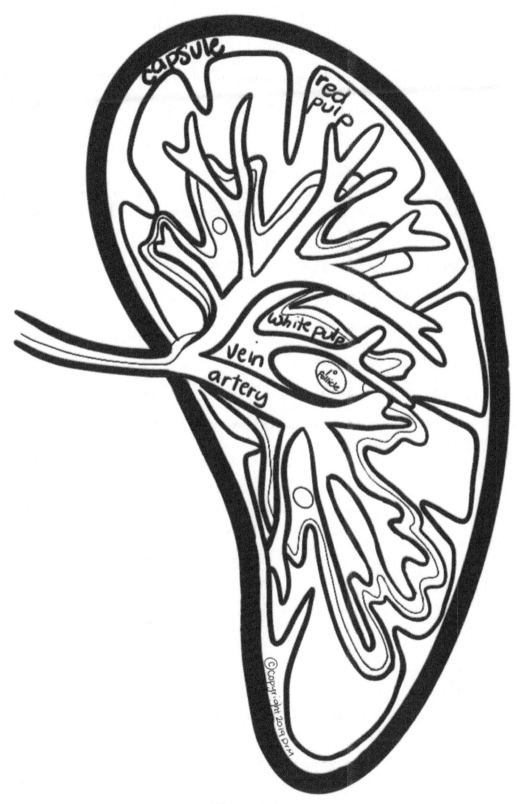

Figure 9-2

C. <u>Thymus</u>-gland is located in the inferior part of the neck and extends into the superior thorax.

    1. Secretes the hormones <u>thymosin</u> and <u>thymopoietin</u> (hormones that force T lymphocytes to fight *specific* pathogens in the immune response).

    2. Largest and most active during <u>childhood</u> (growth stops after adolescence and atrophy occurs).

    3. Primarily composed of densely packed lymphocytes (located in the <u>cortex)</u>. The thymus gland *does not* contain <u>B cells</u>.

D. Aggregates (Clusters) of Lymphoid Follicles

    1. <u>Peyer's Patches</u>-located in the <u>small intestine</u>; structurally similar to tonsils; involved in destroying bacteria that enter into the small intestine and generating memory lymphocytes that provide long-term immunity.

    2. <u>Appendix</u>-located in the large intestine, structurally similar to Peyer's Patches.

E. <u>Tonsils</u>-considered to be the simplest of all the lymphoid organs. (see **Figure 9-3**)

    1. Form a ring around the pharynx.

    2. Named according to *location*.

    3. Gather and remove pathogens entering the pharynx via food or inhaled air.

    4. Internally, contain folds known as <u>crypts</u> which have walls covered by epithelial tissue to trap and destroy bacteria and other pathogens.

    5. Types:

        a. <u>Pharyngeal</u>-located at the *posterior wall of the nasopharynx* near the opening of the nasal cavity into the pharynx; referred to as the <u>adenoids</u> if they are enlarged.

        b. <u>Palatine</u>-paired, located at the rear of the throat (pharynx) on either side of the *posterior end of the oral cavity*; largest and most commonly infected tonsils.

        c. <u>Lingual</u>-paired, located at the *base of the tongue*, one on either side.

Tonsils

Structure	Function/Description	Color
Pharyngeal Tonsil (Adenoid)		
Palatine Tonsil		
Lingual Tonsil		

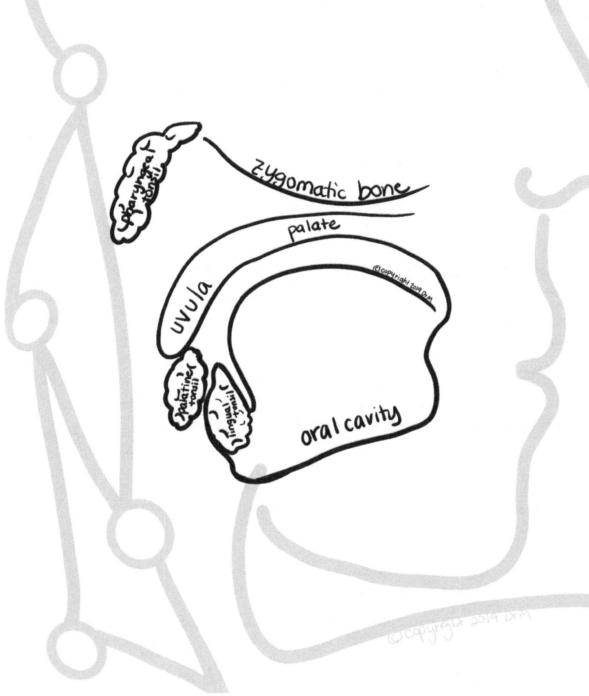

zygomatic bone

palate

pharyngeal tonsil

uvula

palatine tonsil

lingual tonsil

oral cavity

Figure 9-3

Innate and Adaptive Body Defenses

I. Immunity

    A. Resistance to disease which allows the body to maintain its health.

    B. Considered to be a <u>functional system</u> instead of an organ system because it is composed of chemicals and trillions of immune cells inhabiting lymphoid tissue and circulating in body fluids in order to protect the body from infectious microorganisms and cancer cells.

    C. Composed of a variety of cells and structures that must work together to protect the body from <u>bacterial</u>, <u>fungal</u>, and <u>viral infection</u>.

    D. Consists of two primary defense systems that work both <u>independently</u> (separately) and <u>cooperatively</u> (together) to provide resistance to disease. These defense systems are:

        1. Innate (Nonspecific)

        2. Adaptive (Specific)

II. <u>Innate Defenses</u> (Nonspecific)-respond *quickly* to protect the body from pathogens and infection.

    A. Two major lines of defense:

        1. <u>Surface barriers or external body membranes</u>-prevent the penetration of pathogens into the body. Example-skin.

        2. <u>Inflammation</u>-includes a variety of proteins, cells, and phagocytes that *work together* to prevent the spread of pathogens throughout the body.

    B. <u>Surface Barriers</u> (Skin and Mucous Membranes)

        1. Works well as long as the thick keratinized epithelial tissue of the skin is not broken; <u>keratin</u> is also resistant to the acids and bases secreted by most bacteria.

        2. Damaged membranes allow microbes to invade deeper into the body where the internal innate defenses take over to fight off the invaders.

        3. <u>Mucous Membranes</u>-line body cavities that *open directly to the outside* of the body.

        Specific functions of mucous membranes include:

            a. Serve as *sticky surfaces* to trap microorganisms before they enter body systems such as the digestive and respiratory systems.

            b. Some *secrete chemicals* that are toxic to some bacteria. For example, <u>sebum</u> secreted by the skin kills some bacteria.

            c. <u>Mucosa</u>-in the stomach secretes <u>hydrochloric acid</u> and <u>protein-digesting enzymes</u> to kill microorganisms.

            d. <u>Saliva</u>-cleanses the oral cavity and teeth.

            e. <u>Lysozyme</u> (enzyme)-secreted onto the surface of the eye to destroy bacteria.

C. <u>Internal Innate Defenses</u>-help fight off invading microorganisms including <u>phagocytic cells</u>, <u>natural killer cells</u>, <u>antimicrobial proteins</u>, <u>fever</u>, and <u>inflammation</u>.

D. Cells and Chemicals Involved in Internal Innate Defense System

    1. <u>Phagocytes</u>-cells that feed upon and destroy invading microorganisms.

        a. Types of Phagocytic Cells

            1). <u>Macrophages</u>-*primary phagocytes* in the body; derived from <u>monocytes</u> (type of leukocyte or WBC) that leave the bloodstream, enter tissues, and develop into macrophages.

            2). <u>Neutrophils</u>-*most abundant type of leukocyte* (WBC) in the body; become phagocytic when encountering infectious materials in the body.

            3). <u>Eosinophils</u>-another type of *leukocyte* (WBC); can be phagocytic but are best known for fighting parasitic worms.

            4). <u>Free macrophages</u>-*move throughout the body* searching for and destroying foreign invaders; Example-<u>Alveolar macrophages</u> in the lungs.

            5). <u>Fixed macrophages</u>-*permanent* residents of specific organs in the body. Examples-<u>Kupffer cells</u> in the liver and <u>microglia</u> in the brain.

        b. Events in Phagocytosis

            1). <u>Adherence</u>-phagocyte adheres to the pathogen after recognition of either the protein or carbohydrate signature of the pathogen.

                -<u>Opsonization</u>-process in which proteins and antibodies coat the outer covering of a pathogen to provide "handles" for phagocyte attachment to increase the efficiency of phagocytosis.

            2). <u>Phagocytosis of the pathogen</u> (phago=*"eat"*)-cell uses its cell membrane to engulf a pathogen.

    2. <u>Natural Killer Cells</u>-in blood and lymph that can lyse (burst) to kill cancer cells and virus infected cells before the adaptive immune response is initiated.

        a. Cells are *not specific* and develop from <u>granular leukocytes</u>.

        b. <u>Proteins</u> on cell membranes *identify target cells for destruction* by the natural killer cells.

        c. Natural killer cells are *not phagocytic* so destroy target cells by releasing chemicals known as <u>perforins</u> to destroy the nucleus of cells.

E. Inflammation (see **Figure 2-4**, p. 39)

1. Initiated when body tissues are injured; primary goal is to clear the injured area of pathogens, dead cells, and debris so tissue repair can begin.

2. Benefits of inflammation:

a. Prevents the spread of damaging agents into the body.

b. Removes cell debris and pathogens.

c. Sets the stage for repair.

3. Key indicators of inflammation are redness, heat, pain, and swelling.

4. Inflammation Response

a. Begins when chemicals and cells leave blood vessels and move into the injured tissue.

1). Chemicals include cytokines, histamine, kinins, and prostaglandins which promote dilation of small blood vessels in the injured area to increase blood flow.

2). These chemicals also *increase the permeability of blood vessels* so cells and antibodies can move to the site of injury; leads to edema (swelling).

3). Beta defensins-antibiotic-type agents that are often released in the injury site during inflammation to fight bacterial growth.

b. Phagocytic cells also move into the injured area.

1). Leukocytosis-release of phagocytic cells (especially neutrophils) into blood vessels at injury; triggered by leukocytosis-inducing factors.

2). Diapedesis-movement of neutrophils *through the walls* of capillaries into the site of inflammation.

c. In severely damaged areas, pus (mixture of dead neutrophils, broken down tissue cells, and dead pathogens) may accumulate and form an abscess if walled off by collagen fiber because material is not removed.

F. Antimicrobial proteins-attack microbes *directly* or limit the ability of microbes to *reproduce*. Types of antimicrobial proteins include:

a. Interferons-proteins secreted by some cells infected by viruses; stimulate healthy cells to produce a protein known as PKR which prevents viruses from undergoing protein synthesis.

b. Complement System-group of plasma proteins that circulate through the blood in an inactive state until activated by the immune response itself.

1. Destroy cells via cell lysis (bursting).

2. Activated via 2 primary pathways:

a) <u>Classical Pathway</u>-involves the formation of antibodies to destroy invading microbes.

b) <u>Alternative Pathway</u>-occurs when certain complement proteins are triggered by polysaccharides on the membranes of invading microorganisms.

G. <u>Fever</u>-abnormally high body temperature.

1. <u>Pyrogens</u> ("*fire proteins*")-chemicals secreted in response to microbial invasion by <u>leukocytes</u> and <u>macrophages</u> to signal the <u>Hypothalamus</u> to raise body temperature.

2. Mild fever appears to have a *positive* effect on the body because it:

a. Reduces release of certain nutrients by the liver and spleen that are required by microbes to grow and reproduce.

b. Increases metabolism and therefore, the repair processes.

3. Extreme fever can be dangerous because it *denatures enzymes*; can cause seizures in babies.

III. <u>Adaptive Defenses</u> (Specific)-protects the body from a *wide range of microorganisms* and abnormal body cells; turned on by *exposure* to a foreign substance.

A. Important Characteristics:

1. <u>Specific</u>-recognizes and attacks *particular* pathogens or foreign debris in the body.

2. <u>Systemic</u>-immunity is *not restricted* to the site of the initial infection.

3. <u>Sustained</u>-after an initial exposure, it *recognizes* and strongly attacks a *previously encountered* pathogen.

B. <u>Antigens</u>-surface protein on a pathogen that causes **anti**bodies to be **gen**erated by leukocytes; can *mobilize the immune system* and provoke an immune *response*.

1. Classified as being either:

a. Complete antigens

1) <u>Immunogenicity</u>-ability to *stimulate the formation* of specific lymphocytes and antibodies; most proteins, nucleic acids and polysaccharides can serve as complete antigens.

2) <u>Reactivity</u>-ability to *react* with the activated lymphocytes and the antibodies released by immunogenic reactions.

b. <u>Incomplete antigens</u> (haptens)-reactive but *lack immunogenicity* ability to induce a humoral and/or cell-mediated immune responses; small proteins, and certain chemicals (found in poison ivy, detergents etc.) can act as haptens.

2. <u>Antigenic determinants</u>-only *certain parts* of an antigen are immunogenic and bind to *lymphocytes* like enzymes bind to a substrate.

3. <u>Major Histocompatibility Complex</u> (MHC)-("*self antigens*") membrane proteins that act as "special hands" on regular cells and leukocytes; this group of proteins marks cells as "ours".

a. These MHC proteins are:

1) <u>Strongly antigenic</u> to other individuals and is the basis for rejection of tissues and transfusions.

2) <u>Specific</u> to an individual and plays a major role in mobilizing the immune response.

b. Classified as:

1) <u>Class I</u>-possessed by all cells *other than leukocytes*; function is to notify WBCs that an infected cell has been marked for destruction by being displayed on the cell's surface holding an antigen (<u>antibody generating particle</u>).

2) <u>Class II</u>-possessed by *all leukocytes*; show other WBCs which pathogens to search for and destroy because they are displayed like "trophies" on the cell membrane by <u>antigen receptors</u> ("*recognition hands*").

C. <u>Antigen receptors</u>-"*recognition hands*" on lymphocytes made of the glycoproteins or glycolipids of the extracellular matrix. When a pathogen is identified and marked for destruction, the identification triggers *clonal selection* in that lymphocyte where <u>plasma</u> "effector" <u>cells</u> ("fighters") and <u>memory cells</u> (for future fights) are made.

D. Cells in the Adaptive (Specific) Immune System

1. <u>Lymphocytes</u>

a. Originate in the <u>bone marrow</u> from hematopoietic stem cells. When released, lymphocytes mature into either <u>B cells</u> or <u>T cells</u>.

1) <u>T cells</u>-become *immunocompetent* (can recognize a specific antigen by binding to it) in the <u>thymus gland</u>. Only 2% of the T cells produced in the thymus are *released* into the blood. The other 98% are selected against because they cannot actively attach to and destroy antigens.

2) <u>B cells</u>-"kill" by producing antibodies. Antibodies become *immunocompetent* in <u>bone marrow</u>. However, very little is known about this process.

b. Lymphocytes become immunocompetent before meeting the antigens that they must attack and destroy.
c. After becoming immunocompetent, lymphocytes are transported to the *spleen, lymph nodes, and other lymphoid structures* where they can encounter antigens.

2. <u>Antigen-presenting cells</u>-engulf antigens and present fragments of these antigens on *their own surface* so T cells can recognize and destroy the antigen.

E. Types of Immunity in the Adaptive (Specific) Defense System

1. <u>Specific Immune Responses</u>–use <u>lymphocytes</u> (WBC) to fight infections of *specific* pathogens.

a. <u>B</u> (bursa) <u>Lymphocytes</u>–destroy by producing <u>antibodies</u>.

b. <u>T</u> (thymus) <u>Lymphocytes</u>–destroy using <u>chemicals</u>.

1). <u>Cytotoxic T cells</u>–actually *kill* infected cells. (toxic= *"deadly"*)

2). <u>Helper T cells</u>–help turn *"on"* B cells to make antibodies and Cytotoxic T cells to kill; these are the cells are infected and rendered useless by the AIDS virus.

2. Specific Immune Responses:

a. <u>Humoral Immunity</u> (Antibody-Mediated)-produced by <u>antibodies</u> present in the body's fluids. Antibodies <u>bind to pathogens</u>, <u>inactivate them</u>, and <u>mark them for destruction</u> by phagocytes or the complement system. Humoral Immunity refers to *clearing the fluids*, such as blood, using antibodies from B cells. (humoral= *"fluids"*)

1). <u>B-cells</u> mature to become <u>plasma cells</u> that can make <u>antibodies</u> to fight pathogens.

2). B-cell activation is initiated by:

a). <u>Interleukin-2</u> (IL-2) released from a <u>T-Helper cell</u>. (Interleukin-2= *2nd message between WBC*)

b). Plasma cells secrete about 2,000 antibodies per second.

b. <u>Cell-Mediated Immunity</u>-occurs when <u>lymphocytes</u> themselves defend the body from microbial invasion. These cells can produce <u>cell lysis</u> or can initiate an <u>inflammation response</u>. Cell-mediated Immunity refers to the use of T cells to "kill" other infected cells.

1). <u>Cytotoxic T-cells</u>-mature to fight and kill infected cells.

2). <u>T-helper cells</u>-initiate the two types of specific immunity.

a). T-helper connects to the <u>macrophage</u> displaying an MHC type II molecule. It is attracted to the macrophage by <u>Interleukin-1</u> (IL1) allowing the T-helper to "analyze" the antigen so it can tell the other lymphocytes what to "look for". (Interleukin-1= *1st message between WBCs*)

b. <u>Cytokines</u> (Interleukin-2, IL-2) are then released by T-helper cells to relay message to B-cells and Cytotoxic T cells.

3. Cytotoxic T cells

a. Activated by an MHC class 1 molecule or IL-2.

b. Kill infected cells by releasing <u>perforin</u>.

c. <u>Antibodies</u> mark the pathogen parts for disposal by <u>macrophages</u>.

F. <u>Humoral Immune Response System</u>-production of <u>antibodies</u> against a pathogen.

1. Differentiation of B Cells

a. <u>B Cells</u>-activated when *antigens bind to their surface*; this leads to <u>clonal selection</u> where numerous B Cells are formed (<u>cloned cells</u>) that can destroy a <u>particular antigen</u>.

b. Most of these activated B Cells develop into <u>plasma cells</u> (effector cells, "the fighters") which can *secrete antibodies*. These cells survive for only 4- 5 days.

c. Some of the B Cells develop into <u>memory cells</u> which can lead an *immediate attack* if they encounter the *same antigen* a second time in the future.

d. The proliferation and differentiation of plasma and memory cells is known as the <u>Primary Immune Response</u> which occurs on the <u>first exposure</u> to an antigen. It generally takes 10 – 17 days to find right DNA sequence and make antibodies for fighting.

e. <u>Secondary Immune Response</u>-occurs when a person is <u>re-exposed</u> to a particular antigen. This response is *fast and extremely effective* since the immune system is on alert for the antigen. This is known as <u>immunological memory</u>. It takes only 2 – 7 days to feel better from an illness because of memory cells.

2. Types of Humoral Immunity:

a. <u>Active Humoral Immunity</u>-occurs when <u>B Cells</u> *naturally encounter antigens* and *produce antibodies* against them. Active immunity is naturally acquired when a person is exposed to pathogens but can also be artificially acquired when a <u>vaccine</u> is received.

1). <u>Vaccines</u>-contain dead or weak pathogens or their components.
Vaccines provide two benefits:

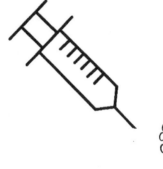

a). Spare us many of the symptoms of an illness.

b). Provide us with immunity against an antigen.

2). <u>Booster shots</u>-may be given to provide extensive immunity to a particular microbe.

b. <u>Passive Humoral Immunity</u>-antibodies are made from the serum of an immune human or animal donor (not naturally encountered). Because B cells are not challenged by antigen, *memory does not occur,* but protection does, as these "borrowed" antibodies degrade in the body.

1). Occurs *naturally in a fetus* when the mother's antibodies cross the placenta.

2). Immune sera are also used to treat snake bites, botulism and rabies. In each of these cases, the protection is short-lived.

3. <u>Antibodies</u> (Immunoglobulins, *"globular protein of the immune system"*, or Ig)-secreted by <u>activated B Cells</u> or <u>plasma cells</u> in response to an antigen; they bind to and remove the antigen.

a. Structure (see **Figure 9-4**)

1). Antibodies have a *loop shape* and are composed of 2 <u>heavy</u> chains and 2 <u>light</u>

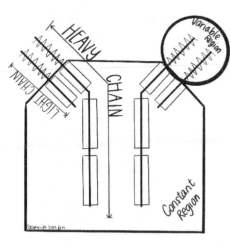

Figure 9-4

chains held together by <u>disulfide bridges</u>. They also contain a variable (V) region and a constant (C) region.

    a). <u>V</u> (Variable) <u>Region</u>-area of the protein that changes to match the pathogen's antigen.

    b). <u>C</u> (Constant) <u>Region</u>-area of the protein that *never changes* and is the part of the antibody where the macrophage can safely grab.

2). <u>Antigen-binding site</u>-shaped to fit a *specific* antigen located at the ends of each arm that make up the V region of the antibody. Each antibody has 2 antigen-binding sites.

    b. <u>Classes of antibodies</u>-based on structure and the specific biological role. The five major classes of antibodies are:

        1) **IgM** (immunoglobin M)-most potent agglutinating antibody; present on surface of B-lymphocytes.

        2) **IgA** (immunoglobin A)-acts as a mucosal barrier.

        3) **IgD** (immunoglobin D)-present on surface of B-lymphocytes.

        4) **IgE** (immunoglobin E)-responsible for allergies.

        5) **IgG** (immunoglobin G)-only antibody class that can cross the placenta.

    c. Antibodies *do not destroy antigens themselves*, but they do *inactivate and tag antigens* for destruction. Types of Antigen-Antibody reactions include:

        1) <u>Complement fixation and activation</u>-antibodies *bind to cells* and *change their shape* triggering complement fixation and cell lysis.

        2) <u>Neutralization</u>-antibodies *block specific sites* on viruses or toxins and *prevent the antigen from attaching to tissue receptors* therefore preventing injury to the tissue.

        3) <u>Agglutination</u>-antibodies can *cause antigens to clump* (<u>agglutinate</u>). Example-occurs when 2 different blood types are in contact.

        4) <u>Precipitation</u>-when large molecules are linked into complexes that *settle out of solution*. These antigens can then be easily removed by phagocytic cells.

G. <u>Cell-Mediated Immune Response</u>

    1. Involves the use of *lymphocytes* (<u>T Cells</u>) to attack and destroy pathogens.

    2. T Cells generally *recognize and respond* to protein antigens displayed on body cell surfaces. Therefore, T cells are geared to attack and destroy body cells infected by pathogens, cancer cells, and transplanted cells.

    3. T Cells are *activated by a recognized antigen*. T Cells must also identify the antigen and normal, healthy

body cells.

      a. <u>MHC Proteins</u>-on cells; act to signal foreign invaders are present in the body.

      b. <u>Steps in T Cell Activation</u>

            1) <u>Antigen Binding</u>-attachment of a T cell to an antigen on a body cell.

            2) <u>Co-Stimulation</u>-T cells must recognize one or more co-stimulatory agents on cells before they can produce clones.

      c. <u>Cytokines</u>-chemicals released by T Cells that help to enhance the immune response.

4. <u>Specific Roles of T Cells</u>

      a. <u>Helper T Cells</u>-stimulate proliferation of other T Cells and B Cells that are attached to an antigen.

      b. <u>Cytotoxic T Cells</u>-directly attack and kill other cells; main targets are virus-infected cells.

      c <u>Suppressor T Cells</u>-suppress the activity of B Cells and T Cells; are thought to inhibit autoimmune reactions.

      d. <u>Gamma Delta T Cells</u>-live in the intestine, their function is unclear.

CHAPTER 10. RESPIRATORY SYSTEM

The Respiratory System

I. Respiratory System-functions by supplying the body with oxygen and disposing of carbon dioxide. The body accomplishes this via four processes (collectively known as respiration) carried out by the Respiratory System in conjunction with the Cardiovascular System:

A. Pulmonary Ventilation-movement of air *into and out of the lungs* (breathing) so the gases are continuously changed and refreshed; carried out by the Respiratory System.

B. External Respiration-movement of oxygen *from the lungs to the blood* and of carbon dioxide *from the blood to the lungs*; carried out by the Respiratory System.

C. Transport of Respiratory Gases-movement of oxygen *from the lungs to the tissue cells* of the body and of carbon dioxide *from the tissue cells to the lungs*; carried out by blood in the Cardiovascular System.

D. Internal Respiration-movement of oxygen *from blood to the tissue cells* and of carbon dioxide from *tissue cells to blood*; carried out by blood in the Cardiovascular System.

Structures of the Respiratory System

II. Anatomy of the Respiratory System (see **Figure 10-11**)

A. Major Structures of the Respiratory System

1. Nose, and Nasal Cavity

2. Larynx

3. Pharynx

4. Trachea

5. Bronchi and smaller branches

6. Lungs with alveoli

7. Paranasal sinuses

B. Composed of two zones:

1. Respiratory Zone-actual site of gas exchange, includes the bronchioles, alveoli, and alveolar ducts.

2. Conducting Zone-includes all other passageways that serve as areas for air to reach exchange zones.

III. Nose and Paranasal Sinuses

A. Nose (**Figure 10-1**)

1. Only visible portion of the Respiratory System.

2. Provides an airway for respiration, moistens and warms air, filters and cleans inspired air, serves as a resonating chamber for speech, and houses the olfactory receptors.

3. Divided into the external nose and the internal nasal cavity.

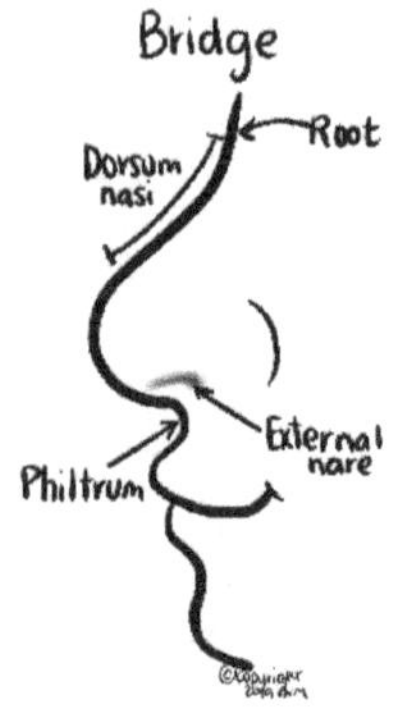

Figure 10-1

a. External features of the nose-root, bridge, dorsum nasi (the length of the nose), apex (tip of the nose), philtrum (concave surface that connects the apex of the nose to the upper lip), and the external nares (nostrils). (see **Figure 10-1**)

b. Large, air-filled space above and behind the nose; formed by the nasal, frontal, and maxillary bones however, it is primarily made of cartilage.

c. Internal nasal cavity-inside and posterior to the external nose.

1). Air enters this cavity by passing through the nostrils (external nares).

2). Divided by a midline known as the nasal septum (formed by the vomer bone, perpendicular plate of the ethmoid bone, and cartilage).

3). The ethmoid bone forms the *roof of the nasal cavity* and the palatine bones form the *base of the cavity*.

4). The internal nasal cavity connects to the pharynx via two *posterior* openings known as internal nares.

5). Vestibule-portion of the nasal cavity just *superior* to the nostrils, lined with sebaceous and sweat glands, and covered by hairs known as vibrissae.

6). Olfactory mucosa-lines much of the nasal cavity and contains *smell receptors*.

7). Respiratory mucosa-also lines much of the nasal cavity and is made of pseudostratified ciliated columnar epithelial tissue and goblet cells (secrete mucous).

8). Nasal Conchae (Superior, Inferior, Medial)-protrude from the *lateral walls* of the nasal cavity; increase mucosal surface area and enhance air flow through the cavity.

B. Paranasal sinuses-located within the frontal, sphenoid, ethmoid, and maxillary bones and serve to lighten the skull; aid in warming and moistening incoming air as well as produce mucus which flows into the nasal cavity.

IV. Pharynx (throat)-funnel-shaped tube that connects the nasal cavity and mouth superiorly to the larynx and inferiorly to the esophagus; serves as a passageway leading from the oral cavity (mouth) and nose to the esophagus and larynx.

Major Regions: (see **Figure 10-2**)

A. Nasopharynx-posterior to the nasal cavity and only serves as an air passageway.

1. Uvula-moves to close off the nasopharynx to prevent food from moving into the nasal cavity during swallowing.

2. Pharyngeal tonsils (adenoids)-located on the posterior wall of the nasopharynx; traps and destroys pathogens entering the nasopharynx via air.

3. Openings into the Nasopharynx:

a. Internal nares (2)

b. Auditory (Eustachian) Tubes (2)-drain the middle ear cavity to equalize pressure in the ear with atmospheric pressure.

B. Oropharynx-posterior to the oral cavity, opens into the mouth through the fauces (arched opening at the back of the mouth leading to the pharynx); both swallowed food and inhaled air pass through this area.

1. Covered by a layer of protective stratified squamous epithelial tissue.

2. Separated from the nasopharynx by the soft palate.

3. Tonsils located in the oropharynx (2 pairs):

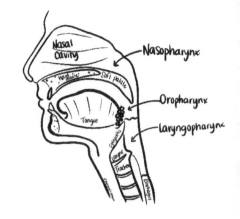

    a. Palatine-in the *lateral walls.*

    b. Lingual-covers the *base of the tongue;* most often removed during a tonsillectomy.

C. Laryngopharynx-opens into the larynx; also serves as a passageway for food and air.   **Figure 10-2**

1. Continuous with the esophagus (tube that carries food to the stomach).

2. Has a role in allowing us to produce certain *vowel sounds.*

V. Larynx (voice box)-two inch long tube that lies at the upper end of the trachea, just in front of the pharynx.

A. Connects the pharynx and trachea and held in place by the hyoid bone.

B. Functions:

1. Serves as an open airway.

2. Routes food and air into the proper channels.

3. Voice production.

C. Lined by stratified squamous epithelium and pseudostratified columnar epithelium (produces mucous that acts as a dust filter).

D. Composed of 9 cartilages that form a box-like structure; most of these are hyaline cartilage. The most common are:

1. Thyroid Cartilage-large, formed by 2 attached cartilage plates that gives a triangular shape to the anterior portion of the larynx; often referred to as the *"Adam's Apple".*

2. Epiglottis-composed of flexible, elastic cartilage and covered by taste buds; attaches to the superior edge of the thyroid cartilage and is free on its other borders; during swallowing, the larynx pulls the epiglottis up to cover the glottis (hollow opening between the vocal cords) to prevent food and liquids from entering the respiratory tract. The cough reflex acts to expel any materials that slip past the epiglottis.

E. Vocal Cords

1. True Vocal Cords-folds of white elastic fibers stretched across the opening of the larynx that vibrate as air rushes up from the lungs to produce sound.

2. False Vocal Cords-located superior to the true vocal cords; do not produce sound and are only involved in helping to close the glottis during swallowing.

F. Sound Production

1. Vibration produces sound waves as air is forced between vocal cords.

2. Waves are modified by the nose, mouth, pharynx, and sinuses (which serve as resonating chambers).

3. More tense vocal cords produce a *higher* pitch. Less tense longer cords produce lower pitch. In adolescent males, the cords begin to thicken and enlarge during puberty, the period that the male's voice "cracks".

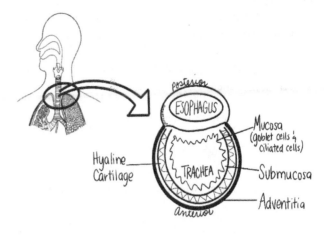

Figure 10-3

G. Laryngitis-inflammation of the vocal folds which can produce hoarseness.

VI. Trachea (windpipe)-wide, hollow cylindrical tube that connects the larynx and the primary bronchi of the lungs; provides passageway for air flow to and from the lungs for respiration. (see **Figure 10-4**)

A. Approximately 4 inches long and 2.5 cm in diameter.

B. Wall of the trachea consists of distinct layers: mucosa (lined with pseudostratified columnar epithelial tissue containing cilia and goblet cells), submucosa, and adventitia. (see **Figure 10-3**)

C. Smoking often destroys cilia in the trachea, so coughing becomes the only way to remove mucus from the trachea.

D. Walls of the adventitia are reinforced internally by 16-20 C-shaped rings of hyaline cartilage to provide the ability to stretch.

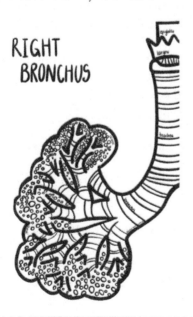

RIGHT BRONCHUS

Figure 10-4

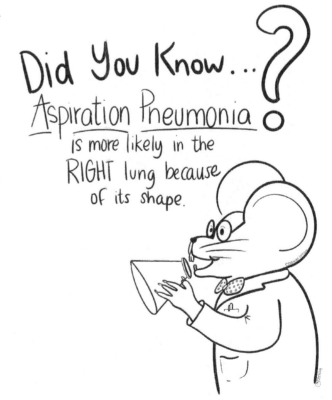

Did You Know...?
Aspiration Pneumonia is more likely in the RIGHT lung because of its shape.

VII. Bronchi and Bronchial Tree (branched airways leading from the trachea to the <u>alveoli</u>, microscopic air sacs in the interior of the lungs where O_2/CO_2 exchange occurs)

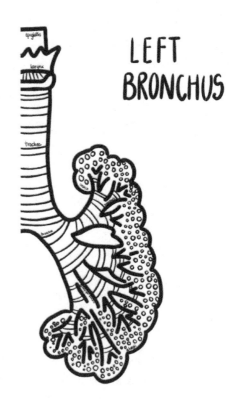

LEFT
BRONCHUS

A. <u>Primary Bronchi</u> (Right and Left)-formed where the trachea branches (near C7). (see **Figures 10-4** and **10-5**)

1. One primary bronchus extends into each lung.

2. Right primary bronchus is wider, shorter, and more vertical than the left, so it is a more common site for objects to become lodged. (see **Figure 10-4**)

B. <u>Secondary Bronchi</u> (branches inside lungs)

1. There are <u>three</u> secondary bronchi in the right lung and <u>two</u> in the left lung.

2. Secondary bronchi branch into smaller <u>tertiary bronchi</u> which further branch into smaller bronchi. There are around 23 orders of branching in the bronchi (often known as the <u>bronchial tree</u>).

Figure 10-5

C. <u>Bronchioles</u>-passageways *smaller than 1 mm*. The smallest of these are known as <u>terminal bronchioles</u> that end in tubes known as <u>alveolar ducts</u>.

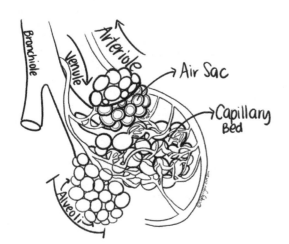

Blood Supply to Alveoli

1. <u>Alveoli</u> (microscopic air sacs at the ends of alveolar ducts)- sites of O_2/CO_2 gas exchange between the air and blood. There are about 3 million alveoli <u>per lung</u>. (see **Figure 10-6**)

2. <u>Alveolar sacs</u>-clusters of alveoli.

3. Walls of the alveoli are covered by a thin layer of simple squamous epithelial tissue (<u>Type I Cells</u>).

a. <u>Type II Cells</u>-scattered among the squamous epithelial cells, secrete <u>surfactant</u> which *reduces the surface tension* of the alveolar fluids and *prevents the walls of the alveoli from sticking together* and collapsing.

b. <u>Pulmonary capillaries</u>-cover the alveoli externally. (see **Figure 10-9**)

Figure 10-6

D. Tissue composition of the walls of the primary bronchi is similar to that of the trachea, however there are some differences:

1. Cartilage rings are replaced by smaller <u>plates</u> of cartilage. There is no cartilage in the smaller bronchioles.

2. <u>Smooth muscle</u> amounts *increase* in the walls of the smaller passageways.

VIII. Lungs and Pleura

    A. Lungs (see **Figures 10-7** and **10-8**)

        a. Main function is the process of gas exchange called respiration (breathing) in which O_2 and CO_2 are exchanged between the inhaled air and the circulating blood.

        b. Cone-shaped; each lung occupies its own <u>pleural cavity</u> but are separated from each other by the <u>mediastinum</u>.

        c. Surrounded *externally* by the ribcage and the diaphragm *inferiorly*.

        d. <u>Apex</u> (pointed tip) of the lung is just deep to the clavicle. The <u>base</u> of the lung sits on the <u>diaphragm</u>.

        e. <u>Hilum</u>-located on the medial surface where the <u>pulmonary blood vessels</u> and <u>primary bronchi</u> enter the lung.

        f. Left lung is *slightly smaller* than the right lung.

            1. <u>Left Lung</u>-has 2 lobes (upper and lower) separated by an <u>oblique fissure</u>. (see **Figure 10-8**)

            2. <u>Right Lung</u>-has 3 lobes (upper lobe, middle lobe and lower lobe). The <u>horizontal fissure</u> divides the upper and middle lobes, while the <u>oblique fissure</u> divides the middle and lower lobes. (see **Figure 10-7**)

        g. Each lobe of the lung contains several <u>bronchopulmonary segments</u> separated from each other by connective tissue walls (<u>septa</u>) and served by its own artery and vein.

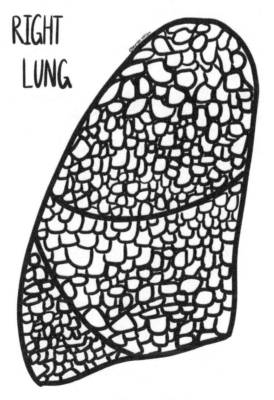

RIGHT LUNG

Figure 10-7

i. Blood supply in the lungs

    1. Pulmonary arteries-carry deoxygenated blood to the lungs, highly branched.

    2. Capillary networks-surround the alveoli, site of oxygen diffusion into the blood.

    3. Pulmonary veins-carry oxygenated blood out of the lungs and back to the heart.

j. Lungs are highly innervated with nerve fibers including sensory fibers, as well as parasympathetic (which constrict), and sympathetic motor fibers (which dilate).

B. Pleura-thin, protective, double layered serous membrane around each lung.

a. Layers that makeup the pleural membranes:

    1. Parietal pleura-covers the thoracic wall and superior portion of the diaphragm.

    2. Visceral pleura (viscera = "*organ*")-covers the external surfaces of the lungs.

b. Pleural cavity-space between these two membranes filled with pleural fluid that acts as a lubricant for breathing.

Breathing (Pulmonary Ventilation)

IX. Breathing (Pulmonary Ventilation)

A. Consists of two phases: inspiration (air flows into the lungs) and expiration (gases exit the lungs).

B. Pressures Associated with Breathing

1. Atmospheric Pressure (P_{atm})-pressure *exerted by the air* (gases) surrounding the body. At sea level, atmospheric pressure is 760 mm Hg (or 1 atm).

2. Intrapulmonary Pressure (P_{pul})-pressure in the *alveoli* that rises and falls with the phases of breathing but will always *equalize with atmospheric pressure.*

3. Intrapleural Pressure (P_{ip})-pressure in the *pleural cavity* that is always about 4 mm Hg *less* than Intrapulmonary Pressure (P_{pul}). As a result, Intrapleural Pressure (P_{ip}) is always negative relative to Intrapulmonary Pressure (P_{pul}).

a. Negative pressure is established:

    1). By natural recoil of the lungs-lungs are *elastic* so will assume the *smallest size* possible.

    2). Due to surface tension of the alveolar fluid-draws the alveoli to their *smallest size*.

b. Because of the strong adhesive force between the parietal pleura and visceral pleura, neither force dominates. Pleural fluid holds the parietal and visceral pleura together tightly so it is difficult to separate the pleura and results in a negative Intrapleural Pressure (P_{ip}).

4. Transpulmonary Pressure-difference between Intrapulmonary Pressure (P_{pul}) and Intrapleural Pressure (P_{ip}) or (P_{pul}-P_{ip}). The greater this pressure is, the larger the lungs are, so it directly prevents the lungs from collapsing.

C. <u>Pulmonary Ventilation</u>-process of <u>breathing</u> (inspiration and expiration).

1. In lungs, *volume changes* lead to *pressure changes* and pressure changes lead to a *flow of gases* in order to <u>equalize the pressure</u>.

2. <u>Boyle's Law</u>-at constant temperature, the pressure of a gas varies inversely with its volume. In other words:

$$P_1V_1=P_2V_2$$

where: P is the pressure of the gas in mm Hg
V is its volume in mm³
1 and 2 represent the initial and resulting condition

a. Gases always fill their container. So, in a large container, the molecules in a given amount of gas will be far apart so the pressure will be low. If the volume of the container is reduced, the gas molecules will be forced closer together and the pressure will rise.

b. This principle can also be applied to the <u>thoracic cavity</u>. When the *volume* of the thoracic cavity *increases*, then the gas *pressure* in the cavity *decreases*, as well as allowing air to rush into the thoracic cavity from the atmosphere.

3. <u>Inspiration</u>-air flows *into* the lungs.

a. <u>Quiet inspiration</u>-normal inspiration produced by:

1). <u>Diaphragm</u>-dome-shaped muscle that separates the thoracic cavity from the abdominopelvic cavity. During inspiration, it contracts, moves inferiorly, and flattens to increase the height (volume) and diameter of the thoracic cavity and expands the lungs.

2). Intercostal Muscle Action

a). <u>External intercostals</u> contract to lift the rib cage and pull the sternum upwards to *increase the volume* of the thorax.

b). As volume increases in the thoracic cavity, the lungs are stretched and <u>intrapulmonary volume</u> increases. As a result, <u>Intrapulmonary Pressure</u> (in the alveoli) drops below atmospheric pressure and air rushes into the lungs.

c). Inspiration ends when the pressure in the alveoli is equal to the atmospheric pressure $P_{pul}=P_{atm}$.

b. <u>Deep</u> (forced) <u>inspiration</u>-occurs during exercise when the thoracic volume is further increased by the actions of accessory muscles (including *scalene, sternocleidomastoid,* and *pectoralis*).

4. <u>Expiration</u>-air flows *out* of the lungs.

a. Passive process that depends more on lung *elasticity* than muscle contraction.

b. As the inspiratory muscles relax and return to their resting state, the rib cage descends and the lungs recoil, decreasing the thoracic and intrapulmonary volumes and compressing the alveoli.

c. Forced Expiration-active process produced by contraction of abdominal wall muscles (primarily oblique and transverse muscles) that depress the rib cage and force the internal organs against the diaphragm.

X. Respiratory Volumes and Pulmonary Function Tests

A. There are four major respiratory volumes that influence the lungs:

1. Tidal Volume (TV)-refers to the 500 mL of air that moves into and out of the lungs during *normal, quiet breathing.*

2. Inspiratory Reserve Volume (IRV)-amount of air that can be *taken in forcibly* beyond the tidal volume (2100 mL to 3200 mL).

3. Expiratory Reserve Volume (ERV)-the amount of air that can be *released* from the lungs after a tidal expiration (1000 mL to 1200 mL).

4. Residual Volume (RV)-the amount of air that *remains* in the lungs even after a strenuous expiration (about 1200 mL).

B. Major Respiratory Capacities

1. Inspiratory Capacity (IC)-*total amount of air* that can be *taken in* after a tidal expiration.

2. Functional Residual Capacity (FRC)-amount of air remaining in the lungs after a tidal expiration.

3. Vital Capacity (VC)-total amount of exchangeable air (approximately 4800 mL).

4. Total Lung Capacity (TLC)-sum of all the lung volumes (normally 6000 mL in males and slightly less in women).

C. Anatomical Dead Space-refers to air that fills respiratory passageways but *never contributes to gas exchange in the alveoli* (usually about 150 mL).

D. Pulmonary Function Tests-used to identify various pulmonary related disorders (such as obstructive pulmonary disease); measured by a spirometer.

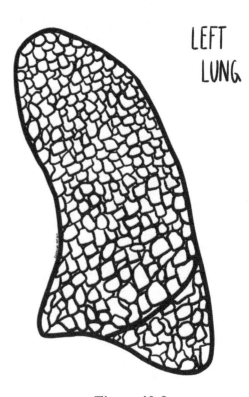

LEFT LUNG

Figure 10-8

XI. <u>Internal Respiration</u> (Capillary Gas Exchange)-movement of oxygen from blood to the tissue cells and of carbon dioxide from tissue cells to blood due to <u>simple diffusion</u> across respiratory membranes. (see **Figures 10-9** and **10-12**)

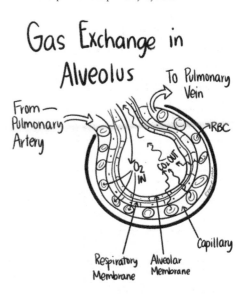

XII. Transport of Oxygen and Carbon Dioxide by the Blood

    A. Oxygen Transport

        1. Oxygen is carried in the blood in 2 ways:

            a. Attached to the <u>hemoglobin</u> within erythrocytes.

            b. Dissolved in <u>plasma</u>.

        2. <u>Hemoglobin</u> (Hb)

            a. <u>Oxyhemoglobin</u> (HbO_2)-the *combination* of oxygen and hemoglobin.   **Figure 10-9**

            b. Four oxygen molecules can attach to hemoglobin. Uptake of *oxygen* molecules *increases dramatically* after the first oxygen attaches to the hemoglobin.

    B. Carbon Dioxide Transport

        1. Normal body cells produce about 200 mL of CO_2 every minute, exactly the amount excreted by the lungs.

        2. Blood transports CO_2 from the tissue cells to the lungs in three forms:

            a. <u>Dissolved in plasma</u>-about 10% of the CO_2.

            b. <u>Chemically-bound to hemoglobin</u>-about 20% of the CO_2.

            c. <u>As bicarbonate ion in plasma</u>-about 70% of the CO_2.

XIII. Gas Exchange in Alveoli (see **Figure 10-9**)

    A. Gas exchange is the delivery of O_2 from the lungs to the bloodstream and the elimination of CO_2 from the bloodstream to the lungs.

    B. Occurs in the lungs between the alveoli (singular=alveolus) and a network of tiny blood vessels called <u>capillaries</u> located in the walls of alveoli.

    C. The walls of alveoli share a membrane with the capillaries so O_2 and CO_2 molecules move freely between the bloodstream and the Respiratory System

        1. O_2 molecules from the inhaled air attach to RBC and travel back to the heart.

        2. Simultaneously, CO_2 molecules in the alveoli are removed from the body with each exhaled breath.

XIV. Respiration Control

    A. <u>Medulla oblongata</u> (Inspiratory Center)-sends impulses to the <u>phrenic</u> and <u>intercostal nerves</u> to force the diaphragm and the intercostals muscles to <u>contract</u> expanding the thorax and allowing *air to rush into the lungs.*

B. <u>Pons Pneumotaxic Center</u> (Pontine Respiratory Group)-impulses from this location <u>inhibit</u> the inspiratory center of the medulla to *regulate the rhythm of breathing*.

Respiratory System (Figure 10-11)

Structure	Function/Description	Color
Larynx		
Trachea		
Bronchi		
Lungs		
Alveoli		
Diaphragm		
Nasal Cavity		
Oral Cavity		
Pharynx		
Bronchiole		

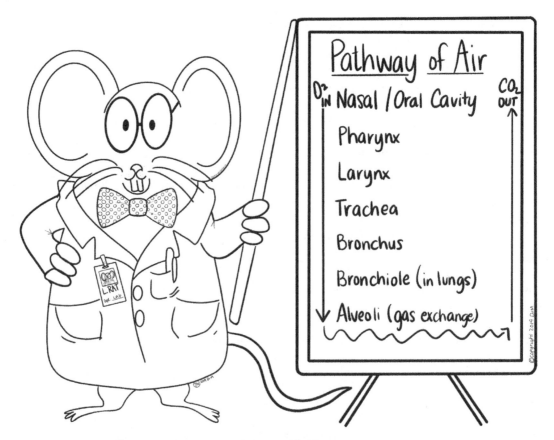

Figure 10-10

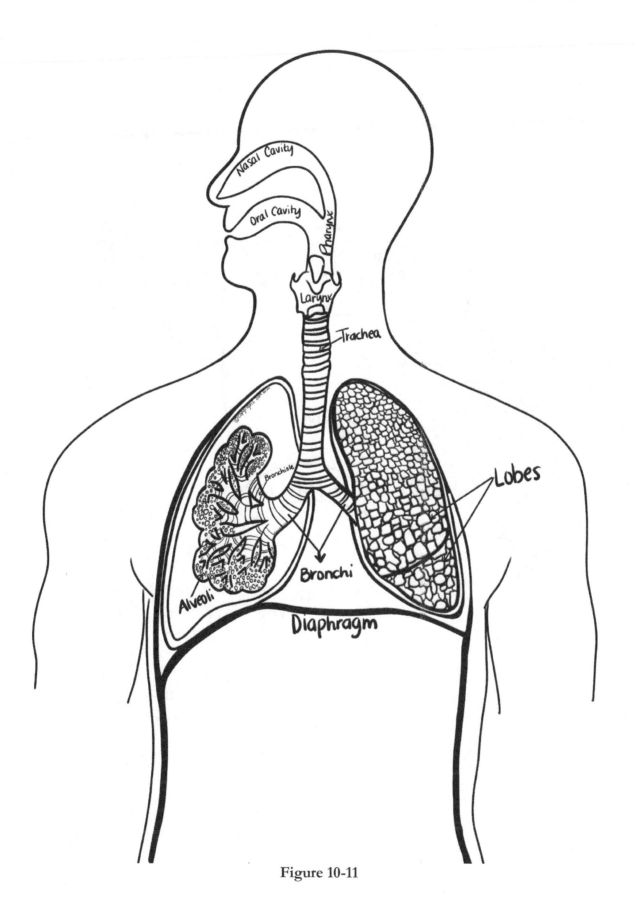

Figure 10-11

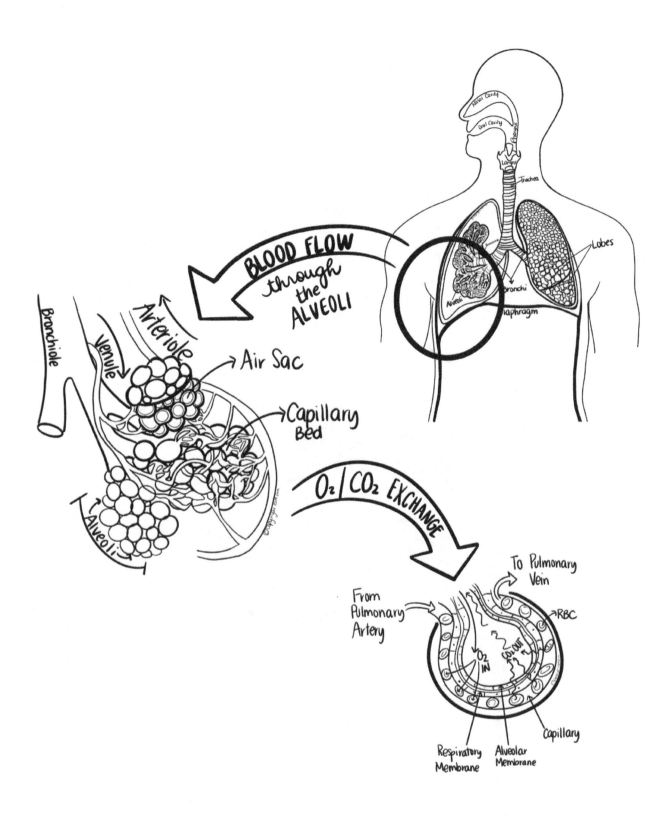

Figure 10-12

CHAPTER 11. DIGESTIVE SYSTEM

The Digestive System

I. Digestive System

A. Functions to take in food, break it down into smaller nutrients, absorb the nutrient molecules into the bloodstream, and rid the body of the indigestible remains.

B. Organs of the Digestive System are Classified into Two Groups:

1. <u>Alimentary Canal</u> (Gastrointestinal or GI Tract)

a. <u>GI Tract</u>-a continuous, muscular tube that winds through the body. Its function is to <u>break food down</u> into small fragments (nutrients) and <u>absorb</u> the fragments through its lining into the blood. Because of this, many people refer to the Digestive System as a "*disassembly line.*"

b. Major organs of the alimentary canal are the mouth, pharynx, esophagus, stomach, small intestine, and large intestine.

2. Accessory Digestive Organs

a. Provide a service to the digestive tract but are not directly located within tube that forms the alimentary canal.

b. Include: teeth, tongue, gallbladder, salivary glands, liver, and pancreas.

II. Major Digestive Processes

A. **I**ngestion-taking food into the digestive tract.

B. **P**ropulsion-*movement* of food through the alimentary canal; includes swallowing and <u>peristalsis</u> (alternate waves of contraction and relaxation of muscles in the walls of organs to squeeze food along through the Digestive System).

C. **M**echanical Digestion-*physically* prepares food for chemical digestion; includes chewing, mixing food with enzymes, churning food in the stomach and <u>segmentation</u> (rhythmic, local constrictions of the intestines). Segmentation <u>mixes</u> food with digestive juices therefore increases the rate of absorption.

D. **C**hemical Digestion-occurs as *enzymes break down food* materials into their primary components; much of this occurs in the <u>lumen</u> of the alimentary canal.

E. **A**bsorption-passage of *digested* end products along with vitamins, mineral and water, from the lumen of the GI tract into the <u>blood</u> or <u>lymph</u>.

F. **D**efecation-process through which *indigestible* wastes are *removed* from the body in the form of feces.

<u>Mnemonic to remember the major digestive processes</u>- **I** **P**lay **M**ostly **C**ards **a**nd **D**ominoes

III. General Arrangement of Organs

    A. <u>Abdominopelvic Cavity</u>-location where most of the digestive organs are located.

    B. <u>Peritoneum</u>-serous membrane that covers the abdominopelvic cavity.

        1. <u>Visceral Peritoneum</u>-membrane that covers the <u>external surfaces</u> of the digestive organs.

        2. <u>Parietal Peritoneum</u>-membrane that <u>lines the wall</u> of the abdominopelvic cavity.

        3. <u>Peritoneal Cavity</u>-space between the two serous membranes that usually contains <u>lubricating fluid</u>.

    C. <u>Mesentery</u>-double layer peritoneum that extends to the digestive organs from the body wall.

        1. Made of two sheets of <u>serous membranes</u> fused back to back.

        2. Provides routes for blood vessels, lymph vessels, and nerves to reach the digestive viscera, in addition to holding organs in place, and storing fat.

        3. <u>Intraperitoneal organs</u>-covered by and held in place by mesentery.

        4. <u>Retroperitoneal organs</u>-lose their mesentery and lie posterior to the peritoneum.

IV. <u>Splanchnic Circulation</u>-includes arteries that branch off the abdominal aorta to serve the <u>digestive organs</u> and <u>hepatic portal circulation</u>. (see **Figure 11-1**)

    A. Major arteries in this circulation include:

        1. <u>Hepatic Artery</u>-supplies blood to the liver, pylorus of the stomach, duodenum, pancreas, and gallbladder.

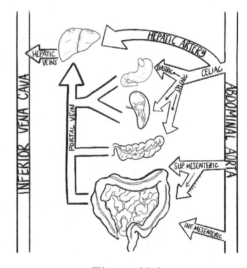

Figure 11-1

        2. <u>Splenic Artery</u>-supplies blood to the spleen, as well as several branches that deliver blood to the stomach and pancreas.

        3. <u>Left Gastric Branches of the Celiac Trunk</u>-supply blood to the stomach.

        4. <u>Superior and Inferior Mesenteric Arteries</u>-supply blood to the large intestine.

    B. <u>Hepatic Portal Circulation</u>-collects nutrient-rich <u>venous</u> blood from the digestive viscera and delivers it to the <u>liver</u> where absorbed nutrients are processed or stored before being released back to the bloodstream for cellular use.

V. Histology

    A. The walls of the alimentary canal (from the esophagus to the anus) contain the same four basic layers (or <u>tunics</u>). Each of these layers is involved in a specific function in the <u>breakdown of food</u>.

B. Basic Layers of the Alimentary Canal: (see **Figure 11-2**)

1. <u>Mucosa</u> (Mucous Membrane)-*innermost* layer; composed of moist epithelial tissue; lines the lumen from the mouth to the anus.

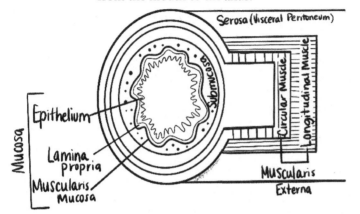

a. Functions:

1). *Secretion* of mucus, digestive enzymes, and hormones.

2). *Absorption* of the end products of digestion into the blood.

3). *Protection* against infectious disease.

Figure 11-2

b. Three Sublayers That Makeup Digestive Mucosa: (see **Figure 11-2**)

1). <u>Lining epithelium</u>-usually simple columnar epithelium with <u>goblet cells</u> which secrete mucous.

2). <u>Lamina propria</u>-loose areolar connective tissue, highly vascular.

3). <u>Muscularis mucosa</u>-smooth muscle cells that produce movement of the mucosa.

2. <u>Submucosa</u>-*external to the mucosa*; composed of <u>connective tissue</u> containing blood vessels, nerve fibers, and lymphatic vessels.

3. <u>Muscularis Externa</u>-involved in *segmentation* and *peristalsis*; composed of two layers of <u>smooth muscle</u> (inner circular layer and outer longitudinal layer). In some areas, the circular layer of smooth muscle thickens to form *sphincters* which keep food moving from one organ to the next.

4. <u>Serosa</u> (the Visceral Peritoneum)-*outermost,* protective layer around each digestive organ; formed by areolar connective tissue covered by <u>mesothelium</u> (a single layer of squamous epithelial tissue).

VI. Nervous System of the GI Tract

A. The alimentary canal has its own nerve supply produced by <u>enteric neurons</u> which communicate with each other in order to regulate the activities within the Digestive System.

B. Two major nerve plexuses found in the walls of the alimentary canal:

1. <u>Submucosal Nerve Plexus</u>-located in the <u>submucosa</u>; regulates the activity of glands and smooth muscle.

2. <u>Myenteric Nerve Plexus</u>-lies in the smooth muscle of the <u>muscularis externa</u>; regulates GI tract motility.

C. <u>Autonomic Nervous System</u> (ANS)-often regulates many of the activities of the enteric neurons in the Digestive System.

VII. **Major Digestive Organs and Structures** (see **Figures 11-13** and **11-14**)

A. <u>Mouth</u>-only structure involved in <u>ingestion</u>; walls of the mouth (oral cavity) are covered by mucosa and stratified squamous epithelium which can withstand friction and stress. The mouth is the beginning of the digestive tract and the location where digestion begins (via chewing and saliva).

Major Structures Associated with the Mouth:

1. <u>Lips and cheeks</u>-composed of a skeletal muscle core covered by skin; function is to keep food between the teeth.

2. <u>Labial frenulum</u>-fold of tissue that attaches lips to the gums.

3. <u>Palate</u>-forms the roof of the mouth.

    a. <u>Hard Palate</u>-anterior portion; supported by the palatine bones and the palatine processes of the maxillae.

    b. <u>Soft Palate</u>- posterior portion; composed of mostly skeletal muscle; rises to close off the nasopharynx when swallowing.

4. <u>Uvula</u>-projects downward from the free edge of the soft palate to hang from the roof of the mouth.

5. <u>Tongue</u>-located in the floor of the mouth; made of bundles of skeletal muscle; function is to hold and position food so it can be mixed with saliva forming a mass called a <u>bolus</u>.

6. <u>Lingual frenulum</u>-fold of mucosa that attaches the tongue to the floor of the mouth.

7. <u>Papillae</u>-cover tongue, store taste buds.

8. <u>Salivary Glands</u>-produce and secrete saliva into the oral cavity. Major extrinsic salivary glands are: (see **Figure 11-3**)

    a. <u>Parotid Gland</u>-large, located anterior to the ear between the skin and masseter muscle. Saliva is carried to the mouth via the Parotid Duct which opens near the second molar.

    b. <u>Submandibular Gland</u>-lies near the mandibular body, duct opens near the lingual frenulum.

    c. <u>Sublingual Gland</u>-located anterior to the submandibular gland, under the tongue; connects to the floor of the oral cavity via 10-12 ducts.

9. <u>Saliva</u>-slightly acidic (pH 6.75-7.00) and composed mostly of water (97-99.5%).

    a. Saliva also contains:

        1). <u>Electrolytes</u>-such as K^+ and Na^+.

        2). <u>Salivary amylase</u>-a key digestive enzyme

        3). <u>Mucin</u>-forms a lubricating mucous when dissolved in water.

        4). <u>Lysozyme</u>-enzyme that inhibits bacterial growth on the teeth.

5). <u>Defensins</u>-a natural antibiotic.

b. Functions of Saliva

1). Cleanses the mouth.

2). Dissolves food chemicals for taste.

3). Moistens food for digestion.

4). Contains various digestive enzymes.

c. Humans secrete about 1000-1500 mL of saliva per day.

d. Salivation is primarily controlled by the Autonomic Nervous System (ANS) via the <u>Glossopharyngeal nerve</u> (CNIX).

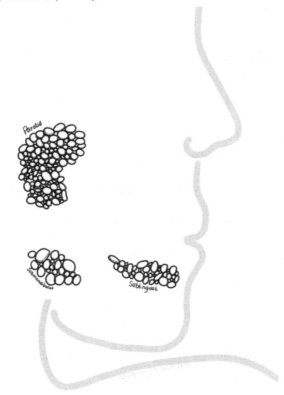

Figure 11-3

Salivary Glands (Figure 11-3)

Structure	Function/ Description	Color
Parotid		
Submandibular		
Sublingual		

10. <u>Teeth</u>-located in sockets (<u>alveoli</u>) of the mandible and maxillae; allow us to grind and tear food as we chew.

a. Humans have two sets of teeth:

1). <u>Primary Teeth</u> (baby or milk teeth)-total of 20; loosen and fall out between the ages of 6 and 12.

2). <u>Permanent Teeth</u>-typically 32 teeth are in the permanent set.

b. Tooth Structure (see **Figure 11-4**)

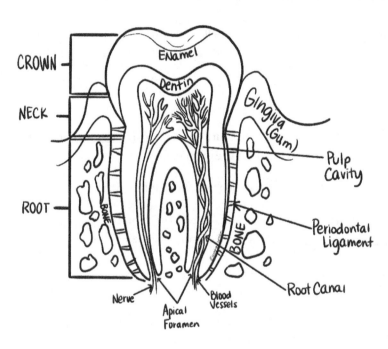

Figure 11-4

1). <u>Crown</u>-exposed portion of a tooth above the <u>gingiva</u> (gums).

2). <u>Enamel</u>-forms the outer covering of a tooth. It is the hardest compound in the body, primarily composed of mineral salts and mineral crystals. Cells that produce enamel erupt when the tooth is damaged.

3). <u>Root</u>-portion of the tooth that is embedded in the jawbone.

4). <u>Neck</u>-connects the crown and root of the tooth.

5). <u>Cementum</u>-calcified material that covers the outer surface of the root and connects the tooth to the <u>periodontal ligament</u> (anchors the tooth into the jawbone) forming a joint known as a <u>gomphosis</u>.

6). <u>Dentin</u>-bonelike material, underlies the enamel of the tooth and forms the bulk of the tooth. It surrounds a <u>pulp cavity</u> that stores blood vessels, nerves, and connective tissue (collectively referred to as <u>pulp</u>).

a). <u>Root Canal</u>-where the pulp extends into the root.

b). <u>Apical Foramen</u>-hole that allows blood vessels and nerves to enter the tooth; found at the end of each root.

c). <u>Odontoblasts</u>-cells responsible for secreting dentin.

d). Enamel, cementum, and dentin are all calcified like bone but are <u>avascular</u> (unlike bone tissue).

B. <u>Pharynx</u> (throat)-connects the oral cavity to the esophagus.

1. Food passes from the mouth into the <u>oropharynx</u> and the <u>laryngopharynx.</u>

2. Histology of the pharynx is essentially the same as the oral cavity.

C. Esophagus-a 25 cm long muscular tube that carries food materials from the laryngopharynx to the stomach; runs straight through the mediastinum of the thorax and pierces the diaphragm at the esophageal hiatus. The esophagus enters the stomach at the cardiac orifice, which is surrounded by the esophageal or cardiac sphincter. Food is pushed along through the esophagus and into the stomach with a series of muscular contractions (called peristalsis).

D. Stomach-organ where chemical breakdown of proteins begins (secretes acid and enzymes) and food is converted into a material known as chyme. The muscles of the stomach contract to churn food and increase digestion. Less than 10% of digestion and absorption of food occurs in the stomach.

Anatomy of the Stomach: (Figures 11-6 and 11-6)

1. Ranges from 15-25 cm in length and can hold up to 4L (1 gallon) of food. When empty, it collapses and folds its mucosa into rugae. It is regulated by the ANS and supplied with blood from branches of the celiac trunk.

2. Major Regions of the Stomach:

a. Cardiac Region (cardia="*near the heart*")-area that surrounds the cardiac orifice (opening where food passes as it enters the stomach from the esophagus).

b. Fundus-dome-shaped portion of the stomach, beneath the diaphragm.

c. Body-midportion of the stomach. The long, convex lateral curve on the left side of the stomach is called the greater curvature while the shorter, concave medial border of the stomach is the lesser curvature.

d. Pyloric Region-lower portion of stomach

1). Pylorus-continuous with the duodenum (first section of the small intestine).

2). Pyloric sphincter-muscular valve that separates the pylorus and the duodenum to regulate and control stomach emptying.

3. Layers of the Stomach:

a. Serosa (outermost layer of the stomach that surrounds the muscular layer)-thin serous membrane made of simple squamous epithelial tissue and areolar connective tissue; has a smooth, slippery surface and secretes thin, watery serous fluid.

b. Muscular Layers (Muscularis)-made of three layers of smooth muscle; contractions of these muscles help mix and break the contents of the stomach into a suspension of nutrients (chyme) and propels it into the duodenum. (see **Figure 11-6**)

- Longitudinal-outer muscular layer; muscle fibers run in a north/south orientation (longitudinally).
- Circular-middle muscular layer; muscle fibers encircle the stomach.
- Oblique-inner muscular layer; muscle fibers run diagonally.

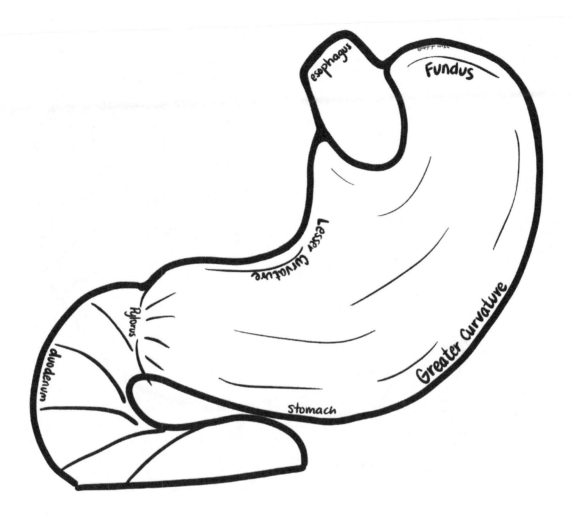

Figure 11-5

Anatomy of the Stomach (Figure 11-5)

Structure	Function/ Description	Color
Fundus		
Greater Curvature		
Lesser Curvature		
Pylorus		

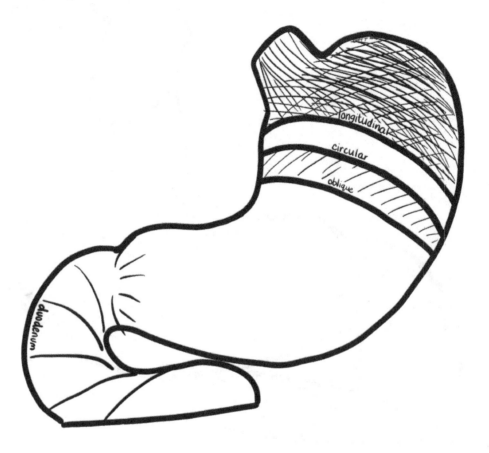

Figure 11-6

Muscular Layers of the Stomach (Figure 11-6)

Structure	Function/ Description	Color
Longitudinal Smooth Muscle		
Circular Smooth Muscle		
Oblique Smooth Muscle		

E. Small Intestine-body's major digestive organ, site where digestion is completed, and location where most absorption occurs. The main function of the small intestine is the absorption of nutrients and minerals from food (90% occurs here).

    1. Anatomy of the Small Intestine (**Figure 11-7**)

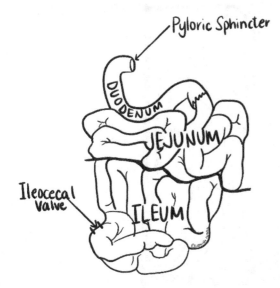

Figure 11-7

        a. Extends from the pyloric sphincter to the ileocecal valve at the large intestine.

        b. Longest organ in the alimentary canal (about 20 feet long).

        c. Subdivisions:

            1). Duodenum-beginning section of small intestine, just after the stomach; immovable, retroperitoneal region of the small intestine that curves around the pancreas; site where the bile duct and pancreatic duct meet to empty their secretions.

            2). Jejunum-2nd part of the small intestine (about 8 ft.); extends from the duodenum to the ileum.

            3). Ileum-last part of the small intestine (about 12 ft.); attaches to the large intestine at the ileocecal valve.

    4. Vagus and Splanchnic Nerves are the major nerve connections to the small intestine.

    5. Microscopic Anatomy of the Small Intestine: (see **Figure 11-8**)

        a. Highly adapted for nutrient absorption due to the length of the small intestine, as well as structural modifications including circular folds, villi, and microvilli which greatly increase the surface area of the organ.

        b. Contains the typical 4 layers of the GI Tract although the mucosa and submucosa are modified for the digestive and absorptive functions.

            1). Mucosa-composed of columnar epithelial cells that are highly adapted for absorption of nutrients. Goblet cells, enteroendocrine cells, and T cells are also abundant in the mucosa of the small intestine. Located just under the mucosal epithelium is the lamina propria (or lamina propria mucosa), which consists of loose connective tissue that fills the spaces between the intestinal glands and forms the cores of the intestinal villi.

            2). Submucosa-composed of areolar connective tissue and contains lymphoid follicles. The aggregated lymphoid follicles are referred to as Peyer's Patches and serve as an important part of the immune system by monitoring intestinal bacteria populations and preventing the growth of pathogenic bacteria.

        c. Villi-small, finger-like projections that extend into the lumen of the small intestine and increase the internal surface area of the intestinal walls, making a greater surface area available for absorption. Each villus is served by an <u>artery</u> (that brings oxygenated blood from the heart) and a <u>vein</u> (that returns deoxygenated blood back to the heart) in order to aid in the absorption of nutrients into the blood stream.

Figure 11-8

Villi of the Small Intestine (Figure 11-8)

Structure	Function	Color
Villi		
Artery		
Vein		
Lamina Propria		
Peyer's Patches		

F. Liver (Accessory Organ)-**Figure 11-9**

1. Main function is to process the nutrients absorbed from the small intestine as well as being responsible for producing the fat emulsifier <u>bile</u>.

2. Largest gland in the body (weighs 1.4kg or 3 Lbs.).

3. Located under the diaphragm so is somewhat protected by the ribcage.

4. Major Lobes of the Liver:

   a. <u>Right Lobe</u>-largest lobe of the liver. It is sub-divided into the right lobe proper, the caudate lobe, and the quadrate lobe.

      1). <u>Caudate Lobe</u>-most posterior of the lobes.

      2). <u>Quadrate Lobe</u>-inferior to the left lobe.

   b. <u>Left Lobe</u>-smaller lobe; separated from the right lobe by a deep fissure.

5. <u>Falciform Ligament</u>-mesentery that separates the right and left lobes of the liver and suspends the liver from the diaphragm and abdominal wall.

6. Bile leaves the liver via several ducts that fuse to form the <u>Common Hepatic Duct</u>. This duct fuses with the <u>Cystic Duct,</u> which drains the gallbladder of bile and forms the <u>Common Bile Duct</u>. (see **Figure 11-10**)

7. <u>Bile</u>-yellow-green solution that contains salts, pigments, cholesterol, fats, phospholipids, and electrolytes. Bile salts and phospholipids are involved in the digestive process, the rest are waste products; humans secrete 500-1000mL of bile daily.

8. <u>Bilirubin</u>-primary pigment in bile that is a waste product of the heme portion of hemoglobin. Bilirubin is actually a breakdown product of erythrocytes (RBC).

Did You Know...?
Cirrhosis of the Liver

- Liver scar tissue gradually replaces healthy liver cells.
- Caused by conditions such as hepatitis and chronic alcoholism.
- Advanced scarring (fibrosis) makes it difficult for the liver to function properly.

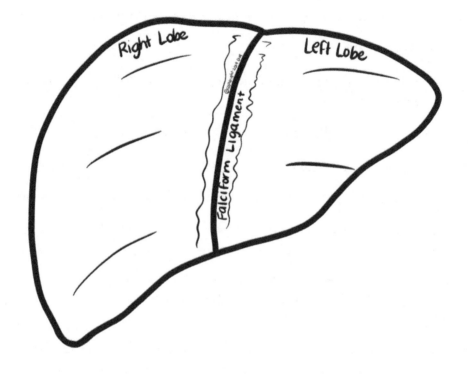

Figure 11-9

Liver (Figure 11-9)

Structure	Function/ Description	Color
Right Lobe		
Left Lobe		
Falciform Ligament		

G. Gallbladder (Accessory Organ)-see **Figure 11-11**

1. Green, thin-walled hollow organ located in a shallow fossa on the ventral surface of the liver on the right side of the abdomen; roughly the size of a kiwi fruit.

2. Stores (and concentrating) bile not immediately needed for digestion or absorption so it is considered an accessory organ for the Digestive System. Bile leaving the gallbladder is 10X more concentrated than the bile entering the gallbladder.

3. Bile is forced out of the gallbladder via the Cystic Duct and then flows into the Common Bile Duct. (see **Figure 11-10**)

H. Pancreas (Accessory Organ)-see **Figure 11-11**

1. Extends from the stomach to the small intestine and encircled by the duodenum.

2. Produces enzymes that breakdown all the major organic molecules found in food so is considered an accessory organ. These enzymes are delivered to the duodenum via the main Pancreatic Duct. (see **Figure 11-10**)

3. Islets of Langerhans (Pancreatic Islets)-small Endocrine glands that release insulin, glucagon, and carbohydrate-digesting hormones.

I. Bile Duct System-the Common Hepatic Duct from the liver and the Cystic Duct from the gallbladder join to form the Common Bile Duct. The Cystic Duct connects the gallbladder (where bile is stored) to the Common Bile Duct which passes through the pancreas before it empties into the duodenum (first part of the small intestine). (see **Figure 11-10**)

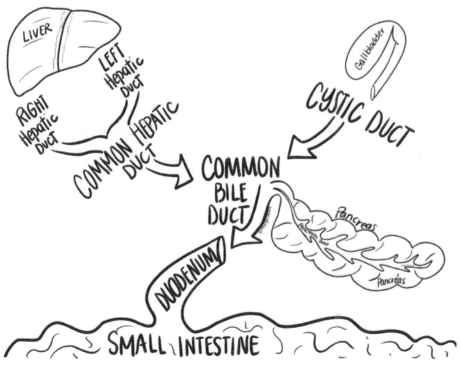

Figure 11-10

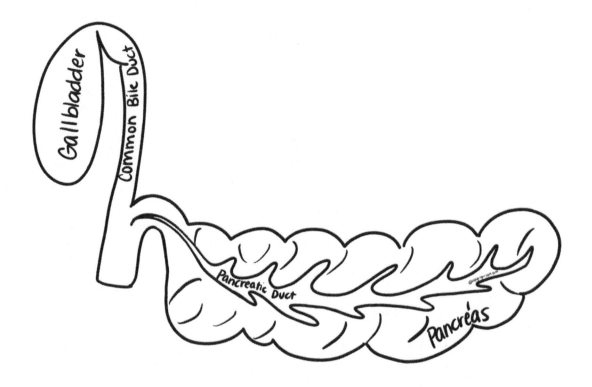

Figure 11-11

Gallbladder and Pancreas (Figure 11-11)

Structure	Function	Color
Gallbladder		
Common Bile Duct		
Pancreas		
Pancreatic Duct		

I. Large Intestine (**Figure 11-12**)

1. Frames and surrounds the small intestine on three sides and extends from the ileocecal valve to the anus. It is about 7cm in diameter and approximately 1.5m long.

2. Functions include absorbing the last amounts of water from indigestible food, as well as storing and removing the waste materials generated as food is broken down in the digestive process (feces).

3. Major Subdivisions:

    a. Cecum-first part of the large intestine, saclike structure that lies below the ileocecal valve in the right iliac fossa.

    b. Vermiform Appendix-mass of lymphoid tissue attached to the surface of the large intestine on the lower right side.

    c. Colon-major regions are named according to the direction through which food travels; includes the ascending, transverse, descending, and sigmoid colon. The sigmoid colon is shaped like an "S" and terminates at the rectum (chamber that connects to the anus and temporarily stores waste).

4. Anal Canal-last portion of the large intestine that opens to the exterior of the body via the anus (exit point for wastes from the digestive tract).

Two Sphincters in the Anal Canal:

    a. Internal Anal Sphincter-composed of smooth muscle, is involuntary.

    b. External Anal Sphincter-composed of skeletal muscle, is voluntary. Both muscles function to open and close the anus. They are ordinarily closed except during defecation.

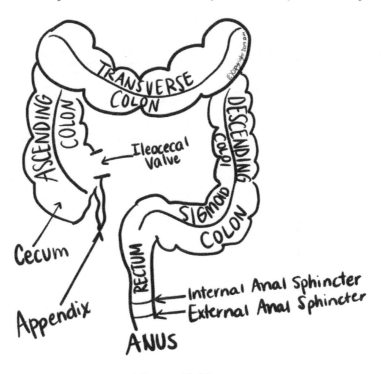

Figure 11-12

Digestive System (Figure 11-13)

Structure	Function	Color
Mouth		
Esophagus		
Stomach		
Liver		
Gallbladder		
Pancreas		
Small Intestine		
Duodenum		
Appendix		
Parotid Salivary Gland		
Sublingual Salivary Gland		
Submandibular Salivary Gland		
Cystic Duct		
Ascending Colon		
Transverse Colon		
Descending Colon		
Sigmoid Colon		
Rectum		
Anus		

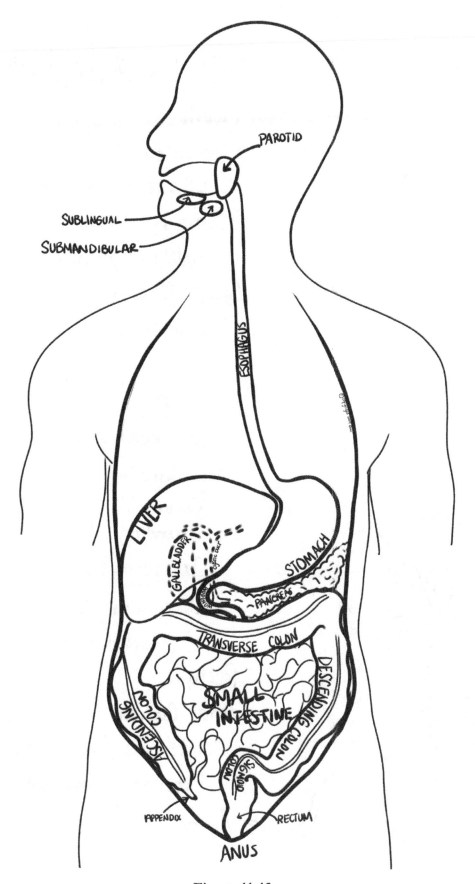

Figure 11-13

Pathway of Food (Digestion)

Mouth

Esophagus

    Lower Esophageal Sphincter (LES)

Stomach

    Pyloric Sphincter

Small Intestine

    Duodenum

    Jejunum

    Ileum

    Ileocecal Valve

Large Intestine

    Cecum

    Ascending Colon

    Transverse Colon

    Descending Colon

    Sigmoid Colon

Rectum

Anal Canal

    Internal Anal Sphincter

    External Anal Sphincter

Anus

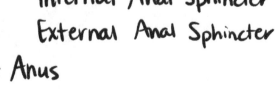

Figure 11-14

278

CHAPTER 12. URINARY SYSTEM

The Urinary System

I. Urinary System (see **Figure 12-1**)

    A. Includes the <u>kidneys</u>, <u>ureters</u>, <u>urethra</u>, and <u>urinary bladder</u>.

    B. <u>Kidneys</u>-primary excretory organs in the human body that removes toxins while returning necessary compounds back to body. Kidneys filter approximately 200 L of fluid every day

    C. Primary Functions of the Urinary System:

        1. <u>Filtering wastes</u> from the blood and removing the wastes from the body via urine.

        2. Forming glucose during times of fasting (<u>Glucogenesis</u>).

        3. Producing the enzyme <u>renin</u> which regulates blood pressure as well as proper kidney functioning.

        4. Producing the hormone <u>erythropoietin</u> which regulates and stimulates red blood cell production.

        5. Metabolizing <u>Vitamin D</u> to its active form.

    D. <u>Ureters</u>-muscular tubes that pushes urine from the kidneys to the urinary bladder.

    E. <u>Urinary Bladder</u>-collapsible muscular sac in the pelvis that temporarily stores urine; located just above and behind the pubic bone.

        1. Interior of the bladder has openings for both ureters and the urethra. The region of the bladder outlined by the three openings is known as the <u>trigone</u>.

        2. When empty, the bladder has a triangular shape and expands as urine accumulates. Maximum capacity of the bladder is approximately 1000mL (2 pints).

    F. <u>Urethra</u>-thin muscular tube that drains urine from the urinary bladder, out of the body.

    G. <u>Micturition</u>-act of emptying the bladder (aka voiding or urination).

        1. Accumulation of about 200 mL of urine in the bladder causes impulses to be transmitted to the brain creating the urge to void.

        2. Involuntary voiding occurs when urine volume exceeds 500-600 mL. About 10 mL of urine remains in the bladder after micturition.

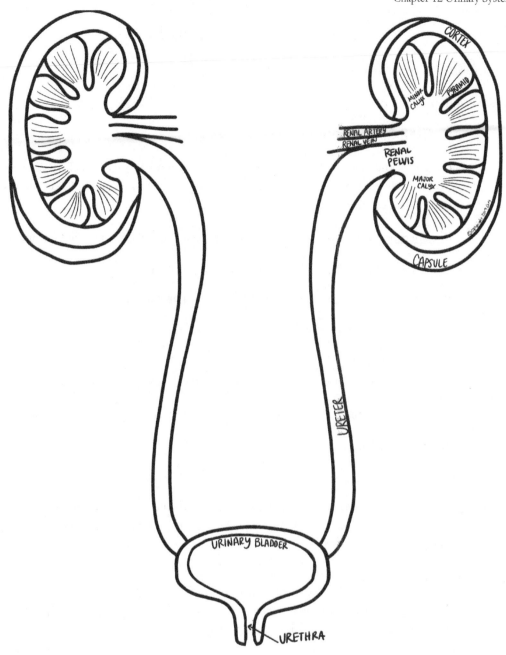

Figure 12-1

The Urinary System (Figure 12-1)

Structure	Function	Color
Kidney		
Ureter		
Urinary Bladder		
Urethra		

External Anatomy of the Kidney

II. External Anatomy of the Kidney (see **Figure 12-3**)

    A. Description:

        1. Bean-shaped.

        2. Located at the back of the abdominal cavity in the lumbar region of the body with one kidney on each side of the spine. The right kidney is generally slightly smaller and lower than the left to accommodate the liver.

        3. <u>Retroperitoneal</u> (located between the dorsal body wall and the parietal peritoneum).

        4. Each kidney weighs 125–170g in males and 115–155g in females.

        5. Surrounded by a tough, fibrous <u>renal capsule</u> and protected by two layers of fat.

        6. Although a single <u>adrenal gland</u> is located on top of each kidney, it exerts essentially no influence on the kidney itself.

        7. Helps the body pass waste as urine and filter blood before sending it back to the heart.

        8. Plays a role in maintaining the balance of body fluids and regulating blood pressure.

        9. Receives 20–25 percent of the heart's output, despite being relatively a small organ.

        10. Receives over a liter of blood each minute and eliminates around 1.5 liters of urine per day.

    B. <u>Renal hilum</u>-small opening on the inner (medial) surface of the kidney located where it curves inward to create its bean shape. It leads into an internal space known as the <u>renal sinus</u> where the <u>ureter</u>, the <u>renal blood vessels</u>, <u>lymphatics</u>, and <u>nerves</u> join.

    C. Support tissue surrounding each kidney:

        1. <u>Renal Capsule</u>-tough, fibrous outer covering of the kidney that <u>prevents infections</u> in surrounding regions from spreading to the kidney.

        2. <u>Fat Capsule</u>-thick layer of adipose tissue that attaches the kidney to the posterior body wall and cushions it against blows.

        3. <u>Renal Fascia</u>-outer layer of fibrous connective tissue that *anchors* the kidney and adrenal glands to surrounding tissues.

Internal Anatomy of the Kidney

III. Internal Anatomy of the Kidney (see **Figures 12-2** and **12-3**)

A. Renal Cortex-outer, superficial part of the kidney located between the renal capsule and the renal medulla; contains the glomerulus and convoluted tubules.

B. Renal Medulla-smooth, inner tissue of the kidney that contains the loop of Henle as well as renal pyramids.

1. The base of each pyramid faces *towards the cortex* and the apex (papilla) points *internally*.

2. Renal Pyramids-consist of six to eight cone-shaped bundles of microscopic urine-collecting tubules that transport urine from the outer part of the kidney (where urine is produced) to the calyces (cup-shaped cavities) where urine collects before it passes through the ureter to the bladder. Renal columns separate the pyramids from each other.

3. Each pyramid and its surrounding tissue makes up one of eight lobes of a kidney.

C. Renal Pelvis-*funnel-shaped* tube that is continuous with the ureter leaving the hilum.

1. Major Calyces (singular=*calyx*)-2 to 3 branching extensions of the renal pelvis, each of which subdivides to form several minor calyces. These major calyces funnel urine through the renal pelvis into the ureter.

2. Minor Calyces-cup-shaped cavities that surround the apex of the renal pyramids. Urine formed in the kidney passes through a renal papilla at the apex into the minor calyx.

a. Calyces collect urine that drains from the papillae and empty it into the renal pelvis. The urine then flows through the renal pelvis and into the ureter, and finally into the bladder where it is stored.

b. Smooth muscle lines the walls of the calyces, pelvis, and ureter and pushes urine through these areas via peristalsis.

Anatomy of the Kidney (Figure 12-3)

Structure	Function/Description	Color
Ureter		
Renal Capsule		
Renal Cortex		
Renal Pyramids		
Minor Calyx		
Major Calyx		
Renal Pelvis		
Renal Medulla		

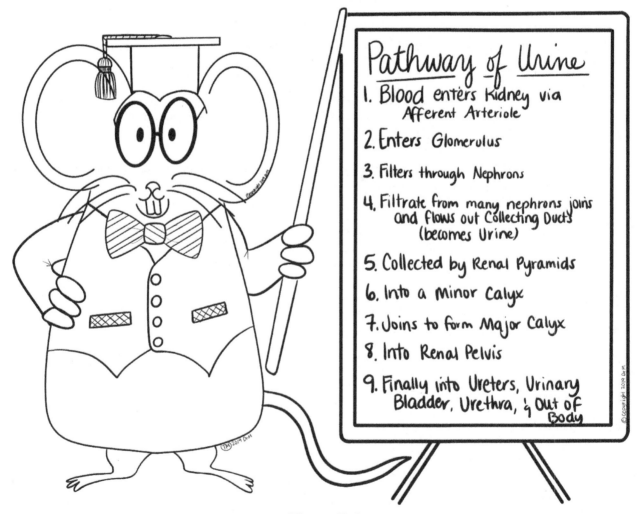

Figure 12-2

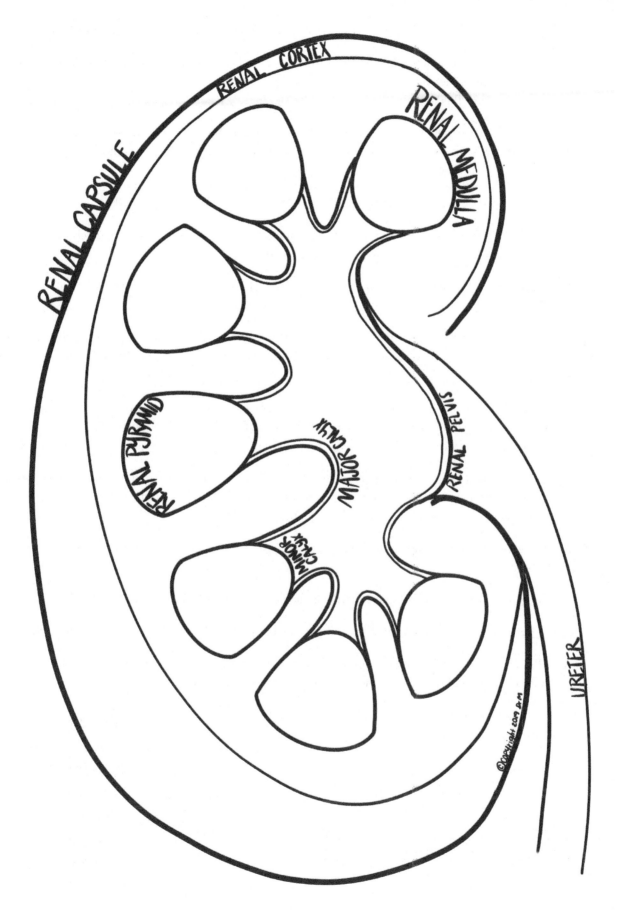

RENAL CORTEX

RENAL CAPSULE

RENAL MEDULLA

RENAL PYRAMID

MAJOR CALYX

MINOR CALYX

RENAL PELVIS

URETER

©COPYRIGHT 2019 D.M.

IV. **Functions of the Kidney**

A. <u>Renin-Angiotensin System</u>-for blood pressure control and electrolyte balance-(see **Figure 12-4**)

1. When blood volume or Na^+ levels are low, or when blood K^+ level is high, the kidney releases the enzyme renin which helps manage the expansion of arteries and the volume of blood plasma, lymph, and interstitial fluid.

2. Renin converts angiotensin (produced by the liver) into the hormone angiotensin I. A second enzyme in the lungs converts angiotensin I into angiotensin II which signals the adrenal glands to release the hormone aldosterone.

3. Aldosterone causes the kidney tubules to retain Na^+ and H_2O and excrete K^+.

4. These hormones work together to increase blood volume, pressure, and Na^+ levels in the blood until the balance of Na^+, K^+, and fluids is restored.

B. <u>Vitamin D Activation</u>-make Vitamin D from foods/sunlight useful to the body; for bone health. (see **Figure 7-7**, p.181)

1. Vitamin D balances calcium and phosphorus in the body by controlling the absorption of these minerals from food and regulating the secretion of Parathyroid Hormone (PTH) by the Parathyroid Glands.

2. If blood calcium levels are low, the Parathyroid Glands can overcompensate by signaling a decrease in kidney function and pulling calcium out of the bones and depositing it into the bloodstream. Excess PTH causes <u>hyperparathyroidism</u> which causes weak bones and bone pain.

3. Produces <u>calcitriol</u>, a hormonally active metabolite of Vitamin D that increases both the amount of calcium the intestines can absorb and the reabsorption of phosphate in the kidney. This helps maintain calcium and phosphorous levels in the blood.

C. Maintains overall fluid balance of the body (<u>homeostasis</u>) by controlling the amount of water excreted from the body.

D. <u>Erythropoiesis</u>-produces the hormone erythropoietin which controls the production of red blood cells.

E. <u>Toxin Removal</u>-filters waste materials from food, medications, and other toxic substances from the blood.

F. Acid-Base Balance-works with the lungs to adjust the pH slowly by altering the excretion of H^+ ions (acidic) into the urine and reabsorbing bicarbonate (basic) from the urine.

1. Acidosis-blood is too acidic; alkalosis-blood is too alkaline (basic).

2. Respiratory acidosis/alkalosis is due to problems with the lungs. Metabolic acidosis/alkalosis is due to problems with the kidneys.

G. An easy way to remember the functions of the kidney is with the mnemonic: <u>BED WETA</u>.

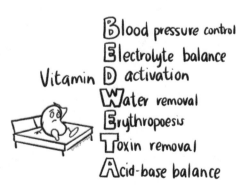

Blood pressure control
Electrolyte balance
Vitamin D activation
Water removal
Erythropoesis
Toxin removal
Acid-base balance

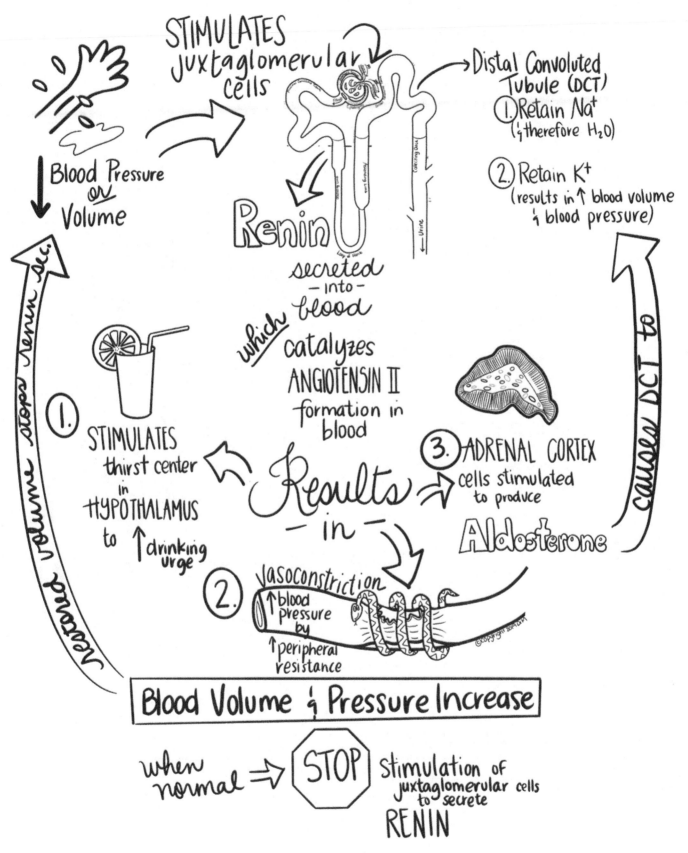

STIMULATES juxtaglomerular cells

Distal Convoluted Tubule (DCT)
1. Retain Na⁺ (& therefore H_2O)
2. Retain K⁺ (results in ↑ blood volume & blood pressure)

↓ Blood Pressure or Volume

Renin secreted — into — blood which catalyzes ANGIOTENSIN II formation in blood

Results — in —

retained volume stops renin sec.

1. STIMULATES thirst center in HYPOTHALAMUS to ↑ drinking urge

3. ADRENAL CORTEX cells stimulated to produce Aldosterone

causes DCT to

2. vasoconstriction ↑ blood pressure by ↑ peripheral resistance

©copyright 2014DM

Blood Volume & Pressure Increase

when normal → STOP stimulation of juxtaglomerular cells to secrete RENIN

Figure 12-4

V. Blood and Nerve Supply to Kidney (see **Figure 12-5**)

A. Kidneys have a huge blood supply via the <u>renal arteries</u> which carries one fourth of the total cardiac output to the kidneys (1200 mL) every minute. Renal arteries branch directly off the Abdominal Aorta.

1. <u>Renal arteries</u> branch into smaller arteries as they reach the kidney: <u>segmental arteries</u> (to the renal sinus), <u>interlobar arteries</u> (supply renal lobes), <u>arcuate arteries</u> (to the base of the renal pyramids and feed into the afferent arterioles which supply the glomeruli), <u>cortical radiate arteries</u> (to the renal cortex).

2. <u>Afferent arteriole</u>-brings *oxygenated* blood into the glomerulus under high pressure. Approximately 1/5 of the fluid that enters will become filtrate and travel into Bowman's space within the Bowman's Capsule which surrounds the glomerulus.

3. <u>Efferent arteriole</u>-how remaining blood leaves the glomerulus. It is still an artery so the blood which leaves the glomerulus is *oxygenated* and remains under high pressure.

4. <u>Renal veins</u> branch off the Inferior Vena Cava and drain the oxygen-depleted blood from the kidneys and ureters.

B. Much of the nervous innervation is provided by the <u>renal Plexus</u>, a network of autonomic nerve fibers that supply the kidney and ureter.

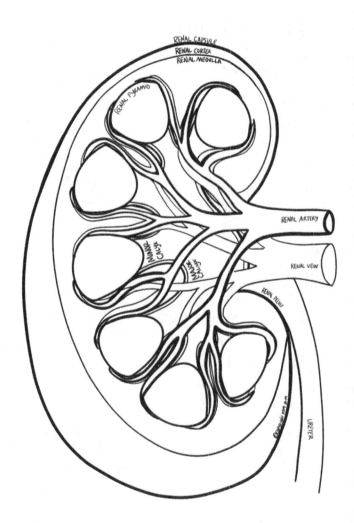

Figure 12-5

Blood Supply to the Kidney (Figure 12-5)

Structure	Function/Description	Color
Renal Artery		
Renal Vein		

Nephron

VI. <u>Nephron</u>-the structural and functional unit of the kidney responsible for cleansing the blood to produce urine. There are over 1 million of these structures in each kidney. (see **Figure 12-6**)

    A. Each nephron consists of:

        1. <u>Glomerulus</u>-high pressure capillary bed.

        2. <u>Renal Tubule</u>-specialized network of ducts.

            a. <u>Afferent Arteriole</u>-feeds the glomerulus where blood is filtered in order to produce a fluid (called <u>filtrate</u>) that is caught by the nephron tubule.

            b. <u>Efferent Arteriole</u>-means by which remaining blood leaves glomerulus; still an artery so blood is oxygenated and remains under high pressure.

            c. <u>Bowman's Capsule</u>-proximal end of the tubule that surrounds the glomerulus and catches the filtered fluid; found in the renal cortex.

            d. <u>Renal Corpuscle</u>-formed by glomerulus and glomerular capsule.

            e. Filtered fluid caught by the glomerular capsule (filtrate) travels through the rest of the tubule to the <u>proximal convoluted tubule</u> (PCT), then to the <u>loop of Henle</u>, and finally to the <u>distal convoluted tubule</u> (DCT) before exiting the nephron into common <u>collecting ducts</u> shared by many nephrons.

B. <u>Glomerular Capillaries</u>-are <u>fenestrated</u> (contain many pores) so large amounts of solute-rich materials can pass from the blood into the <u>glomerular capsule</u> forming material known as <u>filtrate</u> which will be further processed by renal tubules to form <u>urine</u>.

C. <u>Glomerular Capsule</u>-external layer made of simple squamous epithelial tissue. The inner visceral layer (which attaches to the glomerular capillaries) contains <u>podocytes</u> (cells that cling to the glomerulus to form filtration slits where filtrate enters the capsular space).

D. <u>Glomerular Filtration</u>-first step in making urine; occurs as kidneys filter excess fluid and waste products out of the blood into the urine collecting tubules of the kidney to be eliminated from the body.

E. <u>Collecting Ducts</u>-*receive filtrate* from many nephrons and fuse to form the large <u>papillary ducts</u> that deliver urine into the <u>minor calyces</u> via <u>papillae of the pyramids</u>; run through the medullary pyramids and give them their striped appearance. Dips into the renal medulla. Filtrate becomes urine at this point.

F. <u>Proximal Convoluted Tubule</u> (PCT)-walls are covered by cuboidal epithelial cells with microvilli to increase surface area for reabsorbing water and solutes from the filtrate; very little water is removed from this part of the nephron. Found in renal cortex, enters renal medulla at opposite end.

G. <u>Distal Convoluted Tubule</u> (DCT)-site of final step of reabsorption; Found close enough to Bowman's Capsule for further reabsorption of Ca^+, Na^+, and more H_2O to occur. Walls are also covered by cuboidal epithelial cells, but microvilli are less abundant in this region.

H. <u>Juxtaglomerular Apparatus</u> (JGA)-location where the DCT lies against the afferent arteriole. Cells in this arteriole store and secrete <u>renin</u> and monitor blood pressure.

I. Loop of Henle

1. <u>Descending Limb</u>-part of the loop permeable only to H_2O so water leaves filtrate via passive osmosis.

2. <u>Ascending Limb</u>-part of loop that helps make medulla hypertonic (salty) by actively pumping salts (Na^+ and K^+) out of the filtrate into the medulla. This part of the loop is not permeable to H_2O at all.

The Nephron (Figure 12-6)

Structure	Function/Description	Color
Bowman's Capsule		
Glomerulus		
Podocytes		
Afferent Arteriole		
Efferent Arteriole		
Proximal Convoluted Tubule		
Descending Limb of Loop of Henle		
Ascending Limb of Loop of Henle		
Distal Convoluted Tubule		
Collecting Duct		

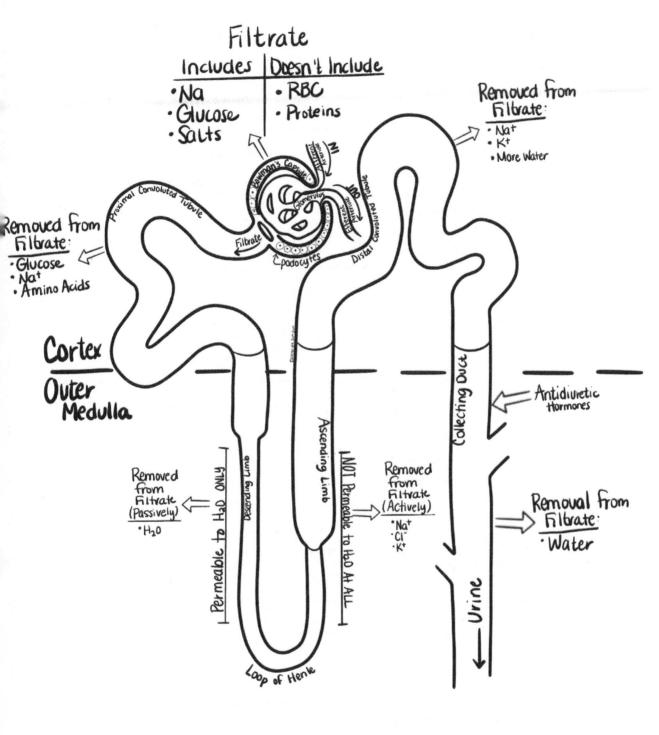

Figure 12-6

VII. **Physiology of the Kidney**

A. Kidneys filter the volume of blood plasma more than 60 times each day and require 20-25% of all oxygen used by the body at rest.

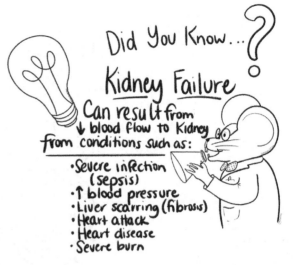

B. Filtrate vs. Urine

   1. Filtrate-contains everything found in blood plasma (including Na^+, glucose, salts) *except for red blood cells and proteins*. It is known as urine after it moves into the collecting ducts because it has lost most of its water, ions, and nutrients.

   2. Urine-contains metabolic wastes and unneeded compounds.

C. Processes Involved in Urine Formation (see **Figure 12-8**)

   1. Filtration (glomerular filtration)-occurs via the glomerulus. (plural=*glomeruli*)

      a. Occurs as blood passes into the glomerulus producing a plasma-like filtrate (minus proteins) which is captured by the Bowman's capsule and funneled into the renal tubule.

      b. Passive process in which hydrostatic pressure forces fluids and solute through a membrane; extremely efficient.

      c. Small molecules (water, glucose, nitrogen wastes) can pass from the blood into the renal tubule. Larger molecules remain to maintain vessel pressures to prevent the complete loss of water from the capillaries.

      d. Glomerular Filtration Rate (GFR)-volume of filtrate formed each minute by the activity of all 2 million glomeruli of the kidneys; measure of overall renal functions. In adults, the GFR is 120-125mL/min.

   2. Reabsorption (tubular reabsorption)-occurs in the renal tubules.

      a. Occurs as the filtrate travels along the length of the Proximal Convoluted Tubules (PCT) and the cells lining the tubule take substances from the filtrate and move them *out* of the tubule *into* the blood.

      b. Includes important molecules such as water, sodium, chloride, and bicarbonate (along with many others). Most organic nutrients (including glucose, amino acids) are reabsorbed into the plasma; water and ion absorption is often regulated by hormones.

      c. Those important molecules would be lost in the urine if not reclaimed by the tubule cells. These cells are so efficient that they can reclaim all the glucose and amino acids and about 80% of the water and important ions lost due to glomerular filtration. The filtrate that is not reabsorbed becomes urine at the base of the collecting duct.

      d. Can be passive (no ATP required) or active (requires ATP) process.

1). <u>Sodium reabsorption</u>-almost always an <u>active</u> process. Sodium ions enter tubule cells from the filtrate and are pumped via a Sodium-Potassium Pump out of the tubule cells before being swept into the peritubular capillaries by the bulk flow of water.

2). <u>Water, nutrient and ion reabsorption</u>-typically occurs via <u>passive</u> processes such as diffusion, osmosis, and facilitated diffusion via <u>aquaporins</u> (channels located at certain areas along the PCT).

e. Differs with Region of Tubule

1). The entire renal tubule is involved in reabsorption, however, the <u>PCT cells are the most active absorbers</u>.

2). <u>Loop of Henle</u>-follows the general rule that *water exits the descending limb* but not the ascending limb and the *opposite is true for solutes.*

3). <u>Distal Convoluted Tubule and Collecting Ducts</u>-reabsorption in these regions is regulated by hormones (aldosterone for sodium reabsorption and PTH for calcium reabsorption).

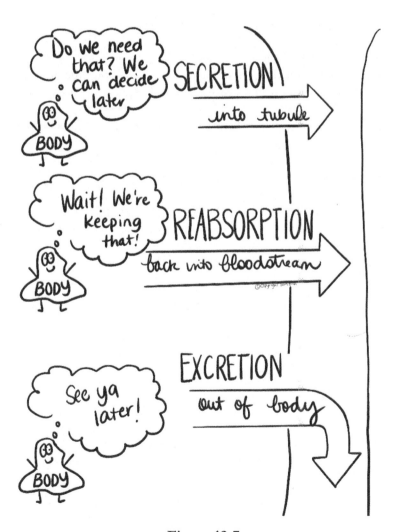

Figure 12-7

3. Secretion (tubular secretion)-occurs mostly in the Proximal Convoluted Tubule (PCT) and Distal Convoluted Tubule (DCT).

   a. Removes substances from the blood that are too large to be filtered (ex: creatinine, drugs, antibiotics, toxins) or those that are in excess in the blood (ex: H^+, K^+). These substances secreted into the tubule leave the body as components of urine.

   b. Important because it:

      1). Disposes of substances not easily filtered from the blood including certain drugs and substances that are tightly attached to plasma proteins.

      2). Eliminates toxic compounds that have been reabsorbed by passive processes (including urea and uric acid).

      3). Removes excess potassium ions from the body.

      4). Regulates blood pH by secreting additional hydrogen ions into the filtrate and retaining bicarbonate by the renal tubules when the blood pH becomes acidic.

VIII. Characteristics of Urine

   A. Color and Transparency-ranges in color from clear to deep yellow.

   B. Odor-may have a slight smell. If allowed to stand, it will begin to develop an ammonia smell as bacteria metabolize urea in the urine. Some drugs, foods and illnesses may alter the odor of urine. For example, the urine of an individual with diabetes mellitus may smell fruity because of its acetone content.

   C. pH-is slightly acidic. Changes in urine pH may indicate a variety of issues including, bacterial infection, an extreme protein diet, a vegetarian diet.

   D. Specific Gravity (mass of a substance to the mass of an equal volume of water)-urine has a fairly high specific gravity.

   E. Chemical Composition-about 95% of the volume of urine is water, the other 5% is made up of urea and nitrogenous wastes (uric acid and creatinine).

IX. Steps in Urine Formation (see **Figures 12-2** and **12-8**)

    A. Bowman's Capsule and Glomerulus

- Found in the <u>renal cortex</u>.
- <u>Filters blood</u> and <u>forms the filtrate</u> which will enter the <u>nephron</u> for further processing and become urine.

    B. <u>Proximal Convoluted Tubule</u> (PCT)-(proximal=*"nearest"* to Bowman's Capsule)

- Found in the <u>renal cortex</u> (1st part after Bowman's Capsule) and enters <u>renal medulla</u> at opposite end.
- In close contact with <u>capillaries</u> so substances (such as glucose, Na, and amino acids) can be *actively removed* from the filtrate and reabsorbed into the bloodstream.
- Very little H_2O (water) is removed in this part of the nephron.

    C. <u>Loop of Henle</u>-dips into the <u>renal medulla</u>

        1. <u>Descending Loop of Henle</u>-(descending=*"down"*); permeable to <u>H_2O ONLY</u> so water leaves the filtrate via <u>passive</u> means (<u>osmosis</u>).

        2. <u>Ascending Loop of Henle</u>-(ascending= *"up"*); NOT permeable to <u>H_2O</u> at all.

- Helps make the medulla a *hypertonic* (salty) environment by <u>actively pumping</u> salts (Na^+, K^+, Cl^-) out of the filtrate into the medulla.
- The hypertonic environment created by the Ascending Loop makes *passive* movement of H_2O into the Descending Loop possible via <u>osmosis</u>.

    D. <u>Distal Convoluted Tubule</u> (DCT)-(distal=*"far away"* from Bowman's Capsule)

- Found in the renal cortex close enough to Bowman's Capsule for *further reabsorption* to occur.
- Substances reabsorbed back into the bloodstream include <u>Na^+</u>, <u>Ca^+</u>, and <u>more water</u>.
- This is the *final step in reabsorption* by the body of necessary materials from the filtrate. What remains in the filtrate is passed into <u>Collecting Ducts</u> as waste to be excreted from the body as <u>urine</u>.

    E. <u>Collecting Duct</u>

- Dips into the <u>Renal Medulla</u> again (because it is a hypertonic/salty environment).
- The final filtrate product joins waste products from multiple nephrons in <u>Collecting Ducts</u>.
- <u>Antidiuretic</u> (ADH) <u>hormones</u>-control the porosity of the Collecting Ducts. Greater porosity means more H_2O leaves.
- After the filtrate (now urine) passes through Collecting Ducts, it travels to the <u>urinary bladder</u> via tubes called <u>ureters</u>. Urine exits the urinary bladder through a tube called the <u>urethra</u>.

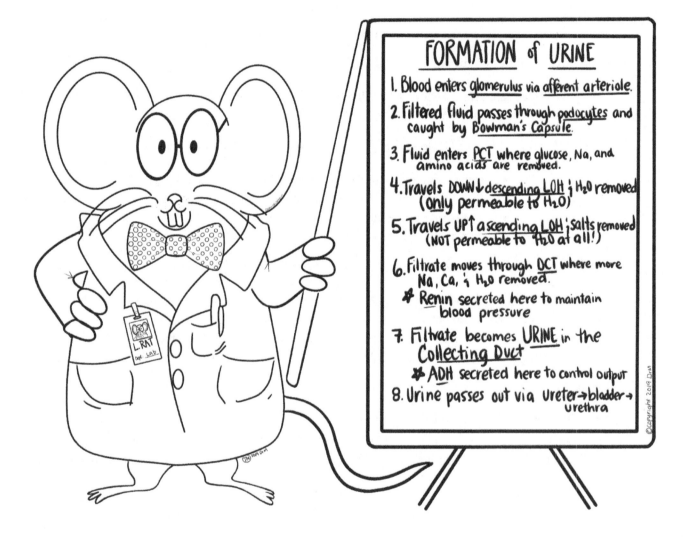

Figure 12-8

CHAPTER 13. REPRODUCTIVE SYSTEM

The Reproductive System

I. Reproductive System

    A. <u>Primary Sex Organs</u>-structures that produce <u>gametes</u> (sex cells) and secrete various <u>sex hormones</u> that regulate reproduction and development; the <u>testes</u> in males and the <u>ovaries</u> in females.

    B. <u>Accessory Reproductive Structures</u> include the various ducts, glands, and external genitalia which support the primary sex organs.

II. Male Reproductive System

    A. Anatomy

        1. <u>Scrotum</u>-sac of skin hanging outside of the abdominopelvic cavity, at the base of the penis. The scrotum houses the paired, oval <u>testes</u>. The testes are held away from the body since sperm are produced in large numbers at about a three degree lower temperature than the body's normal 37 degrees Celsius.

        2. <u>Testes</u>-oval, plum-sized structures that make-up the male external genitalia; produce <u>sperm</u> (gametes) and secrete hormones, primarily testosterone.

        3. <u>Penis</u>-delivers sperm to the female reproductive tract.

            a. <u>Glans penis</u>-enlarged distal tip of the penis covered by a cuff of tissue known as the <u>prepuce</u> or <u>foreskin</u> which is often removed via a circumcision.

            b. Internal Structure of the Penis (Erectile Tissue)

                1) <u>Corpus Spongiosum</u>-central erectile portion of the penis, surrounding the urethra. It expands to form the glans penis.

                2) <u>Corpora Cavernosa</u> (erectile tissue)-paired erectile regions in the penis; fill with blood during an erection.

        4. <u>Male Duct System</u>-known as the <u>accessory ducts.</u> They occur in the following order:

            a. <u>Epididymis</u>-long, coiled tube that rests on the backside of each testicle that functions in the carrying and storage of the sperm cells that are produced in the testes; comprised primarily of the <u>Duct of the Epididymis</u> which functions by absorbing nutrients which are passed to sperm that are stored in the lumen. Sperm are ejaculated from the <u>epididymis</u> (not the testes) into the <u>Ductus deferens</u>.

            b. <u>Vas Deferens</u>-tube from the epididymis that transports mature sperm to the urethra in preparation for ejaculation. It is approximately 18 inches long and serves as a passageway for sperm only. This structure is typically cut in a vasectomy.

            c. <u>Ejaculatory Duct</u>-one inch long tube that penetrates the base of the prostate gland. This duct ejects sperm and seminal fluid into the prostatic urethra.

            d. <u>Urethra</u>-terminal duct that transmits both sperm and urine.

5. <u>Accessory Glands</u>-produce seminal fluids.

    a. <u>Seminal Vesicles</u>-paired structures located on the lower part of the posterior surface of the urinary bladder that secrete alkaline, viscous fluid which activates the whip-like action of the flagella of sperm; major contributors to the production of semen.

    b. <u>Prostate Gland</u>-a single, doughnut-shaped gland inferior to the urinary bladder that secretes a slightly acidic prostatic fluid which gives semen its milky appearance. The muscles of the prostate gland also help propel this seminal fluid into the urethra during ejaculation.

    c. <u>Bulbourethral</u> (Cowper's Gland)-two small pea-shaped structures located below the prostate gland; secrete mucus prior to ejaculation which neutralizes the acidity of the female reproductive system.

6. <u>Semen</u>-refers to sperm plus seminal fluids.

    a. Has a pH of 7.2 to 7.6 and contains enzymes that activate the sperm.

    b. Average ejaculation is about 2.5 to 5 mL.

    c. Males release about 200 million sperm per ejaculation.

B. Physiology

    1. <u>Spermatogenesis</u>-sperm formation, occurs in the seminiferous tubules.

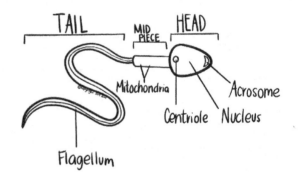

Figure 13-1

        a. Process is regulated by the hormone, <u>Follicle Stimulating Hormone</u> (FSH).

        b. Stages in Spermatogenesis:

            1). <u>Spermatogonium</u>-diploid, 46 chromosomes.

            2). <u>Primary Spermatocyte</u>-chromosomes in tetrads.

            3). <u>Secondary Spermatocyte</u>

            4). <u>Spermatids</u>-haploid, contain single chromosomes.

            5). <u>Spermatozoa</u> or Sperm

        c. <u>Sperm Structure</u>-divided into 2 parts: (see **Figure 13-1**)

            1). <u>Head</u>-contains the <u>nucleus</u> (with chromatin) surrounded by the <u>acrosome</u> which contains enzymes used for penetrating the egg.

            2). <u>Tail</u> (flagellum)-produces wave-like motion to help propel sperm to egg and to help penetrate the egg's surface when it makes contact.

    2. <u>Erection</u>-enables penetration into vagina. Steps in this process include:

a. Impulses from the parasympathetic division of the ANS promote the release of nitric oxide (NO) which causes vasodilation of the arteries and vasoconstriction of the veins of the penis.

b. More blood enters the penis than leaves, allowing blood to fill the spongy tissue of the cavernosa and spongiosa causing the penis to become larger and rigid.

c. Emission-the movement of semen from the genital ducts and glands into the prostatic urethra.

d. Ejaculation-sympathetic response that causes the urethral sphincters to close and propels the semen from the prostatic urethra to the exterior.

e. Sperm account for only about 5% of the total semen weight.

Male Reproductive System (Figure 13-2)

Structure	Function	Color
Epididymis		
Testes		
Vas deferens		
Prostate gland		
Seminal vesicles		
Glans Penis		
Erectile Tissue		
Urinary Bladder		
Urethra		

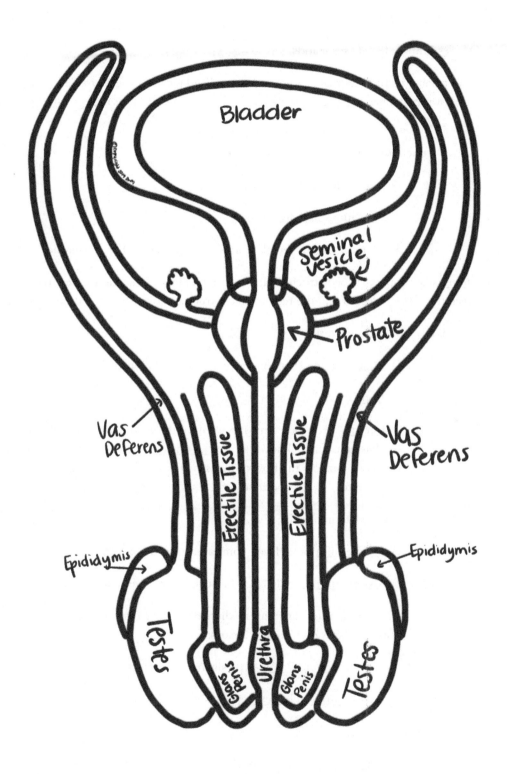

Figure 13-2

III. The Female Reproductive System

    A. Anatomy

        1. <u>Vulva</u>-external genitalia.

        2. <u>Ovaries</u>-primary female sex glands.

            a. Paired structures that are almond-shaped and located on either side of the uterus. The ovaries contain germinal tissue in which are embedded thousands of <u>Graffian</u> <u>Follicles</u> where <u>eggs</u> (ova) develop.

            b. Functions of the Ovaries:

                1). Egg production (<u>oogenesis</u>)

                2). <u>Ovulation</u>-discharge of eggs.

                3). Secretion of the female hormones estrogen and progesterone.

        3. <u>Uterus</u> (womb)-pear-shaped structure that is about 3 inches long and located in the pelvic cavity between the urinary bladder and the rectum. This structure holds the fetus during pregnancy.

            a. Divisions of the Uterus:

                1). <u>Fundus</u>-dome-shaped portion above the fallopian tubes.

                2). <u>Body</u>-central region of the uterus.

                3). <u>Cervix</u>-narrow, lowermost portion of the uterus that protrudes into the vagina and has an opening known as the <u>external os</u>. It is made up of strong muscles and functions to allow the flow of menstrual blood from the uterus into the vagina, as well as directing the sperm into the uterus during intercourse.

            b. Layers of the Uterine Wall:

                1). <u>Perimetrium</u>-outer layer, composed of epithelial tissue.

                2). <u>Myometrium</u>-middle layer, muscular. This layer contracts during childbirth.

                3). <u>Endometrium</u>-inner layer, where the embryo implants during pregnancy. This portion is divided into 2 parts:

                    a) <u>Stratum Basalis</u>-typically remains intact.

                    b) <u>Stratum Functionalis</u>-is shed during menstruation.

            c. Functions of the Uterus:

                1) <u>Menstruation</u>-shedding of the functionalis of endometrium.

                2) <u>Pregnancy</u>-houses embryo during development.

                3) <u>Labor</u>-aids in childbirth.

4. <u>Fallopian</u> (Uterine) <u>Tubes</u>-paired structures that attach to the uterus and extend upward and outward toward the sides of the pelvis and then curve downward to the ovaries. At the ovaries, these expand into a funnel-like section known as the <u>infundibulum</u> which opens into the abdominal cavity and contains finger-like projections known as <u>fimbriae</u> which sweep over the ovaries to pull the egg into the Fallopian Tube.

a. Functions of the Fallopian Tubes:

1) Primary function is to transport sperm towards the egg (released by the ovary) and then to allow passage of the fertilized egg back to the uterus for implantation.

2) Fertilization usually occurs in the Fallopian Tubes.

b. These are the tubes that are cut in a <u>tubal ligation</u>.

5. <u>Vagina</u>-canal that receives the male reproductive cells. It opens to the outside of the body via the vaginal orifice.

a. Functions:

1) Serves as a part of the birth canal.

2) Receives the penis during copulation.

3) Passageway for menstrual flow.

b. <u>Hymen</u>-fold of connective tissue that partially closes the external opening of the vagina.

6. <u>Mammary Glands</u>-located under the pectoralis major muscle.

a. Composed of:

1) <u>Adipose tissue</u>-filling tissue of the mammary glands.

2) <u>Lobes</u>-15-20 of these in each mammary gland; lobes are separated by adipose tissue.

3) <u>Lobules</u>-smaller compartments within the lobes, contain alveoli.

4) <u>Ducts</u>-tubes for excretion of milk.

5) <u>Alveoli</u>-milk secreting cells.

6) <u>Suspensory Ligaments</u>-support the breasts. Also known as Ligaments of Cooper.

b. There are usually 15-20 lobes separated by adipose tissue in the breasts. The lobes are divided into smaller lobules. The alveoli are arranged in clusters in each lobule. The alveoli produce milk which is expelled through a series of ducts.

B. Physiology

1. <u>Oogenesis</u>-occurs in the ovaries, begins at puberty.

a. Regulated by <u>Follicle Stimulating Hormone</u> (FSH).

b. Cells of Oogenesis: (stages that an oocyte completes in order to develop into a mature ovum)

    1). <u>Primordial follicles</u> (Oogonium)-diploid cells (have 2 complete sets of chromosomes).

    2). <u>Primary Oocyte</u>-immature cells in prophase I of meiosis. They remain in this stage until <u>puberty</u>. There are about 1 million of these per ovary.

    3). <u>Secondary Oocytes/First Polar Body</u>-begins around puberty. (see **Figure 13-3**)

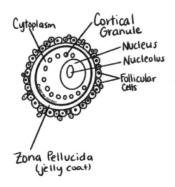

a). After puberty, FSH and LH causes meiosis I to resume, resulting in 2 cells of unequal size, both with 23 dyads. The larger cell is the <u>Secondary Oocyte</u> and the smaller one is the <u>First Polar Body</u>. The polar body will eventually deteriorate, leaving only the secondary oocyte.

b). <u>Secondary Oocyte</u>-contains almost all the cytoplasm and will continue development into the second phase of meiotic cell division.

c). <u>Ovulation</u> occurs at this stage and does not continue unless oocyte is fertilized by a sperm.

Figure 13-3

d). At the time of ovulation, an ootid is released from the follicle and drawn into the Fallopian Tube. If fertilization occurs, the ootid goes through its final state of maturation and becomes an <u>ovum</u> (fully mature egg cell).

    4). <u>Ootid/Secondary Polar Bodies</u>-begins after fertilization

a). If fertilized, the secondary oocyte continues into meiosis II producing two more unequal sized cells-the <u>Ootid</u> (larger cell) and <u>Secondary Polar Bodies</u> (smaller cell).

b). All polar bodies disintegrate leaving the ootid to become the mature ovum.

c). After fertilization. The haploid sperm and haploid egg join their sets of chromosomes together to produce a cell with a full set of chromosomes (called a <u>zygote</u>). This zygote will mature into an <u>embryo</u>, and finally into a baby.

2. Menstrual Cycle

a. Hormones Associated with the Menstrual Cycle (see **Figure 7-4**, p. 177)

    1). <u>Gonadotropin Releasing Hormone</u> (GnRH)-hormone produced by the hypothalamus, that influences the anterior lobe of the pituitary gland to produce the following hormones:

        a). <u>Follicle Stimulating Hormone</u> (FSH):

- Stimulates the growth of the ovum within the follicle.

- Stimulates release of estrogen by the growing follicle.

b). <u>Luteinizing Hormone</u> (LH):

- Induces ovulation.
- Stimulates the ruptured follicle to become the corpus luteum.
- Stimulates the corpus luteum to produce progesterone.

2. <u>Estrogen</u>-hormone produced by the growing follicle.

a). Stimulates growth of the endometrium.

b). Stimulates the development of secondary sex characteristics.

c). Inhibits the release of GnRH and FSH so no other oocytes will be produced.

3. <u>Progesterone</u>-hormone produced by the corpus luteum.

a). Stimulates further growth of the endometrium during pregnancy.

b). Inhibits the production of GnRH and Prolactin.

b. <u>Phases of the Cycle</u>-lasts about 28 days.

1. <u>Menstrual Phase</u>-first 4 or 5 days of the cycle.

a). Functionalis layer of endometrium is shed including about 6-9 ounces of blood, mucus, and epithelial tissue.

b). FSH causes the primary follicles to become secondary follicles.

2. <u>Preovulatory or Follicular Phase</u>-days 6-13.

a). High levels of FSH causes secondary follicle to develop into a mature follicle (<u>Graffian Follicle</u>).

b). <u>Estrogen</u> produced by the growing follicle causes the endometrium to rebuild.

c). On about the 14th day, estrogen acts as a feedback mechanism to inhibit FSS production and inhibit LH production. This leads to <u>ovulation</u>. (see **Figure 7-4**, p. 177)

3. <u>Postovulatory Phase or Luteal Phase</u>-days 15-28.

a). Following ovulation, the level of estrogen drops slightly and LH stimulates the ruptured follicle to become the corpus luteum.

b). The corpus luteum now secretes <u>progesterone</u> and <u>estrogen</u> which is responsible for preparing the endometrium for implantation.

c). Near the end of this phase, FSH secretion gradually increases and LH secretion decreases.

d). The dominant hormone during this phase is <u>progesterone</u>.

4. <u>If fertilization does not occur:</u>

a). Rising levels of progesterone and estrogen from the corpus luteum inhibits GnRH and LH production, causing the corpus luteum to degenerate and become the Corpus Albicans.

b). With the disappearance of the corpus luteum, the production of estrogen and progesterone decreases causing the functionalis of the endometrium to breakdown and the menstrual flow to begin.

c). The decreased amounts of estrogen and progesterone also bring about a new output of FSH causing a new follicle to develop. Birth control pills function by keeping estrogen and progesterone levels high so no new output of FSH will cause a new follicle to form.

5. <u>If fertilization does occur:</u>

a). The corpus luteum is maintained for about 4 months during which time it continues to produce estrogen and progesterone which maintains the endometrium.

b). After the placenta is formed, it begins to produce the hormone <u>Human Chorionic Gonadotrophic Hormone</u> (hCG) which continues to maintain the corpus luteum. The presence of hCG can be detected in urine and blood to check for a positive pregnancy.

c). The placenta also becomes active in estrogen production to support pregnancy and progesterone to support breast development and lactation.

Female Reproductive System (Figure 13-4)

Structure	Function	Color
Ovary		
Uterus		
Cervix		
Fallopian Tubes		
Vagina		

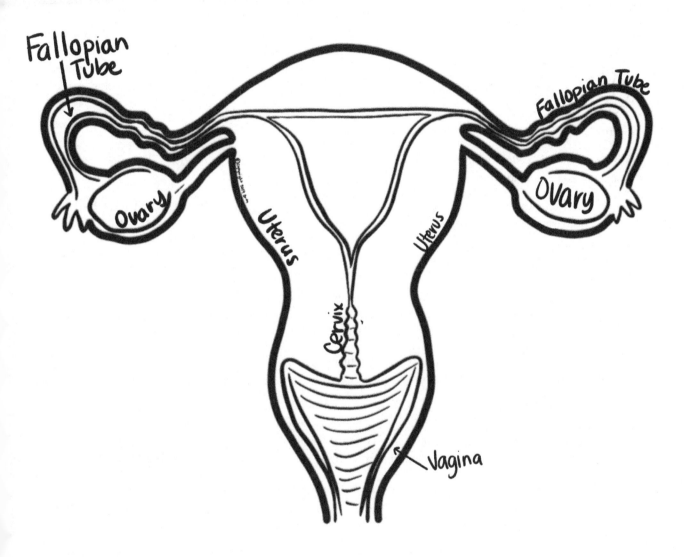

Figure 13-4

Pregnancy and Fetal Development

I. Conceptual Age vs. Gestational Age

A. <u>Conceptual Age</u> (actual embryo or fetal age)-the time elapsed from <u>fertilization of the egg near the time of ovulation</u>.

B. <u>Gestational Age</u> (menstrual age)-the time elapsed since <u>the first day of the last normal menstrual period</u>. Commonly used to determine the age of a pregnancy since most women do not know when ovulation occurred but do know when their last period began. Gestational age is conventionally expressed as completed weeks. So, a 36 week, 6 day fetus is considered to be a 36 week fetus.

II. Classification

A. <u>Zygote</u>-a single-celled organism resulting from a fertilized egg. The zygote divides to become a ball of cells that eventually implants in the wall of the uterus.

1. The first two weeks of pregnancy are counted as the time *prior to ovulation*, in which the body is preparing to release an egg.

2. Week #3 begins with release of an egg (<u>ovulation</u>). If the egg is fertilized, it is known as a <u>zygote</u>. This zygote will then divide and become a collection of cells known as a <u>blastocyst</u>.

3. In week #4 of pregnancy, the blastocyst implants in the wall of the uterus and develops into the placenta and embryo. The blastocyst is considered an <u>embryo</u> at the point when the *amniotic sac develops* (by about day 10 to 12 after fertilization, or at the start of week #5 of pregnancy).

B. <u>Embryo</u>-early stage of human development in which organs and critical body structures are formed. The distinction between an embryo and a fetus is made based on <u>gestational age</u>; roughly corresponds to the <u>5th-10th weeks of pregnancy</u>.

1. The embryonic period is the <u>stage in which most organs are formed</u>, the embryo elongates, and begins to assume a human-like shape. The primitive brain and spinal cord (neural tube) begin to form, as well as the heart and main blood vessels. The heart starts beating by the 6th week.

2. By 12 weeks of pregnancy, most of the baby's organs are formed, including the arms and legs. The brain and spinal cord, however, will continue to develop throughout pregnancy. At the end of the embryonic period, the baby is about 2 inches long.

3. The embryonic period is the critical time when organs are forming. It is also the time of greatest susceptibility to the negative effects of drugs, radiation, and viral infections. As a result, most birth defects occur during this time as well.

C. <u>Fetus</u>-beginning in the 11th week of pregnancy (which is the 9th week of development after fertilization of the egg), an embryo is called a <u>fetus</u>. (See **Figure 13-5**)

1. The embryo is considered a <u>fetus</u> after the embryonic period has ended (at the end of the 10th week of pregnancy). A fetus is a developing baby <u>beginning in the 11th week of pregnancy</u>.

2. The fetal period is a time of <u>growth</u> of the developing baby as the organs and structures formed in the embryonic period continue to grow and develop.

3. The greatest risks of miscarriage are in the very early stages of pregnancy. An estimated 25% or more pregnancies end in the very early stages, often before a woman even knows that she is pregnant

or has missed a menstrual period. Most other miscarriages happen in the first 12 weeks of pregnancy when the embryo is developing.

4. The second trimester begins in the 13th week and the gender of the fetus can be identified by about 14 weeks of pregnancy. The movement of the fetus can be felt somewhere between the 16th and 20th weeks of pregnancy. The baby grows to approximately 2 pounds during the second trimester.

5. The third trimester begins in the 27th week. During this time, the baby assumes the size and characteristics of a newborn and prepares for birth. The fetus will also open its eyes and breathe in the amniotic fluid.

II. <u>Pregnancy</u> (gestation)-average length of human gestation is 280 days, or 40 weeks, from the first day of the woman's last menstrual period.

    A. First Trimester

- <u>Conceptual Age</u>-less than 14 weeks, 0 days
- <u>Gestational Age</u>-3 weeks to 3 months

    B. Second Trimester

- <u>Conceptual Age</u>-14 weeks through 27 weeks, 6 days
- <u>Gestational Age</u>-3.2 months to 6.2 months

    C. Third Trimester

- <u>Conceptual Age</u>-28 weeks through delivery
- <u>Gestational Age</u>-6.4 months to 9/9.4 months

Trimester	Week												
1st		1	2	3	4	5	6	7	8	9	10	11	12
2nd	14	15	16	17	18	19	20	21	22	23	24	25	26
3rd	28	29	30	31	32	33	34	35	36	37	38	39	40

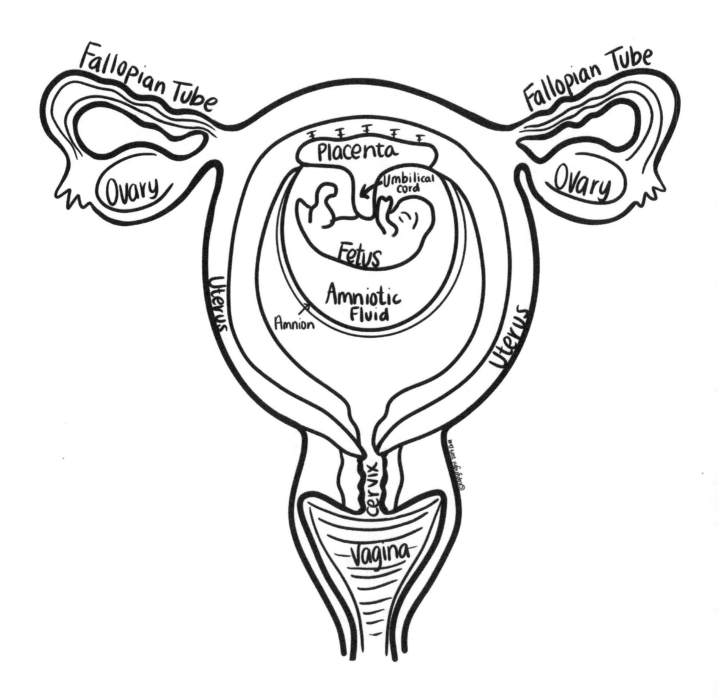

Figure 13-5

Fetal Development

FIRST TRIMESTER (less than 14 weeks)		
Week 1 & 2 of Cycle		During the first two weeks after the last menstrual period, egg follicles mature in the ovaries (under the stimulus of Follicle-Stimulating Hormone (FSH) secreted by the Pituitary Gland). High levels of the hormone Estradiol (produced by the developing egg follicle) cause secretion of Luteinizing Hormone (LH), also secreted from the Pituitary Gland. LH causes release of the egg from its follicle (ovulation). For women with 28-day cycles, ovulation usually occurs on days 13 to 15.
Embryonic Age=1wk	Gestational Age=3wks	If fertilization occurs during the third week of the cycle, the fertilized egg (called a zygote) will begin producing the pregnancy hormone human chorionic gonadotropin (hCG). Human Chorionic Gonadotropin (hCG) first becomes detectable in the mother's blood and urine between 6 and 14 days after fertilization (3 to 4 weeks gestational age). The first signs of pregnancy, fatigue and swollen or tender breasts may be detected. During the 3rd week-the sex of the fetus is determined by the father's sperm and twins may be formed.
Embryonic Age= 2wks	Gestational Age=4wks	The embryo is the size of a pinhead. Most pregnancy tests will be positive at this time.
Embryonic Age=3 wks	Gestational Age=5wks (1.2 mo)	The brain, spine, and heart begin to form. By the end of the week, the heart will be pumping blood. Week 5 is the *beginning of the embryonic period* which lasts from the 5th to the 10th week. Many birth defects occur in the developing embryo during this critical period. Most of these birth defects will have no known cause or be due to a combination of factors (multifactorial).
Embryonic Age=4 wks	Gestational Age=6wks (1.4 mo)	The embryo about the size of a pea with the average length about 0.2 inches (0.4 cm) The eyes, nostrils, and arms begin to take shape. The heart is beating at about 110 beats per minute and can sometimes be seen using a transvaginal ultrasound.
Embryonic Age= 5 wks	Gestational Age=7wks (1.6 mo)	The embryo is about 0. 4 inches (1 cm) long. The hands and feet are forming, as well as the mouth and face. The heart is beating at about 120 beats per minute. Movement of the embryo can be detected by ultrasound.

		By week 7, the trachea and bronchi of the lungs are forming and the pseudoglandular stage of lung development begins
Embryonic Age= 6 weeks	Gestational Age=8wks (1.8 mo)	The average embryo at 8 weeks is 0.6 inches (1.6 cm) long and weighs less than 1/2 ounce (15 grams). The embryo is about the size of a bean. The fingers and toes are developing.
Embryonic Age= 7 weeks	Gestational Age=9wks (2.1 mo)	The heart is beating at about 170 beats per minute. The average embryo at 9 weeks is 0.9 inches (2.3 cm) long and weighs less than 1/2 ounce (15 grams).
Fetal Age= 8 weeks	Gestational Age=10wks (2.3 mo)	The embryo's tail has disappeared, and it is now called fetus. Fingerprints are being formed and bone cells are replacing cartilage. The average fetus at 10 weeks is 1.2 inches (3.2 cm) long and weighs 1.2 ounces (35 grams).
Fetal Age= 9 weeks	Gestational Age=11wks (2.5 mo)	The fetus is starting to have breathing movements and can open its mouth and swallow. The average fetus at 11 weeks is 1.6 inches (4.2 cm) long and weighs 1.6 ounces (45 grams).
Fetal Age= 10 weeks	Gestational Age=12wks (2.8 mo)	The fetus is starting to make random movements. The pancreas is beginning to make insulin and the kidneys are producing urine. The heartbeat can usually be heard with an electronic monitor. The average fetus at 12 weeks is 2.1 inches (5.3 cm) long and weighs 2 ounces (58 grams).
Fetal Age= 12 weeks	Gestational Age=12wks (3 mon)	The average fetus at 13 weeks is 2.5 inches (6.5 cm) long and weighs 2.6 ounces (73 grams). All major organs are formed now, but they are too immature for the fetus to survive out of the womb.

SECOND TRIMESTER (14 weeks through 27 weeks, 6 days)		
Fetal Age= 12 weeks	Gestational Age=14wks (3.2 mon)	The fetus' toenails are appearing, and the gender may sometimes be seen. The average fetus at 14 weeks is 3.1 inches (7.9 cm) long and weighs 3.3 ounces (93 grams).
Fetal Age=13 weeks	Gestational Age=15wks (3.5 mon)	Fetal movement may be sensed by the mother (called quickening). although some don't feel the fetus moving until about 25 weeks. The average fetus at 15 weeks is 6.4 inches (16.4 cm) long and weighs 4.1 ounces (117 grams).
Fetal Age=14-15 weeks	Gestational Age=16-17wks (3.7-3.9 mon)	The average 16 week fetus is 7.1 inches (18.3 cm) long and weighs 5.2 ounces (146 grams). Hearing is beginning to form. Lung development is continuing. The average 17 week fetus is 7.9 inches (20.1 cm) long and weighs 6.4 ounces (181 grams). The pseudoglandular stage of lung development ends at about 17 weeks but there are still no alveoli present, so respiration is not possible at this time.
Fetal Age=16 weeks	Gestational Age=18wks (4.1 mon)	Ears begin to stand out and the fetus is beginning to respond to sound. The average 18 week fetus is 8.6 inches (22 cm) long and weighs 7.9 ounces (223 grams).
Fetal Age=17 weeks	Gestational Age=19wks (4.4 mon)	The ears, nose, and lips are recognizable. The average fetus at 19 weeks is 9.3 inches (23.7 cm) long and weighs 9.6 ounces (273 grams).
Fetal Age=18 weeks	Gestational Age=20wks (4.6 mon)	The fetus is covered in lanugo (fine hair), has some scalp hair, and is capable of producing IgG and IgM (antibodies). The average fetus at 20 weeks is 9.9 inches (25.5 cm) long and weighs 11.7 ounces (331 grams).
Fetal Age=19 weeks	Gestational Age=21wks (4.8 mon)	The fetus is able to suck and grasp and may have episodes of hiccups. Some women begin feeling Braxton Hicks contractions at this time. The average fetus at 21 weeks is 10.6 inches (27.2 cm) long and weighs 14.1 ounces (399 grams).
Fetal Age=20 weeks	Gestational Age=22wks (5.1 mon)	The average fetus at 22 weeks is 11.2 inches (28.8 cm) long and weighs 1.1 pound (478 grams).

		Survival out of the womb at this age would be expected to be less than 10%.
Fetal Age=21 weeks	Gestational Age=23wks (5.3 mon)	The fetus begins to experience rapid eye movements during sleep. The average fetus at 23 weeks is 11.9 inches (30.4 cm) long and weighs 1.2 pounds (568 grams). The entire corpus callosum may be seen using transabdominal ultrasound beginning at this age. Survival out of the womb at this age would be expected to be approximately 33%.
Fetal Age=22 weeks	Gestational Age=24wks (5.5 mon)	The average fetus at 24 weeks is 12.5 inches (32 cm) long and weighs 1.5 pounds (670 grams). The terminal saccular stage of lung development has started in which the air sacs form on the terminal bronchioles. Survival out of the womb at this age would be expected to be approximately 65%.
Fetal Age=23 weeks	Gestational Age=25wks (5.8 mon)	The average fetus at 25 weeks is 13.1 inches (33.6 cm) long and weighs 1.7 pounds (785 grams). The canalicular period of lung development is ending and respiration is possible towards the end of this period. Survival out of the womb at this age would be expected to be approximately 80%.
Fetal Age=24 weeks	Gestational Age=26wks (6 mon)	The fetus can respond to sounds that occur in the mother's surroundings and the eyelids can open and close. The average fetus at 26 weeks is 13.7 inches (35.1 cm) long and weighs 2 pounds (913 grams). Survival out of the womb at this age would be expected to be approximately 87%.
Fetal Age=25 weeks	Gestational Age=27wks (6.2 mon)	The average fetus at 27 weeks is 14.2 inches (36.5 cm) long and weighs 2.3 pounds (1055 grams). Survival out of the womb at this age would be expected to be approximately 94%.

THIRD TRIMESTER (28 weeks through Delivery)		
Fetal Age= 26 weeks	Gestational Age=28wks (6.4 mon)	The fetus has eyelashes and the skin is red and covered with vernix caseosa (waxy substance believed to act as an anti-infective and waterproofing film). The average fetus at 28 weeks is 14.8 inches (37.9 cm) long and weighs 2.7 pounds (1210 grams). Survival out of the womb at this age would be expected to be approximately 94%.
Fetal Age=27-29 weeks	Gestational Age=29-31wks (6.6-7.1 mon)	The average fetus at 29 weeks is 15.3 inches (39.3 cm) long and weighs 3 pounds (1379 grams). The average fetus at 30 weeks is 15.8 inches (40.6 cm) long and weighs 3.4 pounds (1559 grams). The average fetus at 31 weeks is 16.4 inches (41.9 cm) long and weighs 3.9 pounds (1751 grams).
Fetal Age=30-31 weeks	Gestational Age=32-33wks (7.4-7.6 mon)	The fetus is forming muscle and storing body fat. Testicles are descending if the fetus is a boy. The average fetus at 32 weeks is 16.8 inches (43.2 cm) long and weighs 4.3 pounds (1953 grams). The average fetus at 33 weeks is 17.3 inches (44.4 cm) long and weighs 4.8 pounds (2162 grams). The distal femoral epiphysis ossification center can often be seen in 72 % of fetuses at 33 weeks.
Fetal Age=32-34 weeks	Gestational Age=34-36wks (7.8-8.3 mon)	The fetus is now considered to be <u>late preterm</u>. The average 34 week fetus is 17.8 inches (45.6 cm) long and weighs 5.2 pounds (2377 grams). The average 35 week fetus is 18.2 inches (46.7 cm) long and weighs 5.7 pounds (2595 grams). The average 36 week fetus is 18.6 inches (47.8 cm) long and weighs 6.2 pounds (2813 grams). The proximal tibial epiphysis ossification center may be seen in 35 % of fetuses at 35 weeks.
Fetal Age=35-36 weeks	Gestational Age=37-38wks (8.5-8.7 mon)	The fetus is now considered to be <u>early term</u>. The average 37 week fetus is 19.1 inches (48.9 cm) long and weighs 6.7 pounds (3028 grams). The average 38 week fetus is 19.5 inches (49.9 cm) long and weighs 7.1 pounds (3236 grams).

		The proximal humeral epiphysis ossification center may be seen at 38 weeks.
Fetal Age=37-39 weeks	Gestational Age=39-41wks (9.0-9.4 mon)	The fetus is now <u>full term</u>. The average 39 week fetus is 19.8 inches (50.9 cm) long and weighs 7.6 pounds (3435 grams). The average 40 week fetus is 20.2 inches (52 cm) long and weighs 8 pounds (3619 grams). The average 41 week fetus is 20.5 inches (52.7 cm) long and weighs 8.3 pounds (3787 grams).

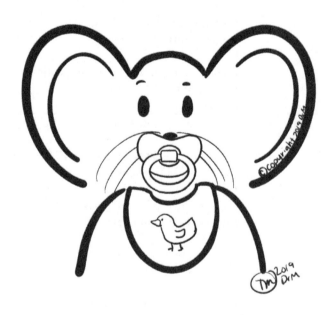

Lactation (Figure 13-6)

After birth, a mother experiences a sharp increase in the levels of the hormone prolactin. This hormone, released from the anterior Pituitary Gland, stimulates milk production for the new infant. This process is called lactation. As the baby nurses, the level of prolactin remains constant and causes the release of the hormone oxytocin from the posterior Pituitary Gland. The more an infant nurses, the more these hormones are produced by the mother's body. This is an example of positive feedback.

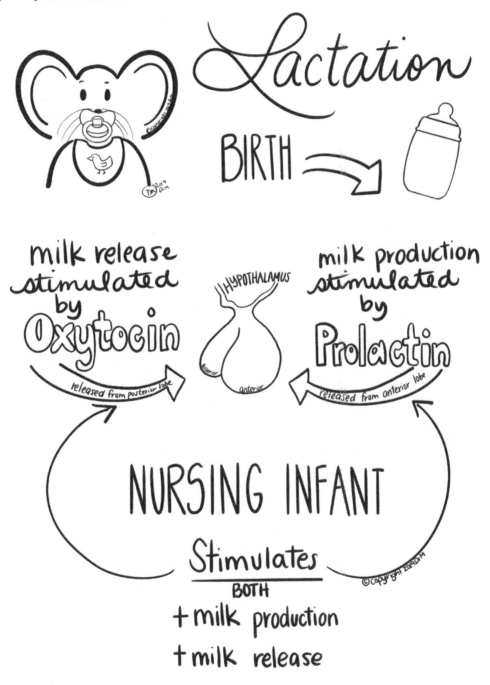

Figure 13-6

Anatomy & Physiology Plain and Simple: A Coloring Review Guide

BONUS MATERIALS

List of Commonly Used Prefixes and Suffixes

Word Part	Meaning	Example(s)
a-, an, non	Without, Not	Apnea, Anuria, Nonstriated
ab-, ef-	Away	Abductor muscle, Efferent Neuron
abdomin-	Abdomen	Abdominopelvic
acou-	Hear	Acoustic
ad-, af-	Toward	Afferent neuron, Adductor muscle
adi-, lip(o)-	Fat	Adipose, Liposuction
-alg	Pain	Neuralgia, Fibromyalgia
ana-	Up	Anabolic reaction
ang(i)-	Vessel	Angiogenesis, Vasodilator
ante-, pre-, pro-	Before	Prenatal, Antebrachial, Promonocyte
anti-, contra-	Against, Resisting	Antibody, Contraception
aqua(e)-, hydr	Water	Aqueous, hydrocephalus
arthr(o), artic-	Joint	Arthritis, Articulation
-ase	Enzyme	Maltase, Lipase
audi-	Hear	Auditory nerve
aut(o)-	Self	Autoimmunity
bi-, di-, diplo-	Two	Bicuspid, Diencephalon, Diplococcus
blast-	Formative cell, bud	Osteoblast
brachi-	Arm	Brachialis
brachy-, brev(i)-	Short	Brachydactyly, Fibularis brevis
brady-	Slow	Bradycardia
bronch-	Airway	Bronchitis
cardi-	Heart	Cardiology
cata-	Down	Catabolic reaction
cent-	100, 100th	Century, Centigram
-centesis	Puncture	Amniocentesis
cephal-, -ceps	Head	Hydrocephalus, Biceps femoris
cerebro-	Brain	Cerebrospinal fluid
chol-, cystic	Gallbladder	Cholecystokinin, Cystic duct
chondr-	Cartilage	Chondrocyte
-cide	Kill	Spermicide
circum-, peri-	Around	Circumcision, Periodontal
-clast	Break, Destroy	Osteoclast
co-, con-, sym-, syn-, sys-	Together, With	Congenital, Synthesis, System
coel-, sinu-	Cavity, Space	Coelom, Frontal sinus
contra-	Against, opposite	Contraception
corp-, soma-	Body	Corpus luteum, Somatic cell
-crine	Secrete, Release	Endocrine gland
cut, derm	Skin	Subcutaneous, Dermatitis
cyan-	Blue	Cyanosis
cysti-	Bladder or sac	Cystoscope
-cyte, -cyto	Cell	Leukocyte
dactyl, digit	Finger or Toe	Syndactyly
dec(k)	10, 1/10th	Decade, Dekagram, Deciliter
dent, don	Tooth/Teeth	Dentalgia, Orthodontist
di-	Two	Diarthrotic
dia-, per-, trans-	Through, Separate, Across	Diarrhea, Permeable, Transcutaneous
diplo-	Double	Diploid

Word Part	Meaning	Example(s)
dys-, mal-	Bad, Painful, Difficult	Dyspnea, Malnutrition, Malabsorption
-ectomy, -tom, -sect	Cut, Cut out	Appendectomy, Lobotomy, Dissect
ecto-	Displaced	Ectopic pregnancy
edem-	Swelling	Lymphedema
-emesis	Vomiting	Hyperemesis
-emia	Blood condition	Hypoglycemia
en, endo-, intra-	Inside, Within	Endosteum, Intraocular
epi-	Upon, Over, Above	Epidermis, Epididymis
equi-, homo-, iso-	Same, Equal, Balanced	Homeostasis, Isotonic
erythr-	Red	Erythrocyte
-esthe	Sensation	Anesthesia
ex-, ecto-	Outside	Extracellular fluid
fasci-	Bundle	Muscle or nerve fascicle
foram-	Opening	Infraorbital foramen
gastr-	Stomach	Gastric bypass surgery
-gen, poie-, blast	Create, Form	Oogenesis, Hemopoiesis, Osteoblast
ger (o, i) -	Aging, Old	Gerontology, Geriatrics
glom-	Ball	Glomerulus
gloss, lingu	Tongue	Hypoglossal, Sublingual
gluc-, gly, -ose	Sugar	Glucose, Glycogen
gyn	Woman	Gynecologist
-gram	Something written	Electrocardiogram (ECG)
-graph	Writing apparatus	Electrocardiograph
-graphy	Use of writing apparatus	Electrocardiography
hem-	Blood	Hemothorax
hemi-, semi-	Half	Cerebral hemisphere
hepat-	Liver	Hepatitis
hex-	Six	Hexose
hist-	Tissue	Histology
hyper-	Over, Excessive	Hypertonic, Hyperesthesia
hypo-, infra-, infer-, sub-	Under, Below, Less	Hypotonic, Infraorbital, Inferior, submandibular
hyster-, metr-	Uterus	Hysterectomy, Endometrium
-iasis, -osis	Condition of	Cholelithiasis, Nephrosis
-itis	Inflammation of	Appendicitis
inter-	Between	Interstitial Fluid
kilo-, milli-	1000, 1000th	Kilogram, Milligram
kin-	To move, Divide	Kinesiology, Cytokinesis
lact-	Milk	Lactose
lapar-	Abdomen	Laparoscopy
leuk(c)-	White	Leukopoiesis
lig-	Connect, Bind	Ligaments, Ligase
-logy, -ist, -ician	Study of, Specialist	Cardiology, Pharmacist, Dietician
lys, lyze	Break apart, Dissolve	Hydrolysis, Lysosome
macr-, mega, magn-	Large	Macrophage, Magnum foramen
mamm-, mass-, pect-	Breast, Chest	Mammary, Mastectomy, Pectoralis
-mania	Obsession, Compulsion	Kleptomania
med-, meso-, meta-	Middle	Mediastinum, Mesoderm, Metaphase
-megaly	Enlargement	Splenomegaly
melano-	Black	Melanocyte

Word Part	Meaning	Example(s)
mens-	Month	Menstrual cycle
-metric, -meter	Measurement, Length	Isometric, Spirometer
micro-, -ole, -ule	Small	Microscope, Arteriole, Venule
mnem-	Memory	Amnesia
mono-, uni-	One	Monozygotic, Unicellular
morph, -plasty	Shape	Morphology, Rhinoplasty
mort, necr-	Death	Post mortem, Necrotic tissue
multi-, poly-	Many	Multinucleate, Polysaccharide
mut-	Change	Mutation
myo-	Muscle	Myopathy, Myofibril
nas-, rhin	Nose	Nasal septum, Rhinovirus
nat-	Birth	Prenatal
neo-	New	Neonatal
nephr-, ren	Kidney	Nephrosclerosis, Renal vein
o(o), ovi	Egg	Oophorectomy, Oviduct
oct	Eight	Octet rule
ocu, ophth, opt, orbit	Eye	Orbicularis oculi, Ophthalmologist
-oid	Resembling, Shape of	Sigmoid colon
olig-	Little, Few	Oliguria
-oma, onco	Tumor	Melanoma, Oncologist
-opia	Vision	Hyperopia
or(a)	Mouth	Orbicularis oris
-scopy	To view, See	Arthroscopic surgery
ost-	Bone	Osteoblast, Osteomyelitis
-ostomy	Make an opening	Tracheostomy
ot	Ear	Otoscope
palp, tact	Touch, Feel	Palpate, Tactile
para	Beside	Parathyroid glands
path	Disease	Pathogenic bacteria
ped, pod	Foot, Feet	Pedal, Podiatrist
pent	Five	Pentose
phago	Eat, Feed	Phagocyte
pharm	Drug	Psychopharmic
-phasia	Speech	Dysphagia
phleb	Vein	Phlebotomist
photo, lumen	Light	Photoreceptor, Gastric lumen
phobia, phobe	Fear	Hydrophobia
phys	Function	Physiology
-plasia	Growth, Formation	Hyperplasia
plegia	Paralysis	Quadriplegia
pnea, spir	Breathing	Apnea, Inspire
pneum, pulmon	Lungs, Air	Pneumothorax, Pulmonary embolus
post	After	Postnatal
prim	First	Primary bronchus
proct	Rectum, Anus	Proctoscope, Proctologist
pseudo	False	Pseudounipolar neuron
psych, phren, -noia	Mind	Psychosis, Schizophrenia
quad, tetra	Four	Quadriceps, Tetralogy of Fallot
re-, retro	Back, Again, Past	Reinfect, Retrograde amnesia

Word Part	Meaning	Example(s)
-rrhea	Flow, Discharge	Diarrhea, Otorrhea
sclero	Hardening	Arteriosclerosis, Scleroderma
sept, tox	Poison, Contaminate	Antiseptic, Cytotoxin
sten	Narrowing	Pyloric stenosis
strat	Layer	Stratified squamous epithelia
super, supra	Above, Over	Superior vena cava, Supraorbital
tachy	Fast	Tachycardia
-tension	Pressure	Hypertension
therm	Heat	Thermoreceptor
thromb	Clot	Thrombocyte
-tonic	Strength	Isotonic
tri-, tert-	Three, Third	Triglyceride, Tertiary bronchus
zyg	Union	Zygote

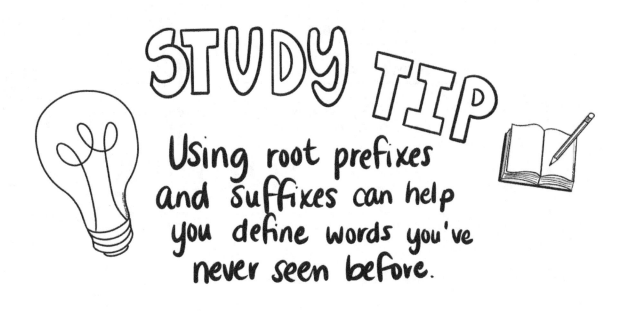

STUDY TIP

Using root prefixes and suffixes can help you define words you've never seen before.

323

EPITHELIAL TISSUE Basics

* Avascular, get nourishment via diffusion

* Lines outer surfaces of organs and blood vessels and inner surfaces of cavities of many organs

* Cells are arranged in sheets over a basement membrane.

* Classified/named according to:

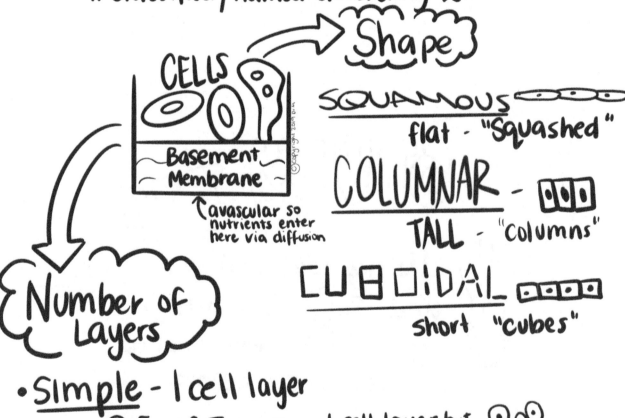

CELLS

Basement Membrane

↑ avascular so nutrients enter here via diffusion

© Copyright 2019 B.M.

Shape

SQUAMOUS
flat - "squashed"

COLUMNAR -
TALL - "columns"

CUBOIDAL
short "cubes"

Number of Layers

• Simple - 1 cell layer
  → PsEUdOSTrAtiFieD - 1 cell layer but different heights
  "fake layers"

• Stratified - 2⁺ cell layers

Simple EPITHELIAL TISSUE

SIMPLE SQUAMOUS

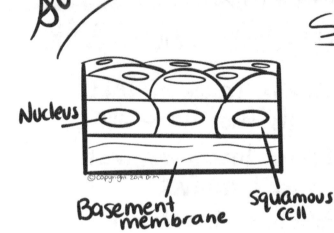

Nucleus

Basement membrane

Squamous cell

©copyright 2019 DrA

- Thin, flat cells in a single layer
- Found lining blood vessels and heart
- Function - diffusion

SIMPLE CUBOIDAL

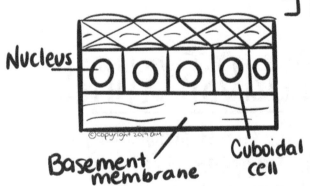

Nucleus

Basement membrane

Cuboidal cell

©copyright 2019 DrA

- Single layer of cube-shaped cells
- Found in walls of small ducts of glands and lining ovary; many kidney tubules
- Function - secretion; absorption

SIMPLE COLUMNAR

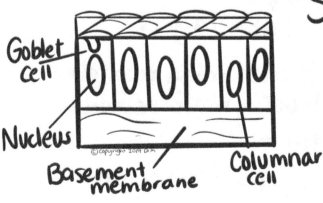

Goblet Cell

Nucleus

Basement membrane

Columnar cell

©copyright 2019 DrA

- Single layer of TALL cells
- May contain goblet cells (secrete mucus)
- Found lining digestive tract
- Function - Absorption, Secretion, & produce mucus

Simple EPITHELIAL TISSUE

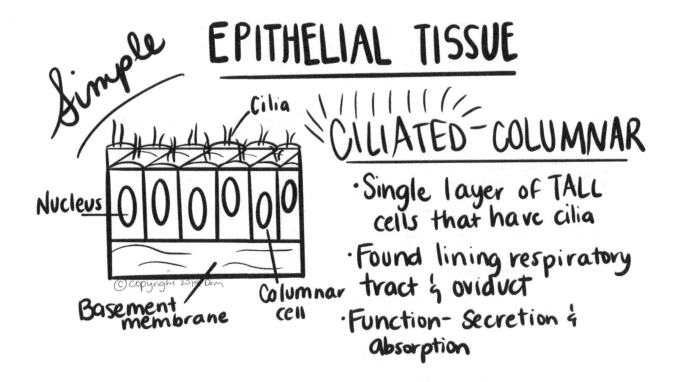

CILIATED - COLUMNAR

- Single layer of TALL cells that have cilia
- Found lining respiratory tract & oviduct
- Function- Secretion & absorption

Cilia

Nucleus

Basement membrane

Columnar cell

PsEudOsTrAtiFieD

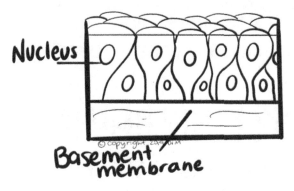

Nucleus

Basement membrane

- Cells are a single layer but appear stratified due to differences in height.
- "Fake layers"
- Found lining respiratory tract & male reproductive tract
- Function-secretion, absorption, & protection

Stratified EPITHELIAL TISSUE

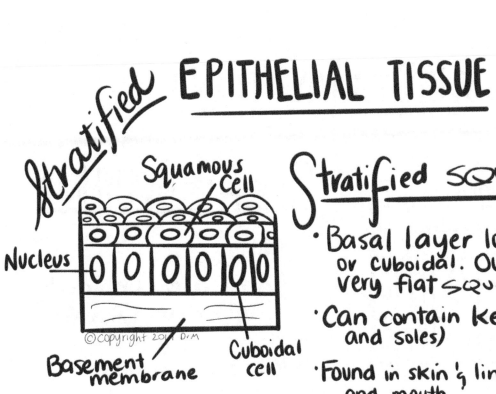

Squamous Cell

Nucleus

Basement membrane

Cuboidal Cell

©copyright 2019 D.M

Stratified SQUAMOUS

- Basal layer low columnar or cuboidal. Outer layer very flat SQUAMOUS cells.
- Can contain keratin (on palms and soles)
- Found in skin & lining esophagus and mouth
- Function- protection

Stratified CUBOIDAL

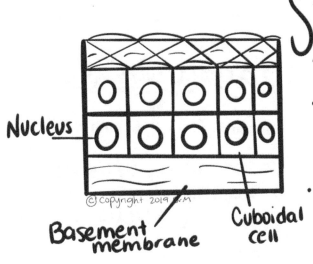

Nucleus

Basement membrane

Cuboidal Cell

©copyright 2019 D.M

- Rare, usually only 2 layers
- Found in some sweat and mammary glands; also in conjunctiva of eye
- Function- secretes and protects

Stratified EPITHELIAL TISSUE

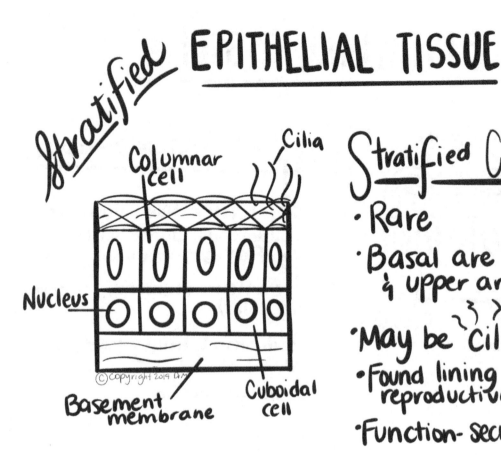

Columnar cell

Cilia

Nucleus

Basement membrane

Cuboidal cell

© Copyright 2019 DM

Stratified COLUMNAR

- Rare
- Basal are cuboidal & upper are COLUMNAR
- May be Ciliated
- Found lining male reproductive tract
- Function- secrete & protect

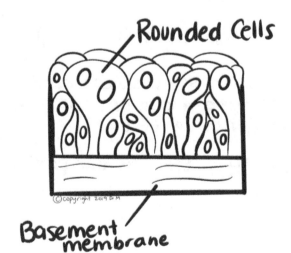

Rounded Cells

Basement membrane

© copyright 2019 DM

Transitional

- Surface cells are rounded
- Found lining urinary organs
- Function- Stretches

~~CONNECTIVE~~ connective TISSUE Basics

* **Found everywhere in the body**
  ↳ most abundant and widely distributed tissue type

* **Made of living cells surrounded by a matrix**

* **Functions** - bind parts together, support & protect organs, insulate, store fuel, and transport substances

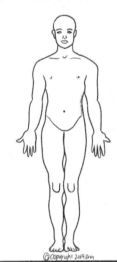
©Copyright 2019 Day

---

① Connective Tissue Proper ⇐ **Classes of Connective Tissue** ⇒ ③ Bone

② Cartilage ⇐ ⇒ ④ Blood

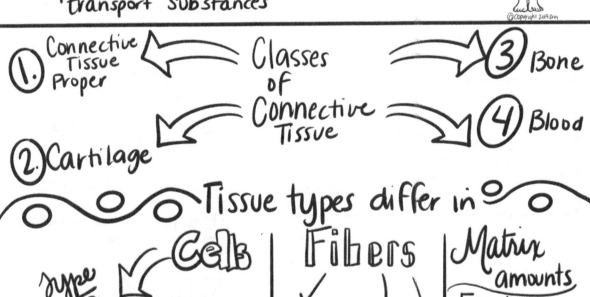

Tissue types differ in

Cells	Fibers	Matrix amounts
Type	Collagen	**Small** (cells/fibers close together)
Fibro = connective tissue proper		↓
chondro = cartilage	Elastic	
osteo = bone		
hemato = blood		**large** (cells/fibers far apart)
Function	Reticular	
−blast = build		
−cyte = maintain (mature cell)		
−clast = break		

329

Loose CONNECTIVE TISSUE Proper

Areolar (LOOSE)

- Made of scattered cells with collagen and elastin fibers
- Fills spaces, surrounds organs, blood vessels, and nerves
- Function-holds organs in place by attaching epithelial tissue to underlying tissue

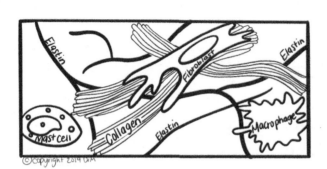

Adipose (FAT)

- Very little matrix
- Each cell has a large droplet of fat
- Found behind eyes, palms, soles, abdomen, and hips
- Functions-cushions & insulates body, stores energy in fat

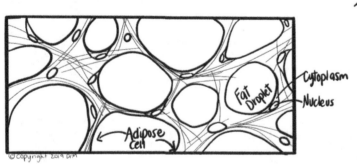

Reticular

- Delicate matrix of reticular fibers & fibroblasts
- Found in the soft structures of liver, lymph nodes, and spleen
- Functions-forms framework of organs, binds smooth muscle cells together

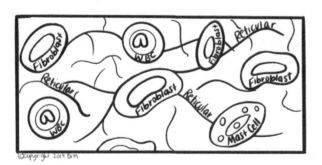

Dense ~~CONNECTIVE~~ connective TISSUE Proper

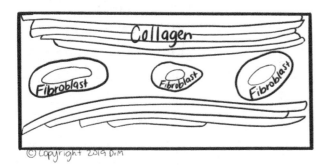

Collagen

Fibroblast Fibroblast Fibroblast

© Copyright 2019 DrM

Dense Regular

- Densely-packed parallel bundles of collagen
- Fibroblast cells are present but scarce
- Make up tendons (bind muscle to bone) and ligaments (bind bones to bones)
- Function - provides connections between different tissues

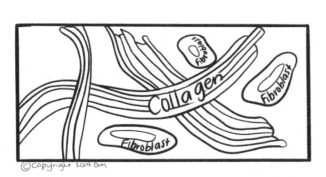

Collagen

Fibroblast Fibroblast Fibroblast

© Copyright 2019 DrM

Dense Irregular

- Collagen fibers in many directions
- Found in dermis of skin and capsules of organs
- Function - provides strength and resists tearing in many directions

Elastic Fibers

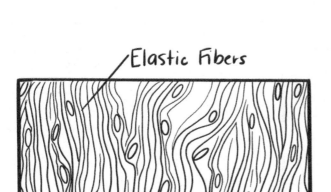

© Copyright 2019 DrM

Nuclei of Fibroblasts

← ∞ Elastic ∞ →

- High concentration of elastic fibers
- Found in walls of large arteries, in some ligaments between vertebrae in neck, and in vocal cords
- Function - allows tissue to return after being stretched

331

Cartilage CONNECTIVE TISSUE

Hyaline Cartilage

- Clear matrix with very little collagen
- "Hyaline" means glass
- Found at ends of bones at joints and sternum, nose, trachea, and larynx
- Function- reduces friction and absorbs shock between bones at joints

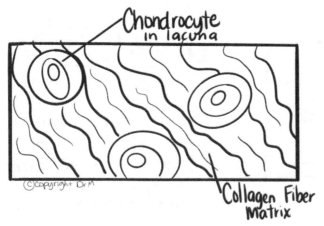

Chondrocytes in lacunae

Clear Matrix

©Copyright 2019 Dr M

Fibro cartilage

- Strong due to large amount of collagen fibers in matrix
- Found in knee and intervertebral disks
- Function- absorbs shock

Chondrocyte in lacuna

Collagen Fiber Matrix

©Copyright Dr M

Elastic Cartilage

- Contains many single elastin fibers in matrix
- Found in ears and epiglottis
- Function- flexibility to withstand repeated bending

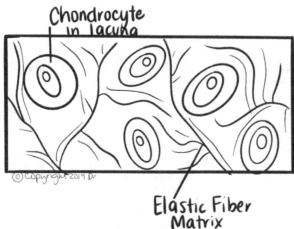

Chondrocyte in lacuna

Elastic Fiber Matrix

©Copyright 2019 Dr

Bone & Blood

CONNECTIVE TISSUE

Osseous (Bone)

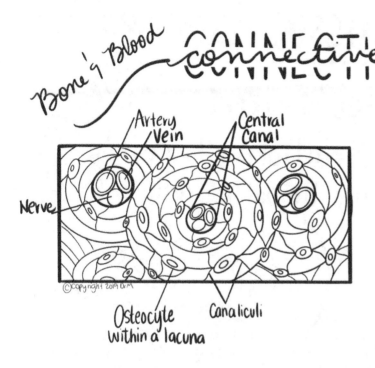

Artery
Vein
Central Canal

Nerve

Osteocyte within a lacuna

Canaliculi

- Osteocytes in a non-living matrix
- Hard yet strong and light
- Composed of several types of cells (osteoclasts, osteoblasts, and osteocytes) responsible for remodeling and maintaining the skeleton
- Function- serves as framework for the body (skeleton)

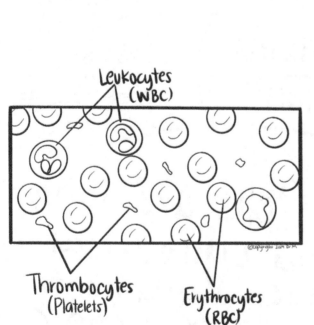

Leukocytes (WBC)

Thrombocytes (Platelets)

Erythrocytes (RBC)

- Has a liquid matrix contained within vessels
- Fibers in matrix are soluble proteins that precipitate during clotting
- Contains 3 types of cells:
  Erythrocytes- red blood cells
  Leukocytes- white blood cells
  Thrombocytes- platelets
- Function- transports O_2/nutrients to cells and CO_2/wastes away from cells

333

MUSCLE TISSUE Basics

* Highly vascularized
* Cells have striations (stripes)
* Nuclei sometimes lie outside cells

©copyright 2019 DvM

* Primary job
   is
~ movement ~

Types of Muscle

smooth

Skeletal

Involuntary
(Smooth & Cardiac)

Voluntary
(Skeletal)

Cardiac

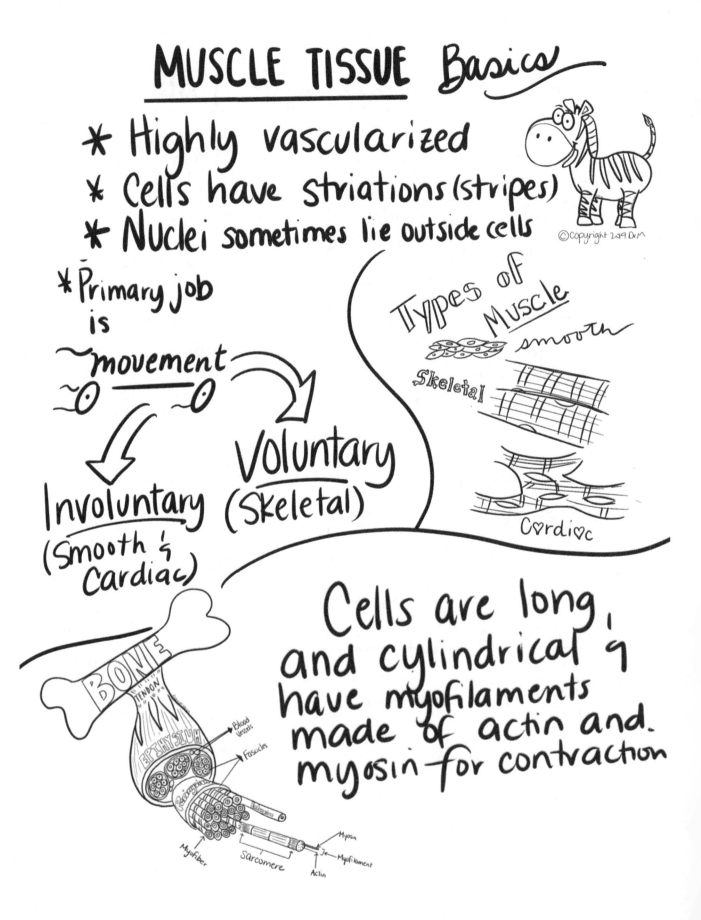

BONE
TENDON
EPIMYSIUM
Blood Vessels
Fascicles
Perimysium
Myofiber
Sarcomere
Actin
Myosin
Myofilament

Cells are long, and cylindrical & have myofilaments made of actin and. myosin for contraction

MUSCLE TISSUE

smooth
- Tapered cells
- Non-striate
- Involuntary
- Makes up inner walls of organs

Nucleus

Skeletal
- Cells with multiple nuclei
- Striated
- Voluntary
- Found attached to bones

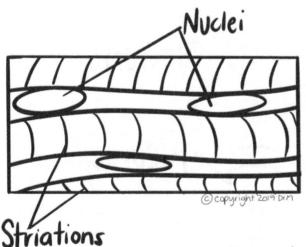

Nuclei

Striations

Cardiac
- Branched cells joined with intercalated disks
- Faint striations
- Involuntary
- Found only in heart

Intercalated Disks

Nucleus   Striations

Nervous TISSUE Basics

* Avascular

* Main component of brain
and   spinal cord

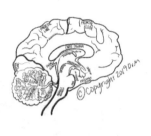

* Made of 2 Kinds of cells:

conducting ⟹ Neurons
conducts impulses

non-conducting ⟹ Neuroglial
protects and supports
neurons

* Specialized tissue found in
Central Nervous System (CNS)
and
Peripheral Nervous System (PNS)

* Job is to regulate and control
body functions

Nervous TISSUE

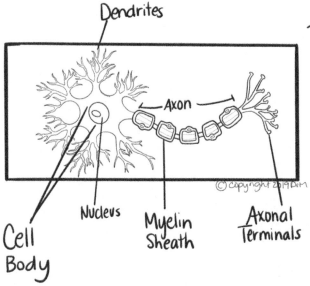

Dendrites

Axon

Cell
Body

Nucleus

Myelin
Sheath

Axonal
Terminals

© copyright 2019 DrM

Neuron

- Branching cell
- Long cytoplasmic extension
- Consists of dendrites, cell body, and axon
- Found in brain, spinal cord, and nerves
- Job is to conduct impulses

Basic Lab Values Reference

Serum Electrolytes

- Calcium: 8.5–10.9mg/L

- Chloride: 98-107

- Magnesium: 1.6-2.6 mg/dL

- Phosphorus:2.5–4.5mg/dL

- Potassium: 3.5-5.1

- Sodium: 135-145 mEq/L

Hematology Values

- RBC: 4.5–5.0million

- WBC: 5,000–10,000

- Platelets: 200,000–400,000

- Hemoglobin: 12–16 g/dL Women; 14–18 g/dL Men

- Hematocrit: 37 – 48% Women; 45 – 52% Men

Arterial Blood Gases (ABGs)

- pH: 7.35-7.45

- pCO2: 35-45 mEq/L

- HCO3: 24-26 mEq/L

- pO2: 80-100%

Chemistry Values

- Glucose: 70–110 mg/dL

- Specific gravity: 1.010–1.030

- BUN: 7–22m g/dL

- Serum creatinine: 0.6–1.35 mg/dL (< 2 in older adults)

- LDH: 100–190 U/L

- CPK: 21–232 U/L

- Uric acid: 3.5–7.5 mg/dL

- Triglyceride: 40–50 mg/dL

- Totalcholesterol:130–200 mg/dL

- Bilirubin: <1.0 mg/dL

- Protein: 6.2–8.1 g/dL

- Albumin: 3.4–5.0 g/dL

How to Draw an EASY Heart Step-by-Step

Instructions	What it Looks Like
1. Start by drawing 2 elementary school era "birds" connected by 2 circles.	
2. Then, add in the Vs (V= Valves)	
3. Connect the wings of the outer "birds" and create the **_myocardium_** (the muscular outer walls of the heart) and draw in the **_septum_** (division of the ventricles) between the 2 circles.	
4. Off the first circle, create the **_pulmonary trunk and the pulmonary arteries_**. • The **_pulmonary trunk_** is a major vessel of the human heart that originates from the right ventricle. It branches into the **_right and left pulmonary arteries,_** which lead to the lungs. Each of these vessels has elastic walls similar to those of the aorta, though somewhat thinner, and **_they are considered to be arteries even though the blood they carry is not oxygenated._** The trunk itself is relatively short and wide. The _function of these vessels is to transmit oxygen-depleted,_	

carbon dioxide-rich blood from the right ventricle to the lungs

5. From the second circle, create the **aorta** which is situated behind the pulmonary trunk and arteries. The aorta is the **largest artery in the body.** The aorta begins at the top of the left ventricle, the heart's muscular pumping chamber. The heart pumps blood from the left ventricle into the aorta through the aortic valve. Three leaflets on the aortic valve open and close with each heartbeat to allow one-way flow of blood.

The aorta is a tube about a foot long and just over an inch in diameter. The aorta is divided into four sections:

• The **ascending aorta** rises up from the heart and is about 2 inches long. The coronary arteries branch off the ascending aorta to supply the heart with blood.

• The **aortic arch** curves over the heart, giving rise to branches that bring blood to the head, neck, and arms.

• The **descending thoracic aorta** travels down through the chest. Its small branches supply blood to the ribs and some chest structures.

• The **abdominal aorta** begins at the diaphragm, splitting to become the paired iliac arteries in the lower abdomen. Most of the major organs receive blood from branches of the abdominal aorta.

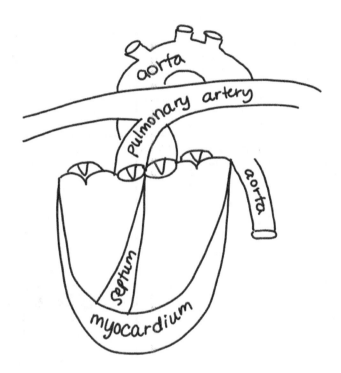

6. Just under the pulmonary trunk and arteries, connect the lines to create the ***left atrium and right atrium***. These are the top 2 chambers and receive blood returning to the heart from the body. ***Label the Right Atrium (R.A.), Left Atrium (L.A.), Right Ventricle (R.V.) and Left Ventricle (L.V).***

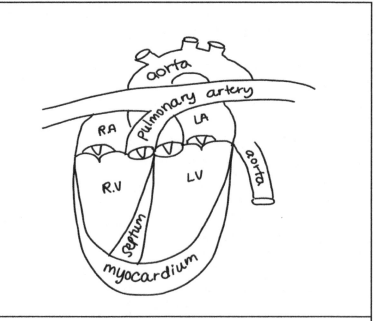

7. Connect the ***pulmonary veins*** to the ***Left Atrium*** on the right side and left side of the heart. *Make sure to draw 4 dots to represent the places where the pulmonary veins return oxygenated blood from the lungs into the left atrium of the heart.*

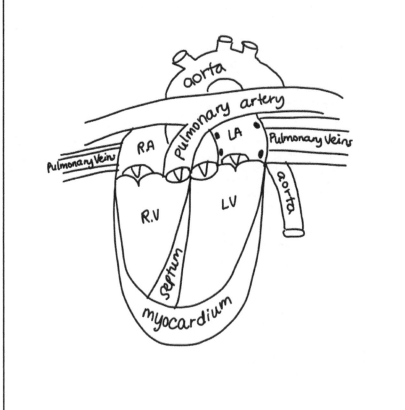

8. Draw the ***Superior Vena Cava*** above the Right Atrium and the ***Inferior Vena Cava*** next to the Right Ventricle. *Make sure to draw 2 dots to represent the places where they return deoxygenated blood from the body into the Right Atrium.*

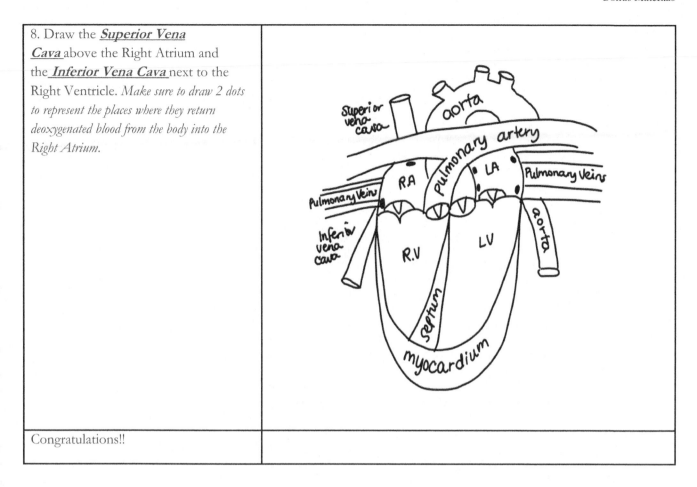

Congratulations!!

To see a video of this drawing, please visit https://ateacherontheedge.wordpress.com/2019/02/12/how-to-draw-an-anatomically-correct-heart-the-easy-way-just-in-time-for-valentines-day/

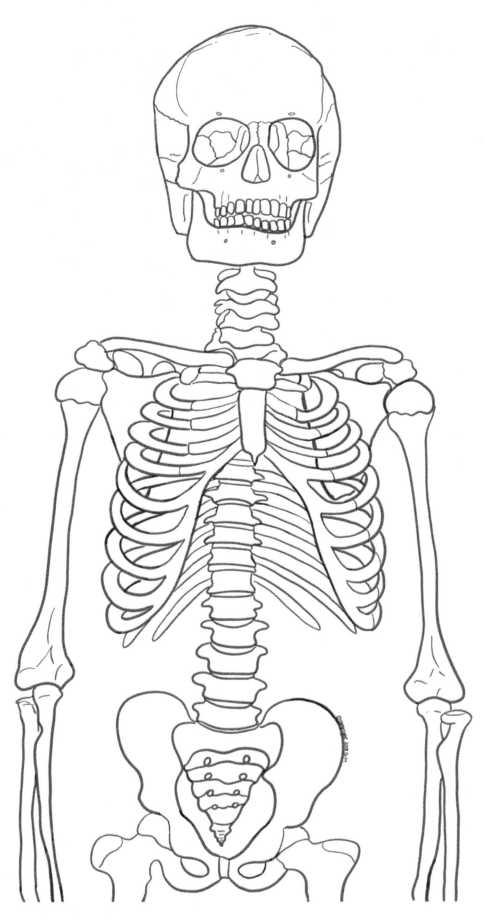

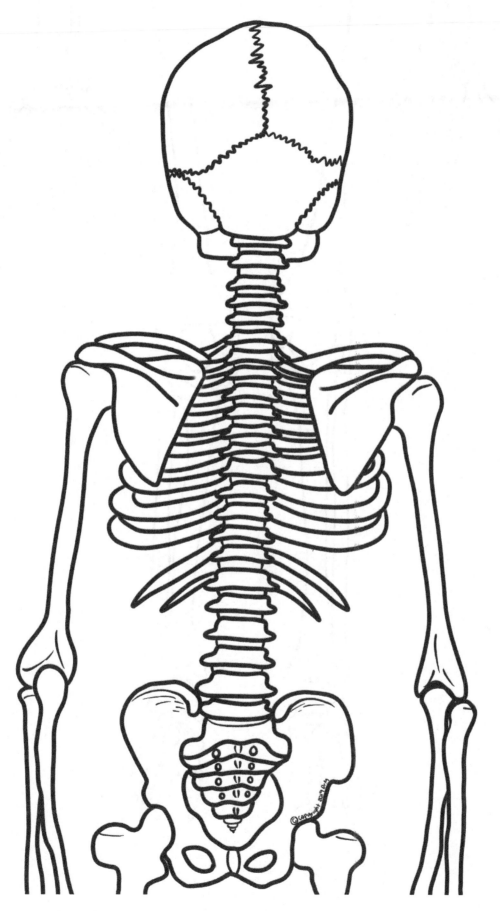

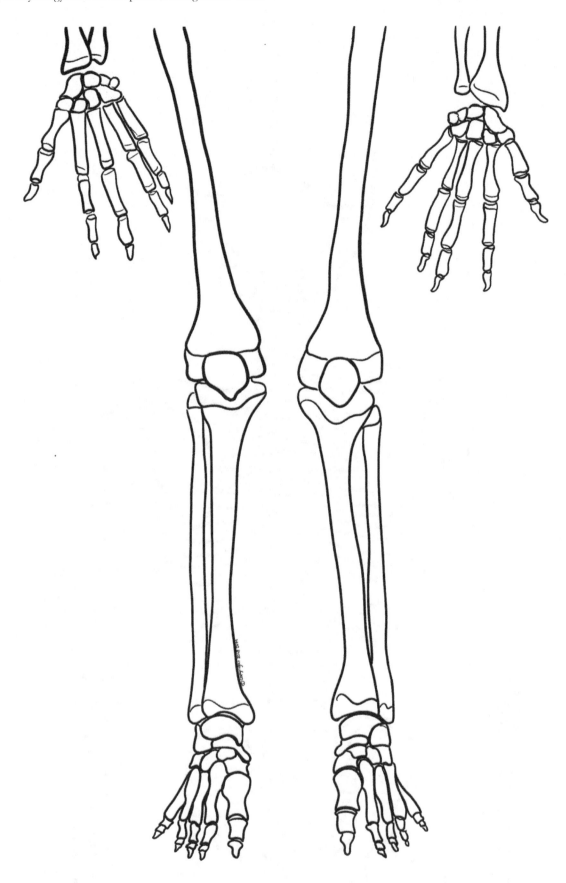

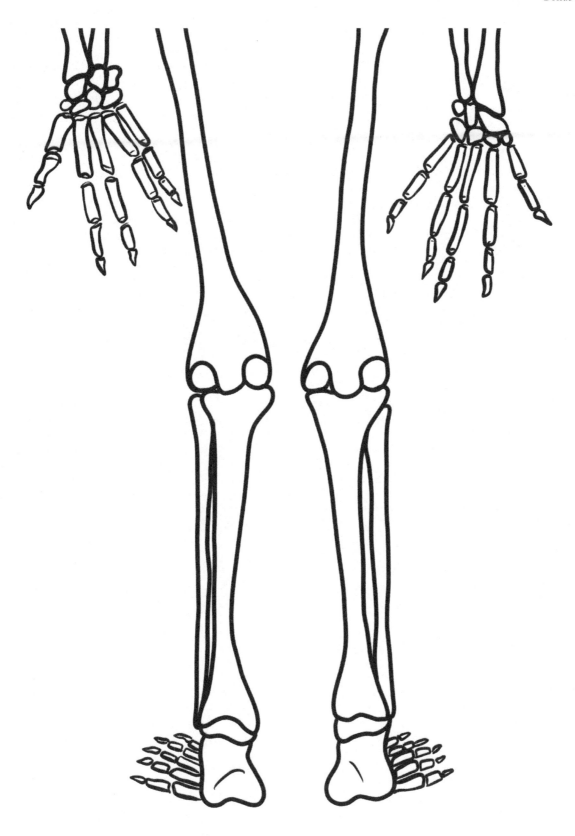

ANSWER KEYS

1. Introduction to Anatomy & Physiology KEY

Body Cavities and Membranes p.14 (Figure 1-7)

Cavity	Location (Dorsal or Ventral)	Membranes That Line this Cavity	Organs/ Structures In this Cavity
Cranial	Dorsal	Meninges	Brain
Spinal (Vertebral)	Dorsal	Meninges	Spinal Cord
Thoracic	Ventral	Serous (Pleura & Pericardia)	Heart, Lungs
Oral	Ventral	Mucosa	Teeth, Tongue, Gums
Otic	Ventral	Mucosa	Middle Ear Bones
Nasal	Ventral	Mucosa	Respiratory & Olfactory Structures
Orbital	Ventral	Mucosa	Eyes
Cardiac (in Thoracic)	Ventral	Serous (Pericardium)	Heart
Mediastinum (in Thoracic)	Ventral	Serous (Pleural)	
Pleural (in Thoracic)	Ventral	Serous (Pleural)	Lungs
Abdominal	Ventral	Serous (Peritoneum)	Kidneys, Ureters, Stomach, Spleen, Liver, Intestines, Gallbladder, and Pancreas.
Pelvic	Ventral	Serous (Peritoneum)	Urinary bladder and Reproductive organs.

Abdominopelvic Regions p. 18 (Figures 1-8 and 1-9)

Region	Organs in this Region
Right Hypochondriac	Liver, Gallbladder, Right Kidney, Small Intestine
Epigastric	Stomach, Liver, Pancreas, Duodenum (first part of small intestine), Spleen, Adrenal Glands
Left Hypochondriac	Spleen, Colon, Left Kidney, Pancreas
Right Lumbar	Gallbladder, Liver, Right Colon

Umbilical	Umbilicus (navel), Jejunum (the part of the small intestine between the duodenum and ileum), Ileum (the third portion of the small intestine, between the jejunum and the cecum), Duodenum
Left Lumbar	Descending Colon (the part of the large intestine that passes downward on the left side of the abdomen toward the rectum), Left Kidney
Right Iliac	Appendix, Cecum (a pouch connected to the junction of the small and large intestines)
Hypogastric	Urinary Bladder, Sigmoid Colon (the S-shaped last part of the large intestine, leading into the rectum), Female Reproductive Organs
Left Iliac	Descending Colon, Sigmoid Colon

Organs and Functions p.22 (Figure 1-10)

Organ/Structure	Function	Body System
Larynx	Speech	Respiratory
Trachea	Air passage	Respiratory
Lungs (R & L)	O_2/ CO_2 exchange	Respiratory
Liver	Detoxify blood	Digestive
Gallbladder	Store bile	Digestive
Cystic Duct	Tube for bile from gallbladder to duodenum	Digestive (*accessory)
Duodenum	1st part of small intestine; bile & pancreatic fluid released here	Digestive
Large Intestine -Ascending Colon -Transverse Colon -Descending Colon -Sigmoid Colon	Absorbs, transports wastes, & reclaims H_2O	Digestive
Appendix	Sm. Pouch of ascending colon (cecum)	Digestive
Heart	Pumps & circulates blood	Cardiovascular
Stomach	Chemical & physical digestion	Digestive

Spleen	Filters blood	Lymphatic/ Immune
Pancreas	Regulates blood sugar	Digestive
Small Intestine	Absorbs nutrients	Digestive
Urinary Bladder	Stores urine	Urinary

I. Body Planes p.24 (Figure 1-11)

Plane	Divides Body Into:
1. Sagittal/ Mid-sagittal (median)	Right and left sides
2. Frontal (coronal)	Anterior (front) and Posterior (back)
3. Transverse (cross-section)	Upper (top) and Lower (bottom)
4. Oblique	Diagonal

II. Directional Terms p. 25

Directional Terms	
Term	**Definition**
Superior (Cranial) "above"	Above; towards head end
Inferior (Caudal) "below"	Below; away from head
Anterior (Ventral) "in front of"	Front; belly side
Posterior (Dorsal) "behind"	Back; back side
Medial "middle"	Towards midline of body
Lateral "side"	Away from midline of body; towards side
Intermediate "between"	Between 2 things
Proximal	Close to body attachment
Distal	Far from body attachment

Supine	Face up; anterior side up
Prone	Face down; anterior side down
Superficial (External)	Towards surface
Deep (Internal)	Away from surface

III. Practice p. 26 (Figure 1-12)

<u>Practice:</u> Describe the anatomical relationship(s) that exist between each of the following parts. (There may be more than one answer for some of them). Always assume the body is in *anatomical position*. Answer should fit into the statement "The _____ is _____(anatomical term) to the _____"

1. elbow and wrist- <u>proximal, superior</u>

2. nose and chin- <u>superior</u>

3. skin and kidneys- <u>superficial</u>

4. lungs and heart-<u>lateral</u>

5. toes to ankle- <u>anterior</u>

6. scalp to skull-<u>superficial</u>

7. diaphragm to lung-<u>inferior</u>

8. heart to diaphragm-<u>superior</u>

9. head to neck-<u>superior</u>

10. esophagus to spine-<u>anterior</u>

11. brain to spinal cord- <u>superior</u>

12. wrist to hand-<u>proximal, superior</u>

13. fingers to hand-<u>distal, inferior</u>

14. kneecap to knee joint-<u>anterior, superficial</u>

15. eyes to nose-<u>lateral</u>

16. ears to head-<u>lateral</u>

17. thumb to hand-<u>superior, lateral</u>

18. little toe to big toe-<u>lateral</u>

19. eyebrow to eye-<u>superior</u>

20. inside corner of eye to outside corner of eye-<u>medial</u>

2. Integumentary System KEY

Layers of Skin p.32 (Figure 2-1)

Structure	Function/ Description
Epidermis	Outer layer of the skin, composed of keratinized stratified squamous epithelial tissue
Stratum Corneum	Outer layer of epidermis; 25 cell layers thick; contains keratin; function is protection; also called horny layer.
Stratum Lucidum	Very thin boundary layer found only in thick skin, commonly found in palms of hands and soles of feet; also called clear layer.
Stratum Granulosum	3-5 cell layers thick; contains lipids to create a water barrier; called the granular layer.
Stratum Spinosum	8-10 cell layers thick; spiny cells are tightly packed; called the prickly layer.
Stratum Basale	1 cell layer thick; contains stem cells; used to repair and produce new cells; also produces melanin also called stratum germanitivum.
Basement Membrane	Lies between the epidermis and the dermis; keeps the outside layer tightly connected to the inside layer.
Dermal Papillae	Projections from the dermis that extend upward into the epidermis; contain nerve endings for touch (Meissner's corpuscles) and capillaries.
Dermis	Deepest portion of the skin.
Pacinian Corpuscle	Detect pressure; found in dermis or hypodermis; also called lamellar corpuscles.
Hair Follicle	Deep in skin; regulate hair growth.
Hair Root	Part of the hair under the skin
Hair Shaft	Visible part of hair.
Sebaceous (Oil) Gland	Located all over body except for palms of hands and soles of feet; open into hair follicles; secrete sebum (oil).
Sebum	Oil secreted by sebaceous glands; functions are to soften hair and skin, waterproof skin, and prevent bacterial growth on skin.
Sudoriferous (Sweat) Gland	Most numerous type of glands; secrete sweat.
Arteriole/Venule	Arterioles distribute blood to capillary beds (sites of exchange with the body tissues). Capillaries lead back to small vessels (known as venules) that flow into the larger veins and eventually back to the heart.

Hypodermis	Not part of the skin but has some skin characteristics; made of mostly adipose tissue; anchors skin to underlying structures; also known as superficial fascia.
Adipose	Fat tissue

Hair Anatomy p.34 (Figure 2-2)

Structure	Function
Connective Tissue Sheath	Covers the outside of the hair follicle and is a layer connected with the dermis.
Hair Bulb	Forms the base of the hair follicle. In the hair bulb, living cells divide and grow to build the hair shaft.
Hair Follicle	Anchors each hair into the skin.
Hair Papilla	Contains many blood vessels that supply nutrients to nourish the growing hair.
Hair Root	Hair begins growing from a root in the bottom of the follicle. The root is made up of cells of protein. Blood from the blood vessels in the scalp feeds the root, which creates more cells and makes the hair grow.
Hair Shaft	The nongrowing portion of a hair that protrudes from the skin.
Sebaceous Gland	Secrete the oily, waxy substance called sebum
Arrector Pili Muscle	Tiny muscle that attaches to the base of a hair follicle at one end and to dermal tissue on the other end; used to generate heat when the body is cold by contracting all at once, causing the hair to stand up on the skin.

Nail Anatomy p.36 (Figure 2-3)

Structure	Function
Lunula	Crescent-shaped whitish area of the bed of a fingernail or toenail. The lunula is the visible part of the root of the nail.
Nail Matrix	Responsible for producing the nail plate itself. The size and thickness of the matrix decide the size and thickness of the nail.
Nail Plate	The fingernail itself; responsible for protection
Dermis	Thick layer of living tissue below the epidermis which forms the true skin, containing blood capillaries, nerve endings, sweat glands, hair follicles, and other structures.
Epidermis	Outermost of the three layers that make up the skin. It provides a barrier to infection from environmental pathogens and regulates the amount of water released from the body into the atmosphere through the skin

Skin p.34 (Figure 2-5)

Structure	Function
Epidermis	Outermost of the three layers that make up the skin. It provides a barrier to infection from environmental pathogens and regulates the amount of water released from the body into the atmosphere through the skin
Arrector pili muscle	Tiny muscle that attaches to the base of a hair follicle at one end and to dermal tissue on the other end; used to generate heat when the body is cold by contracting all at once, causing the hair to stand up on the skin.
Artery	Provide nutrients to the skin and help regulate body temperature.
Dermal Papillae	Increase the surface area of the dermis as well as contain many nerves and blood vessels that project toward the surface of the skin
Hair Follicle	Anchors each hair into the skin
Krause's Corpuscle	Detects cold; in Dermis
Meissner's Corpuscle	Detects touch; in Dermis
Melanin	Blocks UV light and protects deeper layers from its damaging effects.
Nociceptors (Free Nerve Endings)	Detect pain; in Epidermis
Pacinian Corpuscle	Detects pressure; in Dermis
Ruffini Corpuscle	Detects heat; in Dermis
Sebaceous (Oil) Gland	Secrete the oily, waxy substance called sebum
Sebum	Waterproofs and lubricates the skin and hair of mammals.
Sudoriferous (Sweat) Gland	Secrete water (sweat) to the skin surface to regulate temperature.
Tactile Corpuscle	Detects light touch; in Epidermis
Vein	Provide nutrients to the skin and help regulate body temperature.
Dermis	Thick layer of living tissue below the epidermis which forms the true skin, containing blood capillaries, nerve endings, sweat glands, hair follicles, and other structures.
Hypodermis	Subcutaneous layer found just beneath the skin; contains fat used as insulation and padding for the body.
Fat (adipose)	Used for insulation

3. Skeletal System KEY

The Haversian System/ Osteon p.48 (Figure 3-2)

Structure	Description or Function
Central Canal	Opening in the center of an osteon; contains an artery (for oxygenated blood), vein (for deoxygenated blood), & nerve (for electrical impulse); run longitudinally along the long axis of the bone parallel to the bone's surface
Lacuna	"The lagoon"; a cavity that contains a bone cell (osteocytes); arranged in concentric rings
Osteocyte	Mature bone cell; sits within the lacuna and form networks via canaliculi
Matrix	Substance found between cells (intercellular) substance of bone; the part of the bone tissue that forms most of the mass of the bone; comprised of organic and inorganic substances. made of collagenous fibers, ground substance, (the organic parts) as well as inorganic salts (hydroxyapatite).
Artery	For oxygenated blood
Vein	For deoxygenated blood
Nerve	For electrical impulse

Cross-Section of a Long Bone (Lamellar Arrangement) p.50 (Figure 3-3)

Structure	Description or Function
Concentric Lamellae	lamellae around the outside of each osteon (Haversian system)
Interstitial Lamellae	irregular wedges of lamellar bone between osteons
Circumferential Lamellae	lamellae around the outside circumference of the bone

Matching p. 51 Practice   1. D   2. E   3. A   4. C   5. B

Term Group	Which Term Doesn't Belong?	Why Do You Think It Doesn't Belong?
Epiphysis surface, Articular cartilage, Periosteum, Hyaline cartilage	Periosteum	All are part of the end of the bone except the periosteum (membrane on outside of bone not present on epiphysis)
Hematopoiesis, Red marrow, Yellow marrow, Spongy	Yellow Marrow	All are involved in red blood cell production except

bone		yellow marrow (stores fat)
Lamellae, Canaliculi, Circulation, Osteoblasts	Osteoblasts	All involve circulation of nutrients into the bone except osteoblasts (secretes the matrix for bone formation)
Osteon, Canaliculi, Central canal, Marrow cavity	Marrow Cavity	All are part of the Haversian System (osteon) except the marrow cavity (where red &/or yellow marrow is stored)

Anatomy of the Long Bone p.54 (Figure 3-4)

Structure	Description or Function
Epiphysis	ends of bone; made of spongy bone
Diaphysis	shaft of bone; made of compact bone
Periosteum	outside covering of bone; made of fibrous connective tissue
Endosteum	thin vascular membrane of connective tissue; lines the inner surface that forms the medullary cavity of long bones
Articular Cartilage	covers external end (epiphysis) of bone; used to decrease friction at joints; made of hyaline cartilage
Epiphyseal Line/ Plate	also known as the growth plate (in kids); hyaline cartilage plate near the epiphysis in the long bone; where new bone growth in length takes place; plate replace by the epiphyseal line in adults
Medullary Cavity	cavity of the bone shaft (diaphysis); contains yellow marrow (mostly fat) in adults; contains red marrow (for RBC production) in infants
Spongy Bone	also known as cancellous bone or trabecular bone; very porous; highly vascularized and contains red bone marrow that is used in erythropoiesis (RBC production). It is usually located at the ends of the long bones (the epiphyses)
Compact Bone	also known as cortical bone; dense material that is used to create much of the hard structure of the skeleton; formed from osteons, which are circular units of bone material and blood vessels. It is usually located in the diaphysis (shaft) of bone.

Matching: 1. B   2. E   3. A   4. C/D   5. A   6. C

Skeletal System p. 56

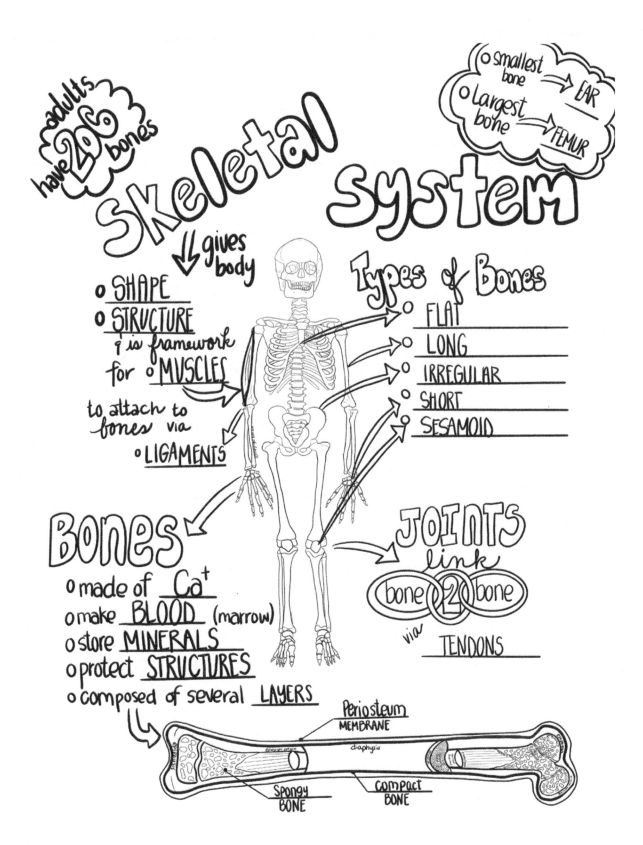

Anatomy of the Skull (Inferior View) p.64 (Figure 3-10)

Structure	Description or Function
Maxilla	Form the upper jaw; hold upper teeth in place
Zygomatic Bone	Cheek bones that articulate with the maxilla, the temporal bones, and the sphenoid bone.
Temporal Bone	Form the temple.
Palatine Bone	Bones that compose the roof of the mouth; hard palate
Vomer	Unpaired facial bone that forms part of the nasal septum.
Parietal Bone	Form most of the sides of the skull.
Styloid Process	Slender spike of bone behind the ear that is the anchor point for neck, tongue muscles, and ligaments that hold the hyoid bone in place.
Jugular Foramen	Hole where jugular vein and 3 cranial nerves pass.
Carotid Canal	Space where carotid artery passes.
Occipital Condyle	Rounded knobs that articulate with vertebrae and allow for head nodding.
Foramen Magnum	Large hole where spinal cord passes through in order to attach to the brain.
Occipital Bone	Back of skull.

Anatomy of the Skull (Lateral View) p.66 (Figure 3-11)

Structure	Description or Function
Frontal bone	Thick plate that forms the forehead.
Infraorbital Foramen	Hole above the eye orbit for blood vessels and nerves
Nasal Bone	Form the bridge of the nose.
Sphenoid Bone	Bat-shaped bone in the middle of the skull that articulates with all cranial bones.
Lacrimal Bone	Smallest and most fragile bones of the face; located at inner corner of eye under tear ducts.
Ethmoid Bone	Upper portion of nasal cavity, forms part of the eye orbits at front of skull. The ethmoid connects to all the bones of the skull and face and essentially holds all of the bones in place.
Maxilla	Form the upper jaw (maxilla is singular). These paired bones hold the upper teeth in place

Zygomatic Bone	cheek bones that articulate with the maxilla, the temporal bones, and the sphenoid bone.
Mental Foramen	Hole in the lower jawbone near the chin; for blood vessels and nerves to pass through.
Mandible	Largest and strongest bone of the face that forms the lower jaw bone; holds the lower teeth in place.
Zygomatic Process of Temporal Bone	Forms cheekbone where it meets the temporal process of the zygomatic bone.
External Auditory Meatus	Pathway running from the outer ear to the middle ear.
Mastoid Process	Bump behind the ear where neck muscles attach.
Styloid Process	Slender spike of bone behind the ear that is the anchor point for neck, tongue muscles, and ligaments that hold the hyoid bone in place.
Temporal Bone	Form the temple
Parietal Bone	Form most of the sides of the skull.
Occipital Bone	Back of skull.
Squamosal Suture	Divides the parietal and temporal bones.
Coronal Suture	Divides the frontal and parietal bones.
Lambdoid Suture	Divides the parietal and occipital bones.
Sagittal Suture	Divides the 2 parietal bones.

Anatomy of the Skull (Frontal View) p.70 (Figure 3-12)

Structure	Description or Function
Frontal Bone	Thick plate that forms the forehead.
Parietal Bone	Form most of the sides of the skull.
Nasal Bone	Form the bridge of the nose.
Sphenoid Bone	Bat-shaped bone in the middle of the skull that articulates with all cranial bones.
Temporal Bone	Forms the temple.
Ethmoid Bone	Upper portion of nasal cavity, forms part of the eye orbits at front of skull. The ethmoid connects to all the bones of the skull and face and essentially holds all of the bones in place.

Zygomatic Bone	Cheek bones that articulate with the maxilla, the temporal bones, and the sphenoid bone.
Lacrimal Bone	Smallest and most fragile bones of the face; located at inner corner of eye under tear ducts.
Maxilla	Form the upper jaw (maxilla is singular). These paired bones hold the upper teeth in place
Perpendicular Plate	Forms part of the nasal septum.
Nasal Conchae	Also called Turbinate, or Turbinal, any of several thin, scroll-shaped bony elements forming the upper chambers of the nasal cavities.
Supraorbital Foramen	Small groove at superior and medial margin of the orbit in the frontal bone for the passage of nerves and blood vessels.
Mental Foramen	Passageway for nerves to the chin.

Vertebral Column p.72 (Figure 3-13)

Structure	Description /Location	Number	Concave/Convex
Atlas	C1 vertebra; has no body.	1	n/a
Axis	C2 vertebra; has the dens process.	1	n/a
Cervical	In neck	7	concave
Thoracic	In chest	12	convex
Lumbar	In lower back	5	concave
Sacral	In hips	1 (5 fused)	convex
Coccyx	Tailbone	1 (4 fused)	n/a

Vertebrae p.75 (Figure 3-14)

Structure	Description or Function
Body of Vertebra	Major weight-bearing structure.
Transverse Process	Project outward to sides.
Spinous Process	Projects up from center.

Left Hand (Palmar and Dorsal Aspects) p.78-80 (Figures 3-15 and 3-16)

Structure	Description
Distal phalanges	Fingertips
Intermediate phalanges	Finger bones located just above the knuckle
Proximal phalanges	Finger bones located just below the knuckle
Metacarpals	Located between the phalanges and carpals; form the palm of the hand
Trapezium	Four-sided bone that articulates with four bones (the 1st and 2nd metacarpals, the scaphoid and the trapezoid); "table"
Trapezoid	Wedge-shaped bone that gets its name due to the similarity to the trapezium. It is the smallest bone in the distal row of carpal bones and articulates with four bones (the 2nd metacarpal, the trapezium, the capitate and the scaphoid bone); "resembles a table"
Scaphoid	Boat-shaped bone that articulates proximally with the radius. It is the largest bone in the proximal row of carpal bone; "boat-shaped"
Capitate	Head-shaped bone that is the largest carpal bone. It articulates with five bones (the 3rd metacarpal, the trapezoid, scaphoid, lunate and hamate); "head-shaped"
Lunate	Crescent-shaped bone that is found centrally in the carpal bones between the scaphoid and triquetrum and articulates proximally with the radius; "moon-shaped"
Hamate	Wedge-shaped bone that articulates with five carpal bones (the 4th and 5th metacarpals, the capitate, the triquetrum and the trapezoid); easily distinguishable due to its shape and a hook-like process which extends towards the palmar surface; "hooked bone"
Triquetrum	Pyramidal bone that lies between the lunate and pisiform bones on the medial side of the proximal row of carpal bones; "three-cornered"
Pisiform (*only seen in palmar view) Figure 3-15	Small round sesamoid bone found in the tendon of the flexor carpi ulnaris. It articulates with the anterior surface of the triquetrum bone and extends anteriorly to form the bump that can be felt at the medial base of the hand; "pea-shaped"
Ulna	Long bone found in forearm that is on the medial side (in anatomical position)
Radius	Long bone found in forearm that is on the lateral side (in anatomical position)

Anatomy of the Right Foot (Dorsal and Plantar Aspects) p.82-84 (Figures 3-17 and 3-18)

Structure	Description
Distal phalanges	Ends of toes
Intermediate phalanges	Toe bones located just above the knuckle
Proximal phalanges	Toe bones located just below the knuckle
Metatarsals	Located between the phalanges and tarsals; form the arch of the foot
Talus	Most superior bone of the ankle (tarsus); rests on top of the calcaneus
Calcaneus	Heel bone; largest and strongest bone of the foot.
Navicular	Located between the head of the talus posteriorly and the three cuneiforms anteriorly. Its name is derived from its resemblance to a small boat.
Medial Cuneiform	Wedge-shaped; named based on their relative position (inside)
Intermediate Cuneiform	Wedge-shaped; named based on their relative position (middle)
Lateral Cuneiform	Wedge-shaped; named based on their relative position (outside)
Cuboid	Articulates posteriorly with the end of the calcaneus. It is the most lateral bone in distal row of tarsal bones.

Bones p.85

Bone	Description of Bone	Number Found in Body
I. Axial Skeleton— Skull & Face		
Cranium (8)		
Parietal	Form roof and sides of cranium	2
Ethmoid	Separates nasal cavity from brain; located at roof of nose between the orbits	1
Sphenoid	Bat-shaped bone that makes up floor of cranium	1
Temporal	Sides and base of cranium around the ear	2
Occipital	Back/base of skull	1
Frontal	Forehead	1

Face (14)		
Vomer	V shaped bone that divides the nasal cavity	1
Nasal Conchae	Scroll-shaped; extends horizontally along lateral wall of nasal cavity	2
Nasal	Bridge of nose	2
Maxilla	Upper bones of jaw; behind upper lip	2
Mandible	Lower jaw	1
Palatine	Roof of mouth	2
Zygomatic	Cheekbones	2
Lacrimal	At corner of each eye where tear duct is located	2
Ear (6)		
Ossicles		
• Malleus	Hammer	2
• Incus	Anvil	2
• Stapes	Stirrup	2
Neck (1)		
Hyoid	U shaped bone in neck where tongue attaches	1

II. Axial Skeleton— Vertebral Column

Backbone (26)		
Cervical Vertebrae	Vertebrae in neck	7
Thoracic Vertebrae	Vertebrae in chest	12
Lumbar Vertebrae	Vertebrae in lower back	5
Sacrum	Broad flat bone at end of backbone; made of 5 bones fused	1
Coccyx	Tailbone; made of 4 bones fused	1
III. Axial Skeleton— Thoracic Cage		
Thoracic Cage (25)		
Ribs		

• True	Attach to sternum	10 (5 pair)
• False	Attach to each other or only to vertebrae (floating)	14 (7 pair)
Sternum	Breastbone	1
IV. Appendicular Skeleton—Pectoral Girdle		
Pectoral Girdle/Upper Limbs (64)		
Scapula	Shoulder blade	2
Clavicle	Collarbone	2
Humerus	Upper arm bone	2
Ulna	Lower arm bone on pink side; forms elbow	2
Radius	Lower arm bone on thumb side; rotates	2
Carpals	Wrist bones	16
Metacarpals	Bones that make up the palm of hand	10
Phalanges (proximal, intermediate, distal)	Fingers	28
Pectoral Girdle/Lower Limbs (62)		
Os Coxa (ilium, ischium, pelvic)	Hip bone	2
Femur	Thigh bone	2
Tibia	Shin bone; larger bone in lower leg	2
Fibula	Smaller bone in lower leg	2
Patella	Kneecap	2
Tarsals	Ankle bones	14
Metatarsals	Bones that make up arch of foot	10
Phalanges (proximal, intermediate, distal)	Toes	28
Total Bones		**206**

4. Muscular System KEY

Head & Neck p.112

Muscle	Action	Number
Frontalis	Raises eyebrows	2
Orbicularis oculi	Closes eyes	3
Temporalis	Moves ears slightly	1
Orbicularis oris	Puckers lips	4
Buccinator	Holds food between teeth when chewing	7
Masseter	Clenches teeth tightly	6
Zygomatic	Raises corner of mouth as in smiling	5
Sternocleidomastoid	Pulls head to 1 side, flexes neck or elevates sternum	9
Trapezius	Shrugs shoulders; rotates & moves scapula	10
Platysma	Draws angle of mouth downward when head leaned back	8

Trunk (Anterior) p.113

Muscle	Action	Number
Pectoralis major	Raises upper arm & pulls it across chest	1
Rectus abdominis	Pulls ribs & pelvis in; curves back as in doing crunches	3
External oblique	Tenses abdominal wall & compresses abdominal contents	5
Internal oblique	Tenses abdominal wall & compresses abdominal contents	4
Transverse abdominis	Compresses abdomen	2

Arm & Forearm (Anterior) p.114

Muscle	Action	Number
Deltoid	Raises upper arm & pulls it slightly forward	1
Triceps brachii	Extends elbow & lower arm	4
Biceps brachii	Flexes elbow & lower arm and rotates hand palm up	3
Brachioradialis	Flexes lower arm (forearm) when palm is down	5
Extensor carpi radialis longus	Extends wrist & abducts hand	8
Extensor digitorum	Extends fingers	7

Extensor carpi ulnaris	Extends wrist & adducts hand	6
Flexor carpi ulnaris	Flexes wrist & adducts hand laterally (towards ulna)	9
Pectoralis major	Raises upper arm & pulls it across chest	2

Hip, Thigh, & Lower Leg (Anterior) p.116

Muscle	Action	Number
Sartorius	"tailor's muscle"; longest muscle; flexes knee & hip, abducts & rotates thigh laterally (as in sitting cross-legged); draws 1 leg over the other	8
Rectus femoris (Quadriceps)	Extends knee	2
Vastus lateralis (Quadriceps)	Extends knee	1
Vastus medialis (Quadriceps)	Extends knee	3
Adductor longus (Adductors)	Adducts & flexes thigh	6
Iliopsoas (Adductors)	Flexes hip at thigh	4
Pectineus (Adductors)	Adducts, flexes, & medially rotates thigh; primary function is hip flexion	5
Gracilis (Adductors)	Adducts (extends) thigh, flexes & medially rotates leg; highest muscle inside thigh	7
Gastrocnemius	Points toes down; flexes (bends) knee; large calf muscle	12
Soleus	Points toes down; small muscle that works with gastrocnemius	11
Tibialis anterior	Flexes foot & raises toes	10
Fibularis	Plantar flexes & everts foot; helps keep foot flat on ground	9

Trunk (Posterior) p.118

Muscle	Action	Number
Trapezius	Shrugs shoulders; rotates & moves scapula	1
Latissimus dorsi	Lowers upper arm & pulls it back	2

Arm (Posterior) p.119

Muscle	Action	Number
Deltoid	Raises upper arm & pulls it slightly forward	2

Triceps brachii	Extends elbow & lower arm	1

Hips, Thigh, & Lower Leg (Posterior) p.120

Muscle	Action	Number
Gluteus maximus	Extends thigh away from body at hip	2
Gluteus medius	Abducts & rotates thigh medially	1
Semimembranosus (Hamstrings)	Flexes (bends) knee, rotates lower leg medially & extends thigh	3
Biceps femoris (Hamstrings)	Flexes (bends) knee, rotates lower leg medially & extends thigh	4
Semitendinosus (Hamstrings)	Flexes (bends) knee, rotates lower leg medially & extends thigh	5
Gastrocnemius	Points toes down; flexes (bends) knee; large calf muscle	6

5. Nervous System KEY

The Neuron p.131 (Figure 5-3)

Structure	Description or Function
Axon	A long, slender projection of a nerve cell (neuron) that typically conducts electrical impulses away from the neuron's cell body.
Axonal Terminals	Located at the end of the axon; contain neurotransmitters.
Cell Body	Contains the nucleus and connects to the dendrites to axons; controls all the function of the neuron.
Dendrite	Brings information into the neuron.
Myelin Sheath	Insulating layer made up of protein and fatty substances that forms around nerves; allows electrical impulses to transmit quickly and efficiently along the nerve cells.
Node of Ranvier	Gaps in the myelin sheath coating on the neural axon that allows the electrical impulse to move quickly down the axon.
Schwann Cell	Makes myelin for the axons of the PNS.
Axolemma	Contains ion channels through which ions can flow rapidly; responsible for maintaining the membrane potential of the neuron.

The Spinal Cord p.138 (Figure 5-6)

Structure	Description or Function
Dorsal Root	Emerges directly from the spinal cord and travels to the dorsal root ganglion.
Dorsal Root Ganglion	Contains the cell bodies of sensory neurons that bring information from the periphery to the spinal cord.
Ventral Root	Contains outgoing, efferent fibers that carry information that controls motor or glandular functions.
Spinal Nerve	A mixed nerve which carries motor, sensory, and autonomic signals between the spinal cord and the body. In the human body there are 31 pairs of spinal nerves that exit on each side of the vertebral column.
Anterior Horn	Contains cell bodies of motor neurons that innervate skeletal muscle to cause movement.
Posterior Horn	Contains interneurons that make connections within the spinal cord, as well as neurons that enter ascending sensory pathways.
Grey Matter	Shaped like a butterfly and consists of cell bodies of interneurons and motor neurons, as well as neuroglia cells and unmyelinated axons.

White Matter	Composed of bundles of myelinated nerve cell processes (or axons) that connect various grey matter areas of the brain to each other and carry nerve impulses between neurons.
Central Canal	Fluid-filled space in the spinal cord that allows for cerebrospinal fluid transport.
Pia Mater	Covers the surface of the brain and spinal cord; contains the cerebrospinal fluid which cushions.
Arachnoid Mater	Middle layer of the meninges that connects the dura mater and pia mater; loosely covers the brain and spinal cord and gets its name from its web-like appearance. It has a rich supply of blood vessels which provide nutrients to nervous tissue.
Dura Mater	Top layer of the meninges, lying beneath the bone tissue.

Areas of the Brain and Associated Functions p.147

	Region	Functions	Arrangement of Grey / White Matter
	I. BRAINSTEM		Grey matter surrounded by white matter
Composed of:			
Cranial Nerve #s 9, 10, 11, 12	(1) Medulla	1. heart rate 2. blood vessel diameter 3. breathing 4. reflex center (vomiting, cough, sneeze, swallow)	
5, 6, 7, 8	(2) Pons	1. contains ascending/descending nerve tracts 2. relay center betw. cerebrum & cerebellum	
3, 4	(3) Midbrain	1. movement of head to respond to light/sound 2. change shape of lens in eye	
	(4) Reticular Formation	Responsible for keeping brain alert	

	Region	Functions	Arrangement of Grey / White Matter
	II. INTERBRAIN (DIENCEPHALON)		Primarily grey matter
Composed of:			
Cranial Nerve #s 1, 2	(1) Thalamus	1. influences mood 2. registers pain 3. relay center to cerebrum 4. memory processing/ learning	

	(2) Hypothalamus	1. temperature 2. hunger 3. thirst 4. pleasure/ displeasure 5. growth 6. secrete & control hormones 7. odor (mammillary body) 8. appetite 9. rage/ anger	
	(3) Pineal Body	1. sexual maturity 2. sleep/wake cycle (secretes melatonin)	
	(4) Limbic System	"emotional brain"; emotion, behavior, motivation, memory, olfaction	
	Region	*Functions*	*Arrangement of Grey / White Matter*
	III. CEREBRUM	1. motor function 2. sensory function 3. association (integrate information)	Grey matter outside, white matter inside
	IV. CEREBELLUM	1. coordination 2. tone 3. balance	

Nervous System p.148 (Figures 5-6 and 5-10)

Structure	Function
Spinal Cord	Roles include relaying messages from the brain to different parts of the body, performing an action, passing messages from sensory receptors to the brain, and coordinating certain reflexes.
Frontal	Controls important cognitive skills in humans, such as emotional expression, problem solving, memory, language, judgment, and sexual behaviors.
Temporal	Involved in primary auditory perception, such as hearing, and holds the primary auditory cortex.
Parietal	Functions in processing sensory information regarding the location of parts of the body as well as interpreting visual information and processing language and mathematics.
Occipital	Primarily responsible for vision
Cerebellum	Receives information from the sensory systems, the spinal cord, and other parts of the brain and then regulates motor movements. It also coordinates voluntary movements such as posture, balance, coordination, and speech, resulting in smooth and balanced muscular activity.
Arbor Vitae	Made of white matter; brings sensory and motor information to and from the cerebellum.

Corpus Callosum	Bridge between right and left hemispheres of brain; primary function of the corpus callosum is to integrate motor, sensory, and cognitive performances between the cerebral cortex on one side of the brain to the same region on the other side.
Pineal Gland	Produces melatonin
Thalamus	Large mass of gray matter in the dorsal part of the diencephalon of the brain with several functions such as relaying of sensory signals, including motor signals to the cerebral cortex, and the regulation of consciousness, sleep, and alertness
Hypothalamus	Small region of the brain located at the base of the brain, near the pituitary gland; plays a crucial role in many important functions including: releasing hormones. regulating body temperature.
Pituitary Gland	Pea-sized *gland* that housed within a bony structure (Sella turcica) at the base of the brain; The *pituitary* controls the function of most other endocrine *glands* and is therefore sometimes called the master *gland*.
Midbrain	Serves important functions in motor movement, particularly movements of the eye, and in auditory and visual processing.
Pons	Involved in the control of breathing, communication between different parts of the brain, and sensations such as hearing, taste, and balance.
Medulla	Directly controls certain ANS responses, such as heart rate, breathing, blood vessel dilation, digestion, sneezing, swallowing and vomiting. It is a portion of the brainstem, located just below the pons and just above the spinal cord.

6. Special Senses KEY

Anatomy of Smell p.154 (Figure 6-2)

Structure	Function/Description
Cribriform Plate	Sieve-like structure of the ethmoid bone that transmits the olfactory nerves which carry the sense of smell.
Nasal Cavity	Large, air-filled space above and behind the nose in the middle of the face.
Nasopharynx	Upper part of the pharynx that connects with the nasal cavity above the soft palate.
Olfactory Bulb	Structure found on the inferior (bottom) side of each cerebral hemisphere; located near the front of the brain.
Olfactory Nerve Fibers	Collection of sensory nerve fibers that extend from the olfactory epithelium to the olfactory bulb, passing through the many openings of the cribriform plate.

The Tongue p.157 (Figure 6-3)

Structure	Function/Description
Circumvallate Papillae	Large, round structures located at the base of the tongue; house several thousand taste buds that allow you not only to taste, but also to detect temperature and touch through sensory cells they contain.
Filiform Papilla	Most common type of lingual papillae; small and round and do not contain taste buds.
Foliate Papillae	Leaf-shaped papillae clustered on the back edges of the tongue; also contain taste buds.
Fungiform Papillae	Mushroom-shaped papillae located primarily at the tip of the tongue; contain taste buds and sensory cells.
Lingual Tonsil	Two small mounds of lymphatic tissue located at the base of the tongue, one on either side.
Palatine Tonsil	Pair of soft tissue masses located at the rear of the throat (pharynx).

The Eye p.162 (Figure 6-6)

Structure	Function/Description
Anterior Chamber	Aqueous humor-filled chamber located between the cornea and iris.

Aqueous Humor	Thin, watery fluid located in the anterior and posterior chambers of the eye; supplies nutrients and nourishment to parts of the eye that lack blood supply and removes waste.
Choroid Coat	Vascular central layer of the eye lying between the retina and sclera. Its function is to provide nourishment to the outer layers of the retina through blood vessels.
Ciliary Body	Part of the eye that includes the ciliary muscle (which controls the shape of the lens) and the ciliary epithelium (which produces the aqueous humor). The vitreous humor is produced in the non-pigmented portion of the ciliary body.
Cornea	Clear, protective outer layer of the eye; serves as a barrier against dirt, germs, and other particles that can harm the eye. The cornea is also capable of filtering out some amounts of the sun's ultraviolet light.
Fovea Centralis	Small, central pit located in the center of the macula lutea of the retina. It is composed of closely packed cones in the eye and is the center of the eye's sharpest vision and the location of most color perception.
Iris	Colored part of the human eye; responsible for controlling the diameter and size of the pupil and therefore, the amount of light reaching the retina.
Lens	Transparent, flexible tissue that is located directly behind the iris and the pupil; helps to focus light and images on the retina (along with the cornea).
Macula	Small, sensitive area in the center of the retina that provides clear central vision. The fovea is located in the center of the macula and provides the sharpest detail vision.
Optic Disk	Disk on the retina at the point where the optic nerve enters the eye; lacks visual receptors and so creates a blind spot.
Optic Nerve	Carries the impulses formed by the retina to the brain.
Posterior Chamber	Vitreous chamber located between the lens and the retina.
Pupil	Hole located in the center of the iris of the eye that allows light to strike the retina.
Retina	Light-sensitive tissue that lines the inside surface of the eye. Cells in the retina convert incoming light into electrical impulses and carry them to the brain via the optic nerve where they are interpreted as visual images.
Sclera	Tough, white outer coating of fibrous tissue that covers the entire eyeball, except for the cornea; where the muscles that move the eye are attached.
Vitreous Humor	Transparent, gel-like substance that maintains the shape of the eye, as well as absorbs shocks to the eye and keeps the retina connected to the back wall of the eye. Light passes through the vitreous on its way to the retina.

The Ear p.166

Structure	Function/Description
Cochlea	Spiral cavity of the inner ear that contains the Organ of Corti that produces nerve impulses in response to sound vibrations.
External Acoustic Meatus	Air-filled tube that extends from the pinna (auricle) of the external ear into the temporal bone to the tympanic membrane.
Incus (Anvil)	Anvil-shaped ossicle in the middle ear that receives vibrations from the malleus and transmits them to the stapes.
Internal Acoustic Meatus	Tube where facial nerve enters the internal auditory meatus.
Malleus (Hammer)	Hammer-shaped ossicle of the middle ear that connects the incus to the tympanic membrane (eardrum).
Oval Window	Membrane-covered opening that leads from the middle ear to the vestibule of the inner ear. The stapes bone transmits vibrations to the oval window. As the stapes bone moves into the oval window, the round window membrane moves out, allowing movement of the fluid and hair cells within the cochlea resulting in hearing.
Pinna (auricle)	Outer ear
Round Window	One of the two openings from the middle ear into the inner ear; allows fluid in the cochlea to move, which in turn ensures that hair cells of the basilar membrane will be stimulated so hearing will occur.
Semicircular Canals	Three small, fluid-filled tubes in the inner ear situated at right angles to each other; provide information about body orientation to the brain to help maintain balance.
Stapes (Stirrup)	Stirrup-shaped ossicle that rests on the oval window and articulates with the incus.
Tympanic Membrane (Eardrum)	Thin layer of tissue that receives sound vibrations from the outer air and transmits them to the ossicles of the middle ear.

7. Endocrine System KEY

Brain p.173 (Figure 7-1)

Structure	Function
Hypothalamus	The link between the endocrine and nervous systems. The hypothalamus produces releasing and inhibiting hormones, which stop and start the production of other hormones throughout the body.
Pineal Gland	Produces melatonin, which helps maintain circadian rhythm and regulate reproductive hormones.
Pituitary Gland	Often called the "master gland" because its hormones control other parts of the endocrine system (namely the thyroid gland, adrenal glands, ovaries, and testes). The hormones of the pituitary gland help regulate the functions of other endocrine glands. It has two parts (anterior and posterior lobe) which have very specific functions.
Anterior Lobe of Pituitary	Releases hormones upon receiving releasing or inhibiting hormones from the hypothalamus. These hormones tell the anterior lobe whether to release more of a specific hormone or stop production of the hormone. Anterior Lobe Hormones: • Adrenocorticotropic hormone (ACTH)-stimulates the adrenal glands to produce hormones. • Follicle-stimulating hormone (FSH)-works with LH to ensure normal functioning of the ovaries and testes. • Growth hormone (GH)-essential in early years to maintaining a healthy body composition and for growth in children. In adults, it aids healthy bone and muscle mass and affects fat distribution. • Luteinizing hormone (LH)-works with FSH to ensure normal functioning of the ovaries and testes. • Prolactin-stimulates breast milk production. • Thyroid-stimulating hormone (TSH)-stimulates the thyroid gland to produce hormones.
Posterior Lobe of Pituitary	Contains the ends of nerve cells which come from the hypothalamus. The hypothalamus sends hormones directly to the posterior lobe via these nerves, and then the pituitary gland releases them. Posterior Lobe Hormones: • Anti-diuretic hormone (ADH)-prompts the kidneys to increase water absorption in the blood. • Oxytocin-involved in a variety of processes, such as contracting the uterus during childbirth and stimulating breast milk production.

Ovaries and Testes p.174 (Figures 7-2 and 7-3)

Structure	Function
Ovary	Secrete hormones (estrogen and progesterone) that are vital to normal reproductive development and fertility.
Testes	Secrete testosterone—a hormone that is vital to the normal development of male physical characteristics.

Parathyroid, Thymus, and Thyroid Glands p.179 (Figure 7-6)

Structure	Function
Parathyroid glands	Produce a hormone called parathyroid hormone (PTH) that raises the blood calcium level by breaking down the bone (where most of the body's calcium is stored) and causing calcium release.
Thymus	Produces several hormones that serves vital roles in the training and development of T-lymphocytes or T cells, an extremely important type of white blood cell.
Thyroid gland	Main role in the endocrine system is to regulate your metabolism by producing T3 and T4 hormones.

Adrenal Gland p.183 (Figure 7-8)

Structure	Function
Adrenal Gland Cortex (outside)	Responsible for producing certain steroid hormones, including aldosterone and cortisol which helps regulate your metabolism, sugar levels, and blood pressure. Adrenal glands are controlled by the pituitary gland.
Adrenal Gland Medulla (inside)	

Pancreas p.184 (Figure 7-9)

Structure	Function
Pancreas	The endocrine component of the pancreas consists of islet cells (islets of Langerhans) that create and release important hormones directly into the bloodstream. Two of the main pancreatic hormones are insulin, which acts to lower blood sugar, and glucagon, which acts to raise blood sugar

8. Cardiovascular System KEY

Arteries & Veins p.194 & 196 (Figures 8-2 and 8-3)

Arteries	Veins
Aorta/Aortic Arch-main artery that carries blood away from your heart to the rest of your body; largest artery in the body. Ascending aorta begins at the heart's left ventricle and extends to the aortic arch, (the bend in the aorta). Arch of the aorta gives off branches to the head and arms.	External Jugular-more superficial of the two jugular veins (other is the internal jugular vein) situated on each side of the neck; drains blood from the head, brain, face and neck and conveys it toward the heart.
Common Carotid Artery-main blood supply to the head and neck.	Subclavian Vein-responsible for draining blood from the upper extremities and returning this blood to the heart.
Brachiocephalic Artery-supplies blood to the right arm and the head and neck.	Superior Vena Cava Vein-returns deoxygenated blood from the systemic circulation (upper half of the body) to the right atrium of the heart.
Subclavian Artery-supplies the arms with blood.	Brachiocephalic Vein-returns oxygen-depleted blood from the upper limbs, neck, and head to the heart.
Axillary Artery-large blood vessel that conveys oxygenated blood to the lateral aspect of the thorax, the axilla (armpit) and the upper limb.	Axillary Vein-large blood vessel that conveys blood from the lateral aspect of the thorax, axilla (armpit) and upper limb toward the heart.
Brachial Artery-major blood vessel located in the upper arm that serves as the main supplier of blood to the arm and hand.	Brachial Vein-deep vein that joins the basilic vein to form the axillary vein; has small tributaries that drain the muscles of the upper arm (such as *biceps brachii* and *triceps brachii* muscles).
Thoracic Aorta-travels through the chest. Its small branches supply blood to the ribs and some chest structures.	Median Cubital Vein-superficial vein of the arm commonly used to draw blood (venipuncture).
Radial Artery-major artery in the forearm; supplies the arm and hand with oxygenated blood from the lung	Renal Vein-carries the blood filtered by the kidney and drains the kidney by connecting it to the inferior vena cava.
Ulnar Artery-main blood vessel of the medial aspect of the forearm; supplies the forearm, wrist, and hand with oxygenated blood.	Inferior Vena Cava-large vein that carries deoxygenated blood from the lower and middle body into the right atrium of the heart.
Palmar Arch-arterial network found in the palm of the hand.	Radial Vein-one of a pair of veins that accompany the radial artery through the back of the hand and the lateral aspect of the forearm; joins the ulnar veins to form the brachial veins.

Renal Artery-branches directly from the aorta and carries blood from the heart to the kidneys.	Ulnar Vein-located in the forearm, next to the ulna bone; drains oxygen-depleted blood from the forearm.
Common Iliac Artery-supplies blood to the pelvic organs, gluteal region, and legs; abdominal aorta divides to form the "common iliac arteries" in the lower abdomen.	Common Iliac Vein-receives blood from the reproductive organs; both internal & external iliac veins join to form the inferior vena cava.
Femoral Artery-large artery in the thigh that is the main arterial supply to the thigh and leg.	Femoral Vein-located in the upper thigh and pelvic region of the human body; drains deoxygenated blood to the leg and pelvic region and transports it to the inferior vena cava.
Popliteal Artery-primary distributor of oxygenated blood to regions around the knee; branches off from the femoral artery and into other significant blood vessels.	Great Saphenous Vein-large, subcutaneous, superficial vein of the leg; longest vein in the body; returns blood from the foot, leg and thigh to the deep femoral vein at the femoral triangle; sometimes stripped out of the leg to eliminate varicose veins; also used as the source of grafts in coronary bypass surgery.
Tibial Artery (anterior & posterior)-posterior tibial artery of the lower limb carries blood to the posterior compartment of the leg and plantar surface of the foot; anterior tibial artery of the leg carries blood to the anterior compartment of the leg and dorsal surface of the foot.	Popliteal Vein-carries blood from the knee (as well as the thigh and calf muscles) back to the heart.
Abdominal Aorta-largest artery in the abdominal cavity that reaches from the chest into the abdomen; supplies blood to the stomach, pelvis, and legs.	Tibial Vein-deep vein of the calf that carry oxygen-depleted blood away from the foot and lower leg, and back toward the heart.

Blood Cells p.203

Cell	Shape	Nucleation/ shape of nucleus / presence of granules in cytoplasm	Estimated Number in 1 drop of blood	Functions
Erythrocyte	Biconcave	Anucleate	4-6 million	Transports O_2 / CO_2
Leukocyte	Spherical	Nucleated	7000- 25,000	Body defense against pathogens
• *Neutrophil*		Multi-lobed (2-4) nucleus; inconspicuous granules	4500-11,000	Phagocytize bacteria
• *Eosinophil*		Bi-lobed nucleus; red granules	100-400	Kill parasitic worms, destroy antigen/antibody complex, inactivate inflammation chemicals of allergy
• *Basophil*		U or S shaped nucleus; large granules	20-50	Release histamine, contain heparin
• *Lymphocyte*		Large spherical or indented nucleus; no granules	1500-3000	Begin immune response
• *Monocyte*		U shaped/ kidney shaped nucleus; no granules	100-700	Phagocytize bacteria & viruses
Thrombocyte	Fragments	Anucleate	250,000- 500,000	Seals small tears in blood vessels, responsible for blood clotting

Heart (Anterior) p.214 (Figure 8-7)

Structure	Function
Superior Vena Cava	Returns deoxygenated blood from the systemic circulation (upper half of the body) to the right atrium of the heart.
Inferior Vena Cava	Large vein that carries the deoxygenated blood from the lower and middle body into the right atrium of the heart.
Brachiocephalic Trunk	First and largest branch of the aortic arch that supplies the head, neck and the right arm.

Left Common Carotid Artery	Main blood supply to the head and neck.
Left Subclavian Artery	Supplies the arms with blood.
Aortic Arch	Gives off branches to the head and arms.
Aorta	Main artery that carries blood away from the heart to the rest of the body; largest artery in the body.
Right & Left Pulmonary Arteries	Arteries in the pulmonary circulation that carry deoxygenated blood from the right side of the heart to the lungs.
Right & Left Pulmonary Veins	Veins that transfer oxygenated blood from the lungs to the heart.
Pulmonary Trunk	Major vessel of the human heart that originates from the right ventricle and branches into the right and left pulmonary arteries that lead to the lungs.
Right Coronary Artery	Supplies blood to the right ventricle and right atrium, as well as the SA (sinoatrial) and AV (atrioventricular) nodes to regulate the heart rhythm. It divides into smaller branches, including the right posterior descending artery and the acute marginal artery; part of the coronary circulation.
Circumflex Artery	Branch of left main coronary artery that supplies blood to the left atrium, side and back of the left ventricle; part of the coronary circulation.
Right Atrium	Right upper chamber of the heart that receives deoxygenated blood from the body through the vena cava and pumps it into the right ventricle where it is sent it to the lungs to be oxygenated.
Right Ventricle	Right lower chamber within the heart that is responsible for pumping oxygen-depleted blood to the lungs.
Left Atrium	Left upper posterior side of the heart that acts as a holding chamber for blood returning from the lungs and as well as a pump to transport blood to other areas of the heart.
Left Ventricle	Left lower portion of the heart separated from the left atrium by the mitral valve; thickest of the heart's chambers and responsible for pumping oxygenated blood to tissues all over the body.
Apex	Most inferior tip of the heart; faces toward the left and inferiorly at the level of the 5th intercostal space.

Heart (Posterior) p.216 (Figure 8-8)

Structure	Function
Superior Vena Cava	Returns deoxygenated blood from the systemic circulation (upper half of the body) to the right atrium of the heart.
Pulmonary Arteries	Arteries in the pulmonary circulation that carry deoxygenated blood from the right side of the heart to the lungs.
Right & Left Pulmonary Veins	Veins that transfer oxygenated blood from the lungs to the heart.
Inferior Vena Cava	Large vein that carries the deoxygenated blood from the lower and middle body into the right atrium of the heart.
Left Atrium	Left upper posterior side of the heart that acts as a holding chamber for blood returning from the lungs and as well as a pump to transport blood to other areas of the heart.
Great Cardiac Vein	Returns deoxygenated blood (metabolic waste products) from the anterior surfaces of the left ventricle.
Right Coronary Artery	Supplies blood to the right ventricle and right atrium, as well as the SA (sinoatrial) and AV (atrioventricular) nodes to regulate the heart rhythm. It divides into smaller branches, including the right posterior descending artery and the acute marginal artery; part of the coronary circulation.
Left Ventricle	Left lower portion of the heart separated from the left atrium by the mitral valve; thickest of the heart's chambers and responsible for pumping oxygenated blood to tissues all over the body.
Middle Cardiac Vein	Relatively large vein that begins near to the apex of the heart on its inferior surface and passes superiorly and to the right in the posterior part of the interventricular groove along with the posterior interventricular artery; drains part of the right and left ventricles and into the coronary sinus at the junction of interventricular and atrioventricular grooves on the posterior surface of the heart.
Posterior Interventricular Artery	Runs in the posterior interventricular sulcus to the apex of the heart where it meets the anterior interventricular artery (also known as the Left Anterior Descending artery). It supplies the posterior third of the interventricular septum. It is typically a branch of the right coronary artery (70%, known as right dominance) but can be a branch of the circumflex coronary artery (10%, known as left dominance) which itself is a branch of the left coronary artery. It is often called the posterior descending artery (PDA).

Heart (Interior) p.218 (Figure 8-9)

Structure	Function
Right Atrium	Right upper chamber of the heart that receives deoxygenated blood from the body through the vena cava and pumps it into the right ventricle where it is sent it to the lungs to be oxygenated.
Right Ventricle	Right lower chamber within the heart that is responsible for pumping oxygen-depleted blood to the lungs.
Left Atrium	Left upper posterior side of the heart that acts as a holding chamber for blood returning from the lungs and as well as a pump to transport blood to other areas of the heart.
Left Ventricle	Left lower portion of the heart separated from the left atrium by the mitral valve; thickest of the heart's chambers and responsible for pumping oxygenated blood to tissues all over the body.
Myocardium	Heart muscle.
Interventricular Septum	Muscular wall separating the ventricles.
Bicuspid (Mitral) Valve	Atrioventricular valve with two flaps (leaflets) that lies between the left atrium and the left ventricle; prevents blood from flowing backward.
Tricuspid valve	Atrioventricular valve with three flaps (leaflets) that lies between the right atrium and the right ventricle; prevents blood from flowing backward.
Pulmonary Semilunar Valve	Semilunar valve that lies between the right ventricle and the pulmonary artery; has three cusps. It opens in ventricular systole (similar to the aortic valve), when the pressure in the right ventricle rises above the pressure in the pulmonary artery. Pressure in the pulmonary artery will close the pulmonary valve at the end of ventricular systole when the pressure in the right ventricle falls rapidly.
Aortic Semilunar Valve	Semilunar valve that lies between the left ventricle and the aorta; normally has three cusps. It is the last structure in the heart the blood travels through before flowing through the systemic circulation.
Right & Left Pulmonary Arteries	Arteries in the pulmonary circulation that carry deoxygenated blood from

	the right side of the heart to the lungs.
Right & Left Pulmonary Veins	Veins that transfer oxygenated blood from the lungs to the heart.
Aorta	Main artery that carries blood away from the heart to the rest of the body; largest artery in the body.
Fossa Ovalis	Depression in the right atrium of the heart on the interatrial septum (wall between right and left atrium). It is the remnant of a thin, fibrous sheet that covered the foramen ovale during fetal development.
Chordae Tendineae	Fibrous cords of connective tissue that connect the papillary muscles to the tricuspid valve and the bicuspid valve in the heart. Often known as the "heart strings".
Superior Vena Cava	Returns deoxygenated blood from the systemic circulation (upper half of the body) to the right atrium of the heart.
Inferior Vena Cava	Large vein that carries the deoxygenated blood from the lower and middle body into the right atrium of the heart.

Heart Conduction System p.226 (Figure 8-14)

Structure	Function
Sinoatrial (SA) Node	Pacemaker; located at the top of the Right Atrium.
Atrioventricular (AV) Node	Controls heart rate; located at the bottom of the Right Atrium.
Atrioventricular (AV) Bundle (Bundle of His)	Relay center between AV Node and rest of heart; located in septum,
Right & Left Bundle Branches	Relay center between AV Bundle and Purkinje Fibers; located in myocardium near apex.
Purkinje Fibers	Stimulate ventricular contraction; located in myocardium throughout ventricles.

9. Lymphatic/Immune System KEY

Lymph Node p.231 (Figure 9-1)

Structure	Function
Afferent Lymph Vessel	Vessel that transports lymph into the lymph node.
Efferent Lymph Vessel	Vessel that transport lymph out of the lymph node.
Cortex	Outer portion of the lymph node that contains follicles with high concentrations of dividing B cells (lymphocytes).
Medulla	Inner portion of the lymph node which contains medullary cords (inward extensions of lymphatic tissue) where antibody-secreting plasma cells are found.
Hilum	Indentation where lymphatic vessels exit lymph node.

Spleen p.232 (Figure 9-2)

Structure	Function
Splenic Artery & Vein	Blood supply to the spleen. The splenic artery supplies oxygenated blood and the splenic vein drains deoxygenated blood.
Capsule	Connective tissue covering which extends inward to divide the spleen into lobules.
Red Pulp	Filters the blood of antigens, microorganisms, and defective or worn-out red blood cells.
White Pulp	Stores large numbers of macrophages and lymphocytes.

Tonsils p.234 (Figure 9-3)

Structure	Function
Pharyngeal Tonsil (Adenoid)	Located behind the nasal cavity, in the roof of the nasopharynx, where the nose blends into the throat.
Palatine Tonsil	Located at the rear of the throat (pharynx).
Lingual Tonsil	Located at the back of the base of the tongue, one on either side.

10. Respiratory System KEY

Respiratory System p.256 (Figure 10-11)

Structure	Function/Description
Larynx	Another name for the voice box. It is a tube about 2 inches (5cm) long in adults located above the trachea (windpipe) in the neck and in front of the pharynx.
Trachea	Another name for the windpipe. It is a wide, hollow tube that connects the larynx (voice box) to the bronchi of the lungs. It provides passageway for air flow to and from the lungs for respiration.
Bronchi	Passageways for air flow to the lungs that become smaller the closer they get to the lung tissue (where they are then considered bronchioles). They further evolve into tiny air sacs called alveoli, the site of oxygen and carbon dioxide exchange in the respiratory system.
Lungs	Main function is the process of gas exchange called respiration (or breathing). In respiration, oxygen from incoming air enters the blood, and carbon dioxide, a waste gas from the metabolism, leaves the blood.
Alveoli	Tiny, balloon-shaped air sacs located at the very end of the respiratory tree and arranged in clusters throughout the lungs. Their function is to exchange oxygen and carbon dioxide molecules to and from the bloodstream.
Diaphragm	Dome-shaped sheet of muscle that separates the thoracic cavity from the abdominal cavity. It is the most important muscle used for inspiration (breathing in) because it increases the length and diameter of the chest cavity and expands the lungs as it contracts.
Nasal Cavity	Large, air-filled space in the middle of the face located above and behind the nose.
Oral Cavity	Another name for the mouth; includes the lips, the lining inside the cheeks and lips, the front two thirds of the tongue, the upper and lower gums, the floor of the mouth under the tongue, the bony roof of the mouth, and the small area behind the wisdom teeth.
Pharynx	Another name for the throat; passageway leading from the mouth and nose to the esophagus and larynx.
Bronchiole	Smaller branch of the bronchial airways in the lungs.

11. Digestive System KEY

Salivary Glands p.264 (Figure 11-3)

Structure	Function
Parotid	Large, located anterior to the ear between the skin and masseter muscle. Saliva is carried to the mouth via the Parotid Duct which opens near the second molar.
Sublingual	Located anterior to the submandibular gland, under the tongue; connects to the floor of the oral cavity via 10-12 ducts.
Submandibular	Lies near the mandibular body; the duct opens near the lingual frenulum.

Stomach p.267 (Figure 11-5)

Structure	Function/ Description
Serosa (Outside)	Outside covering of stomach; thin serous membrane made of simple squamous epithelial tissue and areolar connective tissue; has a smooth, slippery surface and secretes thin, watery serous fluid.
Fundus	Dome-shaped upper portion of the stomach beneath the diaphragm.
Greater Curvature	Long convex curve on the left side of the stomach from the opening for the esophagus to the opening into the duodenum.
Lesser Curvature	Shorter, concave, medial surface of the stomach.
Pylorus	Opening from the stomach into the duodenum (small intestine).

Muscular Layers of the Stomach p.268 (Figure 11-6)

Structure	Function/ Description
Longitudinal Smooth Muscle	Outer layer of smooth muscle.
Circular Smooth Muscle	Middle layer of smooth muscle.
Oblique Smooth Muscle	Inner layer of smooth muscle.

Villi of the Small Intestine p.270 (Figure 11-8)

Structure	Function/Description
Villi	Small, finger-like projections that extend into the lumen of the small intestine that serve to increase the internal surface area of the intestinal walls making a greater surface area available for absorption.
Artery	Carries oxygenated blood from the heart to the villi.
Vein	Carries deoxygenated blood from the villi to the heart.
Lamina Propria	Consists of loose connective tissue which fills the spaces between the intestinal glands and forms the cores of the intestinal villi.
Peyer's Patches	Small masses of lymphatic tissue found throughout the ileum region of the small intestine. They monitor intestinal bacteria populations and prevent the growth of pathogenic bacteria in the intestines.

Liver p.272 (Figure 11-9)

Structure	Function/ Description
Right Lobe	Largest lobe of the liver. It is sub-divided into the right lobe proper, the caudate lobe, and the quadrate lobe.
Left Lobe	Smaller lobe of the liver. It is separated from the right lobe by a deep fissure.
Falciform Ligament	Mesentery that separates the right and left lobes of the liver and suspends the liver from the diaphragm and abdominal wall.

Gallbladder and Pancreas p.274 (Figure 11-11)

Structure	Function
Gallbladder	Hollow structure located under the liver and on the right side of the abdomen; primary function is to store and concentrate bile, a yellow-brown digestive enzyme produced by the liver.
Common Bile Duct	Delivers bile to upper part of small intestine (duodenum).
Pancreas	Secretes enzymes into the small intestine where it continues breaking down food that has exited the stomach.
Pancreatic Duct	Joins the pancreas to the Common Bile Duct to supply digestive enzymes.

Digestive System p.276 (Figure 11-13)

Structure	Function
Mouth	Beginning of the digestive tract; digestion starts here when taking the first bite of food. Chewing breaks the food into pieces that are more easily digested, while saliva mixes with food to begin the process of breaking it down into a form your body can absorb and use.
Esophagus	Muscular tube that goes from the pharynx to the stomach. Food is pushed through the esophagus and into the stomach with a series of muscle contractions called peristalsis.
Stomach	Secretes acid and enzymes that digest food; lined with ridges of muscle tissue called rugae. The muscles of the stomach contract periodically to churn food and enhance digestion. The pyloric sphincter is a muscular valve that opens to allow food to pass from the stomach to the small intestine. Less than 10% of digestion & absorption of food occurs in the stomach.
Liver	Main function within the digestive system is to process the nutrients absorbed from the small intestine. Bile from the liver secreted into the small intestine also plays an important role in digesting fat.
Gallbladder	Hollow structure located under the liver and on the right side of the abdomen; primary function is to store and concentrate bile, a yellow-brown digestive enzyme produced by the liver. Common Bile Duct delivers bile to upper part of small intestine (duodenum).
Pancreas	Secrete enzymes into the small intestine where it continues breaking down food that has exited the stomach. Pancreatic Duct joins the pancreas to the Common Bile Duct to supply digestive enzymes.
Small Intestine	Location where 90% of the digestion and absorption of food occurs; The main function of the small intestine is absorption of nutrients and minerals from food.
Duodenum	1st part of the small intestine; location where digestive enzymes are secreted.
Appendix	Mass of lymphoid tissue attached to the surface of the large intestine on the lower right side.
Parotid Salivary Gland	Large, located anterior to the ear between the skin and masseter muscle. Saliva is carried to the mouth via the Parotid Duct which opens near the second molar.
Sublingual Salivary Gland	Located anterior to the submandibular gland, under the tongue; connects to the floor of the oral cavity via 10-12 ducts.
Submandibular Salivary Gland	Lies near the mandibular body; the duct opens near the lingual frenulum.
Cystic Duct	Tube leading from the gallbladder to the Common Bile Duct where bile is secreted.

Ascending Colon	Carries waste from the cecum superiorly along the right side of the abdominal cavity to the transverse colon.
Transverse Colon	Carries waste across upper horizontal part of the large intestine.
Descending Colon	Carries waste from the splenic flexure inferiorly down the left side to the beginning of the sigmoid colon.
Sigmoid Colon	Part of the large intestine that is closest to the rectum and anus. It lies within the pelvis and forms a loop shaped like an "S".
Rectum	Chamber that connects the large intestine to the anus and serves as a temporary storage for wastes.
Anus	Exit point of the digestive tract.

12. Urinary System KEY

Urinary System p.281 (Figure 12-1)

Structure	Function/Description
Kidney	Primary excretory organs in the human body that removing toxins while returning necessary compounds back to body. Kidneys filter approximately 200 L of fluid every day.
Ureter	Muscular tube that pushes urine into the bladder, where it collects and exits the body.
Urinary Bladder	Muscular sac in the pelvis that stores urine; located just above and behind the pubic bone.
Urethra	Tube that carries urine from the bladder to outside of the body

Anatomy of the Kidney p.285 (Figure 12-3)

Structure	Function/Description
Ureter	Muscular tube that pushes urine into the bladder, where it collects and exits the body.
Renal Capsule	Tough, fibrous outside covering of the kidney that prevents infections in surrounding regions from spreading to the kidney.
Renal Cortex	Outer, superficial part of the kidney between the renal capsule and the renal medulla; contains the glomerulus and convoluted tubules.
Renal Pyramids	Found in the medulla of the kidney; consist of six to eight cone-shaped bundles of microscopic urine-collecting tubules that transport urine from the outer part of the kidney (where urine is produced) to the calyces (cup-shaped cavities) where urine collects before it passes through the ureter to the bladder.
Minor Calyx	Cup-shaped cavities that surround the apex of the renal pyramids. Urine formed in the kidney passes through a renal papilla at the apex into the minor calyx.
Major Calyx	Two or three minor calyces converge to form a major calyx, through which urine passes before continuing through the renal pelvis into the ureter.
Renal Pelvis	Funnel-shaped tube that is continuous with the ureter leaving the hilum.
Renal Medulla	Smooth, inner tissue of the kidney that contains the loop of Henle and the renal pyramids.

Blood Supply to the Kidney p.288 (Figure 12-5)

Structure	Function/Description
Renal Artery	Branch directly off the Abdominal Aorta and supplies the kidneys with blood.
Renal Vein	Drains the kidney and connects the kidney to the Inferior Vena Cava. Renal veins carry the blood filtered by the kidney.

The Nephron p.290 (Figure 12-6)

Structure	Function/Description
Bowman's Capsule	Proximal end of the tubule that surrounds the glomerulus and catches the filtered fluid; found in renal cortex.
Glomerulus	High pressure capillary bed of the nephron.
Podocytes	Cells that cling to the glomerulus to form filtration slips where filtrate enters the capsular space.
Afferent Arteriole	Feeds the glomerulus where blood is filtered in order to produce a fluid (filtrate) that is caught by the nephron tubule.
Efferent Arteriole	Means by which the remaining blood leaves the glomerulus; still an artery so the blood which leaves the glomerulus is oxygenated and remains under high pressure.
Proximal Convoluted Tubule	Found in renal cortex, enters renal medulla at opposite end; in close contact with capillaries so substances (glucose, Na, and amino acids) can be actively removed from the filtrate and reabsorbed into the bloodstream; very little water is removed in this part of nephron.
Descending Limb of Loop of Henle	Part of loop that is permeable to water only so water will leave the filtrate via passive osmosis.
Ascending Limb of Loop of Henle	Part of loop that helps make the medulla a hypertonic (salty) environment by actively pumping salts (sodium etc) out of the filtrate into the medulla. This environment makes passive movement of water (osmosis) into this part of the loop possible.
Distal Convoluted Tubule	Site of the final step in reabsorption by the body of necessary materials from the filtrate; Found in renal cortex close enough to Bowman's Capsule for further reabsorption of sodium, calcium, and more water to occur.
Collecting Duct	Dips into the medulla; site where the final filtrate product joins waste products from multiple nephrons in Collecting Ducts. Filtrate becomes urine at this point and passes through collecting ducts, travels to the urinary bladder via ureters, and exits the body.

13. Reproductive System KEY

Male Reproductive System p.300 (Figure 13-2)

Structure	Function/ Description
Epididymis	A long, coiled tube that rests on the backside of each testicle that functions in the carrying and storage of the sperm cells that are produced in the testes.
Testes	Produce gametes, or sperm, and they secrete hormones, primarily testosterone.
Vas deferens	Transports mature sperm to the urethra (tube that carries urine or sperm to outside of the body) in preparation for ejaculation.
Prostate gland	Main function is to secrete prostate fluid, one of the components of semen. The muscles of the prostate gland also help propel this seminal fluid into the urethra during ejaculation.
Seminal vesicles	Major contributors to the production of semen.
Glans Penis	Distal end of the penis.
Erectile Tissue	Fills with blood during an erection.
Urinary Bladder	Stores urine.
Urethra	Carries urine & semen to outside of the body.

Female Reproductive System p.306 (Figure 13-4)

Structure	Function/ Description
Ovary	Produce the egg cells (called the ova or oocytes).
Uterus	Also known as the womb, is the hollow organ in the female reproductive system that holds a fetus during pregnancy.
Cervix	Lowermost part of the uterus made up of strong muscles. The function of the cervix is to allow flow of menstrual blood from the uterus into the vagina and direct the sperm into the uterus during intercourse.
Fallopian Tubes	Primary function is to transport sperm toward the egg, which is released by the ovary, and to then allow passage of the fertilized egg back to the uterus for implantation.
Vagina	Canal that receives the male reproductive cells.

ABOUT THE AUTHORS

Shelley Hill Montgomery, Ed.D.

From "Medical Mysteries" to "Biology Sketch Notes", Dr. Montgomery inspires teachers to stretch their pedagogy to the edge. After receiving her BS in Biology and MS Education from Samford University, then an Ed.D from The University of Alabama, she has spent the last 24 years arousing curiosity in the minds of high school and college students. She is the author of a successful blog, A Teacher on the Edge and enjoys creating curricula for teachers. She is currently teaching Anatomy and Physiology as well as Forensic Science and enjoying her newly found love for creating student-friendly medical illustrations.

Cat Mueller, RN, BSN, CCRN-CMC, TNCC

Anne Catherine Mueller is the proud daughter of Dr. Shelley Montgomery. She graduated with a BS in nursing science from Samford University in May 2015. She has since gained extensive experience working in ER and Surgical ICU settings. In pursuit of her ultimate career goal, Anne Catherine will soon return to her alma mater to complete her doctorate degree through the school's CRNA program.

Made in the USA
Coppell, TX
07 February 2024

28713229R00227